From Bacteria to Plants

PRENTICE HALL **Science Explorer**

PEARSON
Prentice Hall

Boston, Massachusetts
Upper Saddle River, New Jersey

Pearson Prentice Hall™ is a trademark of Pearson Education, Inc.
Pearson® is a registered trademark of Pearson plc.
Prentice Hall® is a registered trademark of Pearson Education, Inc.

Lab zone™ is a trademark of Pearson Education, Inc.

Planet Diary® is a registered trademark of Addison Wesley Longman, Inc.

Discovery Channel School® is a registered trademark of Discovery Communications, Inc., used under license. The Discovery Channel School logo is a trademark of Discovery Communications, Inc.

SciLinks® is a trademark of the National Science Teachers Association. The SciLinks® service includes copyrighted materials and is owned and provided by the National Science Teachers Association. All rights reserved.

Science News® is a registered trademark of Science Services, Inc.

ISBN 0-13-190272-5

4 5 6 7 8 9 10 11 10 09 08

Everything you need

For Students...

STUDY WORKSHEETS

Section Summaries
• Supports less-proficient readers and English-language learners with easily accessible content summaries

Guided Reading and Study
• Promotes active reading and enhances study skills for all students as they follow along with the text

Review and Reinforce
• Motivates students to build vocabulary, review main ideas, and interpret diagrams, charts, and graphs

Enrich
• Encourages students to apply core concepts in a new context

LABS AND ACTIVITIES

Chapter Project
• Guides students in open-ended inquiry with scoring rubrics and teacher notes

Student Edition Labs
• Provides blackline masters of the Student Edition Labs in an easy-to-grade format

Laboratory Investigations
• Applies and extends key concepts for each chapter using in-depth labs with full support for hands-on inquiry

ASSESSMENT

Performance Assessments
• Assesses problem-solving and process skills with scoring rubrics and suggested outcomes

Chapter and Book Tests
• Monitors student mastery of standards-driven content and skills

For You...

Look for the RED BAR

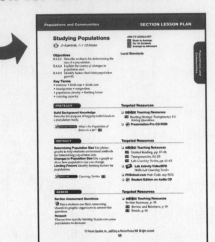

Section Lesson Plans
• Provides section-by-section planning tools that emphasize the National Science Education Standards

Teacher Notes
• Includes point-of-use support for Chapter Projects, Laboratory Investigations, and Performance Assessment

Answer Keys
• Complete answers for all worksheets

Look for the COLOR TRANSPARENCY PLANNER

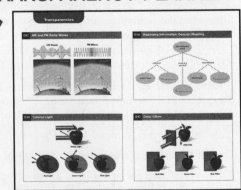

Transparency Thumbnails
• Enables full-color review of all the transparencies that support the chapters

Contents

From Bacteria to Plants

Science Explorer • *Target Reading Skills Handbook*

☉ Target Reading Skills

Identifying Main Ideas

Identifying the main idea helps you understand what you are reading. Sometimes the main idea can be easy to find. For example, suppose that you are reading just one paragraph. Very often you will find the main idea in the first sentence, the topic sentence. The other sentences in the paragraph provide supporting details or support the ideas in the topic sentence.

Sometimes, however, the first sentence is not the topic sentence. Sometimes you may have to look further. In those cases, it might help to read the paragraph and summarize what you have read. Your summary can give you the main idea.

A textbook has many paragraphs, each one with its own main idea. However, just as a paragraph has a main idea and supporting details, so does the text under each heading in your textbook. Sometimes the main idea is the heading itself. Other times it is more difficult to find. You may have to infer a main idea by combining information from several paragraphs.

To practice this skill, you can use a graphic organizer that looks like this one.

Main Idea		
Detail	**Detail**	**Detail**
a.	b.	c.

Outlining

Outlining shows you how supporting details relate to main ideas. You can make an outline as you read. Using this skill can make you a more careful reader.

Your outline can be made up of sentences, simple phrases, or single words. What matters is that you follow a formal structure. To outline while you read, use a plan like this one.

I. Section Title
  A. Main Heading
    1. Subheading
      a. Detail
      b. Detail
      c. Detail

The main ideas or topics are labeled as Roman numerals. The supporting details or subtopics are labeled A, B, C, and so on. Other levels of supporting information can be added under heads. When you outline in this way, you are deciding just how important a piece of information is.

Science Explorer ▪ *Target Reading Skills Handbook*

Comparing and Contrasting

You can use comparing and contrasting to better understand similarities and differences between two or more concepts. Look for clue words as you read. When concepts or topics are similar, you will probably see words such as *also, just as, like, likewise,* or *in the same way.* When concepts or topics are different, you will see *but, however, although, whereas, on the other hand,* or *unlike.*

To use this skill, it sometimes helps to make a Venn diagram. In this type of graphic organizer, the similarities are in the middle, where the two circles overlap.

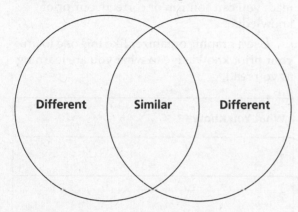

Relating Cause and Effect

Identifying causes and effects can help you understand the relationships among events. A cause is what makes something happen. An effect is what happens. In science, many actions cause other actions to occur.

Sometimes you have to look hard to see a cause-and-effect relationship in reading. You can watch for clue words to help you identify causes and effects. Look for *because, so, since, therefore, results, cause,* or *lead to.*

Sometimes a cause-and-effect relationship occurs in a chain. For example, an effect can have more than one cause, or a cause can have several effects. Seeing and understanding the relationships helps you understand science processes. You can use a graphic organizer like this one.

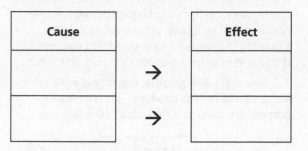

Asking Questions

Your textbook is organized using headings and subheadings. You can read the material under those headings by turning each heading into a question. For example, you might change the heading "Protecting Yourself During an Earthquake" to "How can you protect yourself during an earthquake?" Asking questions in this way will help you look for answers while reading. You can use a graphic organizer like this one to ask questions.

Question	Answer

Science Explorer ▪ *Target Reading Skills Handbook*

Sequencing

Sequencing is the order in which a series of events occurs. As you read, look for clue words that tell you the sequence or the order in which things happen. You see words such as *first, next, then,* or *finally.* When a process is being described, watch for numbered steps. Sometimes there are clues provided for you. Using the sequencing reading skill will help you understand and visualize the steps in a process. You can also use it to list events in the order of their occurrence.

You can use a graphic organizer to show the sequence of events or steps. The one most commonly used is a flowchart like this one.

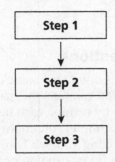

Sometimes, though, a cycle diagram works better.

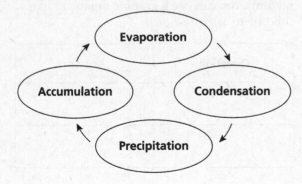

Using Prior Knowledge

Use prior knowledge to relate what you are reading to something that you already know. It is easier to learn when you can link new ideas to something that is already familiar to you. For example, if you know that fish are actually breathing oxygen that is dissolved in water, you wil be able to understand how or why gills work.

Using prior knowledge can help you make logical assumptions or draw conclusions about what you are reading. But be careful. Your prior knowledge might sometimes be wrong. As you read, you can confirm or correct your prior knowledge.

Use a graphic organizer like this one to link your prior knowledge to what you are learning as you read.

What You Know
1.
2.
3.

What You Learned
1.
2.
3.

Science Explorer ▪ *Target Reading Skills Handbook*

Previewing Visuals

Looking at visuals before you read can help you better understand a topic. Preview the visuals by reading labels and captions. For example, if you preview the visuals in a chapter about volcanoes, you will see more than just photographs of erupting volcanoes. You will see maps, diagrams, and photographs of rocks. These might tell you that you will learn where volcanoes are found, how they form, and what sort of rock is created when volcanoes erupt. Previewing visuals helps you understand and enjoy what you read.

One way to apply this strategy is to choose a few photographs, diagrams, or other visuals to preview. Then write questions about what you see. Answer the questions as you read.

Identifying Supporting Evidence

In science, you will read about hypotheses. A hypothesis is a possible explanation for scientific observations made by scientists or an answer to a scientific question. A hypothesis is tested over and over again. The tests may produce evidence that supports the hypothesis. When enough supporting evidence is collected, a hypothesis may become a theory.

Identifying supporting evidence in your reading can help you understand a hypothesis or theory. Evidence is made up of facts. Facts are information that can be confirmed by testing or observation.

When you are identifying supporting evidence, a graphic organizer like this one can be helpful.

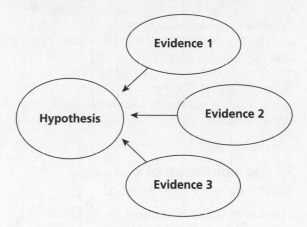

Building Vocabulary

To understand what someone is saying, you have to know the language that person is speaking. To understand science, you need to know what the words mean.

There are many ways to build your vocabulary. You can look up the meaning of a new word in a dictionary or glossary. Then you can write its definition in your own words. You can use the new word in a sentence. To figure out the meaning of a new word, you can use context clues or surrounding words. Look for prefixes and suffixes in the new word to help you break it down. Building vocabulary will get easier with practice.

Guidelines for Laboratory Safety

This section on laboratory safety is included as a resource for the teacher. Rather than providing definitive rules and regulations, the information is intended to be the basis for the establishment of safe laboratory practice. Pearson Prentice Hall and its consultants make no claims as to the completeness of this material. Not all the precautions necessitated by the use, storage, and disposal of materials are covered here. Additional steps and safeguards may be required.

Responsibilities of the Teacher and the School

Laboratory safety is a shared responsibility. Both the school and the teacher need to be sure that all educational activities protect and promote the health and safety of students and the environment. To accomplish this goal, teachers need to understand the hazards, precautions, and emergency procedures associated with laboratory activities. When schools or teachers fail to live up to this responsibility, their behavior may be considered negligent. As a result, they may be liable for resulting injuries.

The best way to avoid being considered negligent is to ask yourself four simple questions:

1. What are the hazards?
2. What are the worst things that could happen?
3. What do I need to do if they do happen?
4. What are the prudent practices, protective facilities, and protective equipment needed to minimize the risk?

Be sure that you can answer all four of these questions before starting any science activity or demonstration. Then you can reduce the risks to an acceptable level—a level where the educational benefits of the activity outweigh the risks.

General Safety Strategies

Teachers should promote a "safety first" philosophy through personal example and by the careful planning and implementation of safety strategies.

The following strategies will help create an enjoyable, instructional, and safe environment.

1. Set up a safety committee made up of both teachers and administrators. Arrange to meet regularly to set safety policies for the school, discuss any safety problems that might arise, and organize periodic inspections of classrooms and laboratory equipment.
2. Establish a safety and health reference shelf in a resource center.
3. Develop detailed plans explaining what to do in case of emergency, including spills, cuts, burns, electric shock, poisoning, and fire. Review the procedures periodically throughout the school year.
4. Inform students of these emergency plans and carry out unannounced drills.
5. Explain to students how to use the intercom or other available means of communication to get help during an emergency.
6. Keep up to date in first aid and CPR (cardiopulmonary resuscitation) training.
7. Post emergency phone numbers for ambulance, fire, police, hospital, and the poison control center next to the telephone.
8. Perform laboratory investigations before assigning them to students. Take note of any potential hazards; devise plans for dealing with any possible mishaps or emergencies.
9. Emphasize safety considerations in pre-lab discussions. Display posters dealing with safety issues in the classroom as reminders.
10. Keep classroom aisles and exits free of obstructions.

11. During an investigation, move about the classroom to keep a constant watch for potentially dangerous situations.

12. Curtail inappropriate behavior immediately. Wild play and practical jokes are forbidden during labs. Once students realize that the practice of safety is a required part of the course, they will accept a serious approach to laboratory work.

13. Never leave students unattended while they are engaged in science activities.

14. Require proper clothing at all times. Insist that long hair, dangling jewelry, and loose clothing be restrained; do not allow students to wear open shoes.

15. Insist that students wear safety goggles when the lab requires it.

16. Encourage students to keep lab work space neat and clear of extraneous objects, such as books and jackets.

17. Make sure that investigations utilizing toxic, fuming, or flammable materials are performed under a fume hood.

18. Keep the fume hood clear of unnecessary chemicals and equipment. Have the fume hood checked periodically to ensure that it is operating safely and efficiently.

19. Demonstrate to students the proper handling of glass materials, such as beakers and graduated cylinders.

20. Only wastepaper should be discarded in wastepaper receptacles. Keep a separate container for broken glass.

21. Substitute plastic containers for glass ones whenever possible, including graduated cylinders and beakers.

22. Consider the use of dispensing containers for liquids. They help prevent spills, skin contact with chemicals, and waste.

23. Use hot plates in place of open flames whenever possible. Never use open flames or hot plates when flammables are present in the room.

24. Use only nonmercury thermometers in investigations that call for the measurement of temperature.

25. Do not permit students to insert glass tubing or thermometers into rubber stoppers. If necessary, do this task yourself. When inserting these items into rubber stoppers, use safety stoppers, which have holes with beveled edges and are easier to use. Use glycerin or water to lubricate the glass.

26. All electrical equipment used in the lab should have GFI (Ground Fault Interrupter) switches.

27. Do not leave equipment that is operating or plugged in unattended.

28. When working with live animals or plants, check ahead of time for students who may have allergies to the specimens.

29. Students should wear disposable nitrile, latex, or food-handling gloves when handling live animals or nonliving specimens.

30. Wearing safety equipment is required of all students.

31. Report in writing unsafe conditions to the department head, maintenance director, and principal.

32. Have clearly defined penalties for violations of safety rules. Have these penalties approved and supported by the principal.

33. Document safety training, rules violations, and penalties in your records.

34. Keep a record of injuries and incidents (close calls), no matter how minor they may seem. Discuss these events at a department meeting to avoid similar occurrences.

Guidelines for Laboratory Safety *(continued)*

35. As a class, review the safety rules and symbols. Make sure students understand the safety rules.

36. Require students to sign the safety contract.

37. Conduct quarterly inspections of the classrooms and storage areas to maintain safe conditions.

Safety Equipment

Any classroom where laboratory investigations are performed should contain at least one each of the following pieces of safety equipment: (1) fire extinguisher, (2) fire blanket, (3) fire alarm, (4) phone or intercom to the office, (5) eyewash station, (6) safety shower, (7) safety hood, and (8) first-aid kit. If any of these basic pieces of safety equipment are not available, you may need to modify your laboratory program until the situation is remedied.

Make sure students know the location and proper use of all safety equipment. Where appropriate and practical, have students handle or operate the equipment so that they become familiar with it. Make sure all safety equipment is in good working order. All malfunctions should be promptly reported in writing to the proper school or district administrator.

Fire equipment At the beginning of the school year, you may wish to give each student the opportunity to actually operate a fire extinguisher, as the sound and action of a CO_2 fire extinguisher can be quite alarming to those who have never used one. You may also want to have students practice smothering imaginary flames on one another with the fire blanket.

Eyewash station The eyewash station should be used if chemicals are splashed onto the face or eyes. The exposed area should be left in the running water for five to ten minutes.

Safety shower The shower is used when chemicals have been spilled on a student's body or clothing. The student should stand under the shower until the chemical is completely diluted. Have a bathrobe or some type of replacement clothing handy in case the student's clothing is so badly contaminated that it must be removed.

You may want to set up one or two spill kits in your laboratory. The contents of a spill kit are used to neutralize chemicals, such as acids and bases, so that they can be cleaned up more easily. Baking soda (sodium bicarbonate) can be used to neutralize acids. Vinegar (acetic acid) can be used to neutralize bases. Commercial spill kits for acids, bases, and a number of other chemicals are available from supply houses.

Safety hood Use a safety hood whenever students are working with volatile or noxious chemicals. Make sure that the room is well ventilated when students are using any kind of chemicals or are working with preserved specimens. Warn students of the flammability and toxicity of various chemicals.

First-aid kit A typical first-aid kit contains an assortment of antiseptics, bandages, gauze pads, and scissors. Most also contain simple instructions for use. Be sure to read the instructions if you are not familiar with basic first-aid procedures. A first-aid kit should be taken on all field trips. For field trips, you may wish to add such items as a bee-sting kit, meat tenderizer, tweezers, and calamine lotion. Do not dispense medication (including aspirin).

Guidelines for the Use and Care of Animals

Animals are an essential part of a science curriculum. The judicious use of live or preserved animals can help students realize that the study of science is relevant, fascinating, and rewarding. It is important to be aware of and sensitive to ethical and practical concerns when studying animals. The purpose of this section is to discuss some realistic guidelines for using animals in the classroom.

1. Whenever possible, live animals should be observed in their natural habitats or in zoos, parks, and aquariums.

2. Check the state and federal codes regarding animal welfare that apply in your area. You may also wish to refer to guidelines published by the National Science Teachers Association, the National Association of Biology Teachers, and the International Science Fair. Make students aware of all safety rules and regulations regarding animals.

3. Before bringing a live animal into the classroom, determine whether a proper habitat can be maintained in the classroom. Such a habitat includes temperature, space, and type of food. Students should have a clear understanding of the appropriate care needed by the live animals brought into the classroom. Do not allow students to tap on animal enclosures or otherwise disturb the animals.

4. No wild vertebrate animals should be brought into the classroom. Purchase animals from a reputable dealer only.

5. Live animals should be nonpoisonous and healthy. Any mammals used in the classroom should be vaccinated against rabies unless the animals were purchased recently from a reliable scientific supply company. Quarantine any animal to make sure it is disease-free before bringing it into the classroom.

6. Make sure that the living quarters of classroom animals are clean, located away from stressful situations, appropriately spacious, and secure enough to confine the animal. You may wish to lock cages to prevent the accidental release of animals; the small padlocks used on luggage are good for this purpose.

7. Remove wastes from animal living quarters daily. Thoroughly clean animal living quarters periodically to ensure that they are odor and germ-free. Provide a daily supply of fresh water and any other needs specific to the particular animal.

8. Provide for the care of animals during weekends and school vacations. Inform the custodial staff of the presence of animals and warn them of any special requirements. For example, turning off the aquarium pump to save electricity or spraying the classroom for insects can be fatal to animals.

9. Students should be instructed how to handle each species brought into the classroom. Make students aware that they can receive painful wounds from the improper handling of some animals.

10. Animals should be handled only if necessary. If an animal is frightened or excited, pregnant, feeding, or with its young, special handling is required.

11. Students should thoroughly clean their hands after handling animals or the quarters containing animals.

12. Animals should be returned to their natural habitat after an observation period of not longer than 14 days. However, laboratory-bred animals or species that are not native to an area should not be released into the environment.

13. If an animal must be euthanized, do not allow students to watch. Contact the local humane society for advice.

Guidelines for the Use and Care of Animals *(continued)*

14. Before performing any experiment involving live animals, check local and state regulations. In some states, certification is required before a teacher is permitted to experiment with animals.

15. No animal studies involving anesthetic drugs, pathogenic organisms, toxicological products, carcinogens, or radiation should be performed.

16. Any experiment requiring live animals should have a clearly defined objective relating to the teaching and learning of some scientific principle.

17. No experimental procedures that will cause pain, discomfort, or harm to animals should be done in the classroom or at home.

18. Surgical procedures should not be performed on live animals.

19. If fertilized bird eggs are opened, the embryo should be destroyed humanely two days before it would have hatched, at the latest.

20. When working with preserved animals, make sure that students maintain a serious and respectful attitude toward the specimens.

Handling Ethical Issues

There is much controversy regarding the use of animals in scientific research. This controversy extends to preserved animals in dissections as well as to live animals in experiments. Although the debate over what uses of animals are appropriate in a science classroom can be emotionally charged, it can also provide an opportunity for students to closely examine a current issue. You may wish to have students read current literature on the subject and contact groups and individuals with varying points of view.

Stress that it is important to make a rational, informed decision before taking a stand on any issue. Point out that it is vital to know and understand the arguments on all sides of an issue. Help students analyze the sources they find in terms of bias and the reliability and objectivity of the author(s). Help them to distinguish between fact and opinion. Encourage them to question what they read and hear. Challenge them to discover the hidden assumptions and implications of different points of view.

If dissections are a part of your curriculum and a student chooses to avoid dissections because of ethical concerns, respect that student's opinion. Point out, however, that no simulation or videotape can completely replace hands-on experience.

Guidelines for Safe Disposal of Laboratory Wastes

Every effort should be made to recover, recycle, and reuse materials used in the laboratory. When disposal is required, however, specific procedures should be followed to ensure that your school complies with local, state, and federal regulations.

1. Discard only dry paper into ordinary wastebaskets.

2. Discard broken glass into a separate container clearly marked "For Broken Glass Only."

3. Acidic or basic solutions need to be neutralized before disposal. Slowly add dilute sodium hydroxide to acids and dilute hydrochloric acid to bases until pH paper shows that they are no longer strongly acidic or basic. Then flush the solutions down the drain with a lot of water.

4. Before each investigation, instruct your students concerning where and how they are to dispose of chemicals that are used or produced during the investigation. Specific teacher notes addressing disposal are provided on each lab as appropriate.

5. Keep each excess or used chemical in a separate container; do not mix them. This allows for possible recycling or reuse. It also eliminates unexpected reactions or the need for expensive separation by a contractor if the wastes must be disposed of professionally.

6. Only nonflammable, neutral, nontoxic, nonreactive, and water-soluble chemicals should be flushed down the drain.

7. When growing bacterial cultures, use only disposable petri dishes. After streaking, the dishes should be sealed and not opened again by students. After the lab, students should return the unopened dishes to you and wash their hands with antibacterial soap.

8. For the safe disposal of bacterial cultures, autoclave the petri dishes and discard them without opening. If no autoclave is available, carefully open the dishes (never have a student do this), pour full-strength bleach into the dishes, and let them stand for a day. Then pour the bleach from the petri dishes down a drain and flush the drain with lots of water. Tape the petri dishes back together and place them in a sealed plastic bag. Wrap the plastic bag with a brown paper bag or newspaper and tape securely. Throw the sealed package in the trash. Thoroughly disinfect the work area with bleach.

9. To grow mold, use a new, sealable plastic bag that is two to three times larger than the material to be placed inside. Seal the bag and tape it shut. After the bag is sealed, students should not open it. To dispose of the bag and mold culture, make a small cut near an edge of the bag and cook the bag in a microwave oven on a high setting for at least one minute. Discard the bag according to local ordinance, usually in the trash.

Laboratory Safety

Laboratory Safety · *Science Safety Rules*

Science Safety Rules

To prepare yourself to work safely in the laboratory, read the following safety rules. Then read them a second time. Make sure you understand and follow each rule. Ask your teacher to explain any rules you do not understand.

Dress Code

1. To protect yourself from injuring your eyes, wear safety goggles whenever you work with chemicals, flames, glassware, or any substance that might get into your eyes. If you wear contact lenses, notify your teacher.

2. Wear an apron or a lab coat whenever you work with corrosive chemicals or substances that can stain.

3. Tie back long hair to keep it away from any chemicals, flames, or equipment.

4. Remove or tie back any article of clothing or jewelry that can hang down and touch chemicals, flames, or equipment. Roll up or secure long sleeves.

5. Never wear open shoes or sandals.

General Precautions

6. Read all directions for an experiment several times before beginning the activity. Carefully follow all written and oral instructions. If you are in doubt about any part of the experiment, ask your teacher for assistance.

7. Never perform activities that are not assigned or authorized by your teacher. Obtain permission before "experimenting" on your own. Never handle any equipment unless you have specific permission.

8. Never perform lab activities without direct supervision.

9. Never eat or drink in the laboratory.

10. Keep work areas clean and tidy at all times. Bring only notebooks and lab manuals or written lab procedures to the work area. All other items, such as purses and backpacks, should be left in a designated area.

11. Do not engage in horseplay.

First Aid

12. Always report all accidents or injuries to your teacher, no matter how minor. Notify your teacher immediately about any fires.

13. Learn what to do in case of specific accidents, such as getting acid in your eyes or on your skin. (Rinse acids from your body with plenty of water.)

14. Be aware of the location of the first-aid kit, but do not use it unless instructed by your teacher. In case of injury, your teacher should administer first aid. Your teacher may also send you to the school nurse or call a physician.

15. Know the location of the emergency equipment such as the fire extinguisher and fire blanket.

16. Know the location of the nearest telephone and whom to contact in an emergency.

Heating and Fire Safety

17. Never use a heat source, such as a candle, burner, or hot plate, without wearing safety goggles.

18. Never heat anything unless instructed to do so. A chemical that is harmless when cool may be dangerous when heated.

19. Keep all combustible materials away from flames. Never use a flame or spark near a combustible chemical.

20. Never reach across a flame.

21. Before using a laboratory burner, make sure you know proper procedures for lighting and adjusting the burner, as demonstrated by your teacher. Do not touch the burner. It may be hot. Never leave a lighted burner unattended. Turn off the burner when it is not in use.

22. Chemicals can splash or boil out of a heated test tube. When heating a substance in a test tube, make sure that the mouth of the tube is not pointed at you or anyone else.

23. Never heat a liquid in a closed container. The expanding gases produced may shatter the container.

24. Before picking up a container that has been heated, first hold the back of your hand near it. If you can feel heat on the back of your hand, the container is too hot to handle. Use an oven mitt to pick up a container that has been heated.

Laboratory Safety ▪ *Science Safety Rules*

Using Chemicals Safely

25. Never mix chemicals "for the fun of it." You might produce a dangerous, possibly explosive substance.

26. Never put your face near the mouth of a container that holds chemicals. Many chemicals are poisonous. Never touch, taste, or smell a chemical unless you are instructed by your teacher to do so.

27. Use only those chemicals needed in the activity. Read and double-check labels on supply bottles before removing any chemicals. Take only as much as you need. Keep all containers closed when chemicals are not being used.

28. Dispose of all chemicals as instructed by your teacher. To avoid contamination, never return chemicals to their original containers. Never pour untreated chemicals or other substances into the sink or trash containers.

29. Be extra careful when working with acids or bases. Pour all chemicals over the sink or a container, not over your work surface.

30. If you are instructed to test for odors, use a wafting motion to direct the odors to your nose. Do not inhale the fumes directly from the container.

31. When mixing an acid and water, always pour the water into the container first and then add the acid to the water. Never pour water into an acid.

32. Take extreme care not to spill any material in the laboratory. Wash chemical spills and splashes immediately with plenty of water. Immediately begin rinsing with water any acids that get on your skin or clothing, and notify your teacher of any acid spill at the same time.

Using Glassware Safely

33. Never force glass tubing or a thermometer into a rubber stopper or rubber tubing. Have your teacher insert the glass tubing or thermometer if required for an activity.

34. If you are using a laboratory burner, use a wire screen to protect glassware from any flame. Never heat glassware that is not thoroughly dry on the outside.

35. Keep in mind that hot glassware looks cool. Never pick up glassware without first checking to see if it is hot. Use an oven mitt. See rule 24.

36. Never use broken or chipped glassware. If glassware breaks, notify your teacher and dispose of the glassware in the proper broken-glassware container.

37. Never eat or drink from glassware.

38. Thoroughly clean glassware before putting it away.

Using Sharp Instruments

39. Handle scalpels or other sharp instruments with extreme care. Never cut material toward you; cut away from you.

40. Immediately notify your teacher if you cut your skin when working in the laboratory.

Animal and Plant Safety

41. Never perform experiments that cause pain, discomfort, or harm to animals. This rule applies at home as well as in the classroom.

42. Animals should be handled only if absolutely necessary. Your teacher will instruct you how to handle each animal species brought into the classroom.

43. If you know that you are allergic to certain plants, molds, or animals, tell your teacher before doing an activity in which these are used.

44. During field work, protect your skin by wearing long pants, long sleeves, socks, and closed shoes. Know how to recognize the poisonous plants and fungi in your area, as well as plants with thorns, and avoid contact with them. Never eat any part of a plant or fungus.

45. Wash your hands thoroughly after handling animals or a cage containing animals. Wash your hands when you are finished with any activity involving animal parts, plants, or soil.

End-of-Experiment Rules

46. After an experiment has been completed, turn off all burners or hot plates. If you used a gas burner, check that the gas-line valve to the burner is off. Unplug hot plates.

47. Turn off and unplug any other electrical equipment that you used.

48. Clean up your work area and return all equipment to its proper place.

49. Dispose of waste materials as instructed by your teacher.

50. Wash your hands after every experiment.

Laboratory Safety

Laboratory Safety • *Safety Symbols*

Safety Symbols

These symbols appear in laboratory activities. They warn of possible dangers in the laboratory and remind you to work carefully.

Safety Goggles Wear safety goggles to protect your eyes in any activity involving chemicals, flames or heating, or glassware.

Lab Apron Wear a laboratory apron to protect your skin and clothing from damage.

Breakage Handle breakable materials, such as glassware, with care. Do not touch broken glassware.

Heat-Resistant Gloves Use an oven mitt or other hand protection when handling hot materials such as hot plates or hot glassware.

Plastic Gloves Wear disposable plastic gloves when working with harmful chemicals and organisms. Keep your hands away from your face, and dispose of the gloves according to your teacher's instructions.

Heating Use a clamp or tongs to pick up hot glassware. Do not touch hot objects with your bare hands.

Flames Before you work with flames, tie back loose hair and clothing. Follow instructions from your teacher about lighting and extinguishing flames.

No Flames When using flammable materials, make sure there are no flames, sparks, or other exposed heat sources present.

Corrosive Chemical Avoid getting acid or other corrosive chemicals on your skin or clothing or in your eyes. Do not inhale the vapors. Wash your hands after the activity.

Poison Do not let any poisonous chemical come into contact with your skin, and do not inhale its vapors. Wash your hands when you are finished with the activity.

Fumes Work in a ventilated area when harmful vapors may be involved. Avoid inhaling vapors directly. Only test an odor when directed to do so by your teacher, and use a wafting motion to direct the vapor toward your nose.

Sharp Object Scissors, scalpels, knives, needles, pins, and tacks can cut your skin. Always direct a sharp edge or point away from yourself and others.

Animal Safety Treat live or preserved animals or animal parts with care to avoid harming the animals or yourself. Wash your hands when you are finished with the activity.

Plant Safety Handle plants only as directed by your teacher. If you are allergic to certain plants, tell your teacher; do not do an activity involving those plants. Avoid touching harmful plants such as poison ivy. Wash your hands when you are finished with the activity.

Electric Shock To avoid electric shock, never use electrical equipment around water, or when the equipment is wet or your hands are wet. Be sure cords are untangled and cannot trip anyone. Unplug equipment not in use.

Physical Safety When an experiment involves physical activity, avoid injuring yourself or others. Alert your teacher if there is any reason you should not participate.

Disposal Dispose of chemicals and other laboratory materials safely. Follow the instructions from your teacher.

Hand Washing Wash your hands thoroughly when finished with the activity. Use antibacterial soap and warm water. Rinse well.

General Safety Awareness When this symbol appears, follow the instructions provided. When you are asked to develop your own procedure in a lab, have your teacher approve your plan before you go further.

Name _____ Date _____ Class _____

Laboratory Safety Contract

I, _____ ,

(please print full name)

have read the Science Safety Rules and Safety Symbols sections, understand their contents completely, and agree to demonstrate compliance with all safety rules and guidelines that have been established in each of the following categories:

(please check)

❑ Dress Code

❑ General Precautions

❑ First Aid

❑ Heating and Fire Safety

❑ Using Chemicals Safely

❑ Using Glassware Safely

❑ Using Sharp Instruments

❑ Animal and Plant Safety

❑ End-of-Experiment Rules

_____

(signature)

Date _____

Name _____ Date _____ Class _____

Social Studies: Squanto

The paragraphs below describe Tisquantum, a Native American of the Pawtuxet tribe, who was also known as Squanto. Read the paragraphs and answer the questions that follow on the lines below.

Little is known about Squanto's early life in New England beyond the fact that he learned English from English settlers. Then, in 1614, he was captured and enslaved by an English captain and taken to Spain. When he was finally able to return to America, he joined a trading and exploring expedition of the Newfoundland Company. Squanto acted as a guide and interpreter on this trip, which resulted in a map of the natural resources along the New England coast.

When Squanto returned to his home, he found that most of the members of his tribe, the Pawtuxet, had been killed by disease. So, Squanto joined a neighboring tribe, the Wampanoags. In 1620, the Pilgrims began to build a colony at Plymouth, where the Pawtuxet tribe had once lived. The following year, Squanto helped to bring about a peace treaty between the Pilgrims and the Wampanoag tribe. In the treaty, the two groups agreed that they would not attack each other and that they would defend each other if one was threatened. Later that year, the Pilgrims celebrated the harvest with the Wampanoag tribe. This was the forerunner of our Thanksgiving celebration. Squanto lived with the Pilgrims at Plymouth until his death in 1622. He taught them many skills they needed to survive in America, including how to grow corn and where to catch fish.

1. How might Squanto's knowledge of English have helped him return home?

   _____

   _____

2. Why do you think Squanto made a good guide for the expedition of the Newfoundland Company?

   _____

   _____

3. How might American history have been different if Squanto had refused to teach the English how to survive in America?

   _____

   _____

4. Why do you think the Pilgrims didn't know how to grow corn?

   _____

   _____

Name _____ Date _____ Class _____

Social Studies: Acres of Corn Planted

Each state in the map below contains two numbers. The top number is equal to the number of thousands of acres of corn planted in that state during 1998. For example, the top number in the state of Texas is 2,300. This means that 2,300,000 acres (2,300 × 1,000 acres) of corn were planted in Texas during 1998. The bottom number in each state is equal to the percentage change in the number of acres of corn planted from 1997 to 1998. For example, the number of acres of corn planted in Texas during 1998 was 15 percent greater than the number of acres planted during 1997. If the bottom number in a state is negative, fewer acres of corn were planted in 1998 than in 1997.

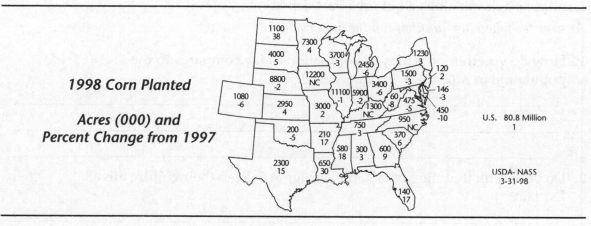

1998 Corn Planted

Acres (000) and Percent Change from 1997

U.S. 80.8 Million 1

USDA- NASS 3-31-98

Answer the following questions on the lines below.

1. Which state planted the most acres of corn in 1998?

   _____

2. Which state had the highest percentage increase in the number of acres of corn planted from 1997 to 1998?

   _____

3. How many acres of corn did the state of Illinois plant in 1998?

   _____

4. How many fewer acres of corn did the state of Illinois plant in 1998 compared to 1997? Round your answer to the nearest hundred thousand acres.

   _____

5. Which states planted more than five million acres of corn in 1998?

   _____

6. How many thousand acres of corn did the state of Oklahoma plant in 1997?

   _____

Interdisciplinary Exploration ▪ *Corn—The Amazing Grain*

Social Studies: The Maya

The Mayan civilization lasted over 3,000 years, from about 2,000 B.C. to about A.D. 1521, just before the Spanish began to rule Mexico. However, the Spanish never succeeded in eliminating the Mayan language, dress, or religious ceremonies. Small Mayan groups still exist today.

The Maya were an agrarian society centered on corn. They developed methods of irrigation and had a religious system based on worshipping the gods of the sun, moon, rain, and corn. They believed the corn god would give them a good harvest if they worshipped him. Besides corn, the Maya also grew beans, squash, yucca, and a kind of sweet potato. However, corn was the principal part of their diet. For example, they ate tamales and tortillas and drank atole, a hot breakfast drink.

Answer the following questions on the lines below.

1. How do you think the Mayan population today compares to the population in A.D. 1521? Explain.

   _____

   _____

   _____

2. Do you think that the Maya had to struggle to keep their culture alive? Explain.

   _____

   _____

3. What do you think *agrarian* means? What words in the second paragraph help you understand the meaning of the word *agrarian*?

   _____

   _____

4. What is *atole* made from? How do you know?

   _____

   _____

5. Modern farmers use pipes, hoses, and sprinklers to irrigate their crops. Think of some methods that the ancient Maya may have used to irrigate their crops.

   _____

   _____

   _____

Name _____ Date _____ Class _____

Interdisciplinary Exploration • *Corn—The Amazing Grain*

Language Arts: Write a Letter

In your text, you read about the mysterious maiden who left the family when her husband's brother insulted the bread she had made.

1. Imagine you are the brother. Your family urges you to write the corn maiden a letter of apology. Reread the story and then write your letter. You can use the paragraph starters on the lines below or use your own ideas and write your letter on a separate sheet of paper.

   Dear Sister-in-law,

   Please forgive me for insulting the bread you made. I am a great hunter and I thought

   _____
   _____
   _____
   _____

   Now I know the Great Spirit gave us the corn so we would

   _____
   _____
   _____
   _____

   Without corn to make bread, our people will

   _____
   _____
   _____
   _____

   So please forgive me.
   Sincerely,

2. What kind of person do you think the brother was? How do you know?

   _____
   _____
   _____

Name _____ Date _____ Class _____

Language Arts: Got an "Ear" for Corny Words?

With a partner, brainstorm a list of words and phrases relating to corn. On the lines below, list all the words and expressions you can think of that contain the word corn. *When you have run out of ideas, use a dictionary, thesaurus, or encyclopedia to help you find more words and expressions. Record your results on the lines below. Use the words and expressions as inspiration for a short story about corn. Use as many of the words as you can in your story.*

Words or expressions that contain the word *corn*.

_____

_____

_____

_____

_____

_____

_____

_____

_____

_____

_____

Use the words and expressions on your list to write a short story about corn. Your story may be about the value of corn for an ancient civilization, the reaction of the Europeans in the 1500s when they tasted corn for the first time, a farm where corn is grown, or any other aspect of corn. Be creative.

Name _____ Date _____ Class _____

Language Arts: The Other Corn Goddess

The paragraphs below explain the origin of the English word corn *and explain how the word is used in the folk tales of another ancient culture. Read the paragraphs and answer the questions that follow on the lines below.*

The English word *corn* comes from an Old English word for *grain*. There are written records that prove that this word was used as early as the 9th century, well before Europeans were first introduced to corn in South and Central America. In the United States, *corn* refers strictly to one grain, also known as *maize*, but the word *corn* is used by English speakers outside the Americas to refer to a grain that is important in their culture, such as wheat or barley.

This explains the ancient Greek story of Demeter, known as the corn goddess because she was believed to be responsible for the growth of grain. According to legend, Demeter's daughter Persephone was kidnapped by the god of the underworld. When Demeter took a long journey to find her daughter, there was a great famine because in her grief she had stopped tending to the harvest of the grain. In order to restore the natural harvest, a powerful god rescued Persephone and allowed her to live with her mother for three seasons of the year. For the fourth season, however, she returned to the underworld. This legend was thought to explain why the fields were barren during one season out of the year.

1. How is the ancient Greek story of Demeter similar to the story of the Corn Goddess?

   _____

   _____

2. Brainstorm a list of foods that you think might serve the same purpose for other cultures as corn for the Native Americans and grain for the ancient Greeks. For example, for many people rice is an important food.

   _____

   _____

3. Find out about legends in other cultures that are similar to the legend of the Corn Goddess or of Demeter, or write your own. Write a paragraph describing the similarities between the legends.

   _____

   _____

   _____

   _____

Interdisciplinary Exploration

Interdisciplinary Exploration ▪ *Corn—The Amazing Grain*

Science: How to Plant Corn

The following instructions can be found on a packet of field corn. Read the instructions and answer the questions that follow on the lines below.

Culture: Plant early to assure good, dry ripeness. Sow around last frost date in spring, 2.5 cm deep, about 3 seeds per 30 cm, in rows 75-90 cm apart. Thin to 20-30 cm apart. Plant in blocks of at least 4 rows to assure complete pollination and well-filled ears. Isolate from sweet corn, because pollen from field corn will reduce its sweetness. Cultivate shallowly as plants become large to avoid trimming roots.

Harvest: Pick after husks are drying and kernels are becoming hard. Hang or spread out in an airy place under cover to complete drying before shelling. Improperly dried corn will spoil.

Notes: Corn germinates best at soil temperature of 65–85 °F (18–29 °C). Many growers plant early in colder soil. Take care to avoid wet pieces of ground. We suggest treating seeds with chemicals that kill fungus to help prevent seed rot in these cold and/or wet soils. The cooler and more northerly the location, the longer field corn takes to mature.

Insect Pests: Chop or plow under corn stubble in the fall to discourage overwintering of insects such as corn borers. Where borers are evident in a crop, some control is offered with regular spraying with rotenone or pyrethrum or with other sprays recommended to kill insects.

1. There are 200 seeds in the packet and you plant four rows of seeds. Each seed is spaced the maximum recommended distance. How long are your rows of corn?

   _____

2. Do the seed suppliers expect every seed to sprout? Explain your reasoning.

   _____

   _____

   _____

3. What happens if you plant corn in cold wet soil?

   _____

   _____

   _____

4. Would you expect corn to mature faster in Indiana or Minnesota? Explain your reasoning. _____

   _____

   _____

5. What is a corn borer? What does it feed on?

   _____

   _____

Name_____ Date_____ Class_____

Science: How Does Popcorn Pop?

In this activity, you will learn how popcorn pops and then perform an experiment. Follow the instructions step by step and record your results on the lines below.

Popcorn is a special kind of corn that has hard kernels. When popcorn is harvested, it is dried for a certain amount of time so that it will have the correct moisture content. Moisture inside the kernel expands when it is heated. It pushes out the starchy part of the kernel, popping it through the seed coat. The "white bloom" that results is much larger than the original kernel.

In this activity, you will find out how drying commercial popcorn affects how well it pops.

Materials

unpopped popcorn

either: oil and pot with lid

or: popcorn popper

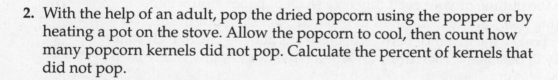

Seed coat
protects the kernel

Bran is made from
the seed coat

Stored food
*inner starchy part that
feeds the embryo*

Embryo
*the part of the seed
that will develop into
a new corn plant*

Corn oil is made from
the embryo

1. Count 100 unpopped popcorn kernels and spread them out on a tray. To dry the kernels, either place the tray in a warm area where it will be undisturbed for a week or bake the popcorn kernels for 90 minutes at 200 °F with the supervision of an adult.

2. With the help of an adult, pop the dried popcorn using the popper or by heating a pot on the stove. Allow the popcorn to cool, then count how many popcorn kernels did not pop. Calculate the percent of kernels that did not pop.

_____

3. Count 100 kernels of popcorn fresh from the container. Pop the fresh popcorn. Allow the popcorn to cool, then count how many popcorn kernels did not pop. Calculate the percent of kernels that did not pop.

_____

4. Compare the failure rate of dried popcorn to the failure rate of fresh popcorn. How do they compare?

_____

5. What can you conclude about how moisture affects the popping ability of popcorn?

_____

Interdisciplinary Exploration ▪ *Corn—The Amazing Grain*

Science: Build a Maize Maze

In this activity, you will read about a maize maze and then follow the instructions for building your own, step by step.

In 1996, an Iowa businessman named Paul Christophers decided to build a maize maze as a fund raiser for local nonprofit organizations. With the help of an architectural student, Mr. Christophers designed a maze to celebrate Iowa's 150th anniversary. The maze said "Iowa 150" and featured Iowa's original state emblem. A farmer donated his time and machinery to plant the corn, and a seed company donated the seed.

The maze covered a seven-acre piece of land; Christophers believed it was the world's largest maze. The corn stalks were placed about 75 cm apart to make a maze containing nearly 5 kilometers of paths. Christophers expected people to need nearly two hours to work their way through the maze.

In this activity, you will design and plant your own maze. You can use corn seeds, but sunflower seeds will sprout faster. Your maze should be growing well within a week.

Materials

- corn or sunflower seeds
- potting soil
- seed tray about 2 inches deep; the larger the surface area the better

1. Trace the outline of your seed tray on a sheet of paper. You will be planting seeds about 2 cm apart to make the walls of your maze. You should make the distance between your walls about 4 cm. Sketch walls lightly in pencil and then draw an X or a large dot to show where each seed will go.

2. Fill your seed tray three-quarters full with potting soil. Following your maze design, lay your seeds out in the tray. Do not push them into the soil. Simply lay them flat.

3. Gently add the last one quarter of potting soil. Do not pat the soil down or press on it; if you do, the seeds will not be able to sprout. Gently water the tray so the surface is evenly damp. Make sure the soil is damp but not wet when you touch it. Then place your tray in a bright location. Direct sun is helpful but not necessary.

4. Check the soil every day for about a week. Within a week, most of your seeds should have sprouted and be at least 2 cm tall.

5. Display your maze with your original design.

Name _____ Date _____ Class _____

Mathematics: World Corn Production and Use

Study the tables from the U.S. Department of Agriculture on the next page. Then answer the following questions on the lines below. Round all percents to the nearest whole percent. For example, if the answer you calculate is 22.0561%, round it to 22%.

1. Which country was the second highest producer of corn in 1996/97?
   _____

2. In 1997/98, more corn was used than was produced. Where do you think the extra corn came from? Explain your reasoning.
   _____
   _____
   _____

3. In 1997/98, which countries (of those countries listed in both tables) produced more corn than they used?
   _____

4. Which country's corn production increased the most between 1996/97 and 1997/98? By how many metric tons did production increase in that country?
   _____
   _____

5. Which country's corn use increased the most between 1996/97 and 1997/98? By how many metric tons did use increase in that country?
   _____
   _____

6. What percent of the world's corn did the United States produce in 1996/97?
   _____

7. What percent of the world's corn did the United States consume in 1996/97?
   _____

8. What percent of the world's corn did the United States consume in 1997/98?
   _____

9. By how many percentage points did the United States' share of world consumption change from 1996/97 to 1997/98?
   _____

Interdisciplinary Exploration • *Corn—The Amazing Grain*

Mathematics: World Corn Production and Use

	Production 1996/97 (1000s of metric tons)	Production 1997/98 (1000s of metric tons)
Brazil	35,800	33,000
Canada	7,380	7,180
China	127,470	105,000
Egypt	5,825	5,700
Hungary	5,900	6,200
India	10,100	10,000
Indonesia	6,500	6,500
Mexico	19,500	18,500
Romania	9,610	12,500
South Africa	9,012	7,500
United States	236,064	237,897
Yugoslavia	7,600	9,500
Others	111,286	119,052
TOTAL	592,047	578,529

	Use 1996/97 (1000s of metric tons)	Use 1997/98 (1000s of metric tons)
Brazil	37,150	34,300
Canada	7,650	7,950
China	115,353	121,250
Egypt	8,907	8,900
Hungary	5,350	5,000
India	10,100	10,000
Indonesia	7,344	7,200
Mexico	23,441	22,600
Romania	9,080	10,550
South Africa	8,062	7,900
United States	179,190	195,208
Yugoslavia	7,200	7,875
Others	163,890	167,593
TOTAL	573,637	595,776

Name _____ Date _____ Class _____

Mathematics: Volume Increase of Popcorn

In this experiment, you will calculate the increase in volume after popcorn is popped. Follow the instructions step by step and record your results on the lines below.

Materials

- unpopped popcorn
- either oil and pot with lid or popcorn popper
- graduated two-cup measuring cup showing eighths of a cup

1. Measure 1/8 of a cup of popcorn kernels in the measuring cup. Predict how much popped popcorn will result from this volume of kernels to the nearest 1/8 of a cup. Write your prediction here.

   _____

2. With the help of an adult, pop the popcorn using the popper or by heating a pot on the stove.

3. Pour the popcorn into the measuring cup. Shake the cup gently to help the popcorn settle, but do not squash the popcorn into the cup. Record the volume of popcorn here. If there is more popcorn than will fit in the measuring cup, fill the cup to the two-cup line, empty the cup, and fill the cup again with the remaining popcorn. Add the two volumes to find the total volume of the popped popcorn.

   _____

4. To find the increase in volume, subtract the volume of the unpopped popcorn (1/8 c) from the total volume of the popped popcorn.

   _____

5. Find the percent increase in volume. For example, if you began with 1/8 cup and the volume increased by 5/8 cup, 5/8c ÷ 1/8c = 5. The volume increased 5 times or by 500%.

   _____

6. Estimate what volume of unpopped kernels you would need to pop to fill a gallon milk container with popped popcorn.

   _____

Social Studies: Squanto

1. Answers may vary. Sample: Because he knew English, he would be able to tell the story of his capture to the people on board the English ship. As a result, they might have agreed to let him return to America with them.

2. He grew up in New England, so he was familiar with the land. Also, he could translate between English and his own Native American language. This could be useful in arranging trade between the English and the Native Americans.

3. Accept all reasonable answers. Sample: The English settlers might have died. As a result, a successful British colony might not have been established for many years.

4. The Pilgrims didn't know how to grow corn because corn was not native to England where the Pilgrims came from.

Social Studies: Acres of Corn Planted

1. Iowa
2. North Dakota
3. 11,100,000 acres
4. 100,000 acres
5. Iowa, Illinois, Nebraska, Minnesota, Indiana
6. 211

Social Studies: The Maya

1. Accept all reasonable answers. Sample: Many probably speak Spanish as well as the Mayan language. Modern Mayan groups probably still eat some of the same foods, such as tamales and tortillas, as the Maya who lived long ago.

2. Answers may vary. Sample: Yes, I think they had to struggle to keep their culture alive because the Spanish brought their own customs, language, and religion to Mexico. When the Spanish began to rule, they probably tried to impose their own culture on the Native Americans.

3. *Agrarian* means "agriculture" or "relating to farming." Corn; irrigation; harvest

4. *Atole* is made from corn. The previous sentence says corn was a principal part of the Maya's diet.

5. Accept all reasonable answers. Sample: The Maya may have dug irrigation ditches and built troughs to direct water toward their fields. They may have built dams to collect river water or rain water.

Language Arts: Write a Letter

1. Accept all letters that are supported by details from the text. Make sure the letter content is consistent with the story.

Sample letter: Dear Sister-in-law, Please forgive me for insulting the bread you made. I am a great hunter and I thought you were threatening my power. I was afraid that if our people started to eat bread, they wouldn't want to eat meat anymore. Then there would be no need for hunters.

Now I know the Great Spirit gave us the corn so we would have something to eat when our hunters can't find game. Without corn to make bread, our people will go hungry this winter. Our children will cry, and some of us may even starve. Now I understand how wrong I was to dishonor the Great Spirit's gift.

2. The brother was proud, arrogant, and rude; otherwise he would not have thrown the bread on the ground.

Language Arts: Got an "Ear" for Corny Words?

Accept all words and expressions that contain corn. Samples are: corn bread, corn flakes, corn meal, corn dogs, corn syrup, corn oil, popcorn, canned corn, creamed corn, candy corn, corn stalk, caramel corn, sweet corn, Indian corn, corn-on-the-cob, cornstarch, cornfields, cornrows, peppercorn, corned beef, corny, cornball, cornucopia, cornflower

Students' stories will vary but should use as many "corn" words as possible and should be about corn in some way.

Language Arts: The Other Corn Goddess

1. In both stories, a famine occurs when the corn goddess goes away.

2. Answers will vary. Samples: rice, potatoes, barley, wheat

3. Students' answers will vary. Many cultures have stories about an Earth mother or goddess of harvests or agriculture. There are also many stories about how certain important foods came into existence. Students' comparisons should describe the similarities between the legends.

Science: How to Plant Corn

1. 5 m

(200 seeds) / (4 rows) = (50 seeds) / (row)

(50 seeds) / (row) × (10 cm) / (seed) = (500 cm) / (row)

2. No. Reasoning may vary; sample: they tell you to plant 1 seed every 10 cm but later you thin to 1 seed every 20 to 30 cm so they expect some seeds to fail.

3. It does not sprout and fungus grows on it.

4. Indiana is further south than Minnesota so I expect corn to mature faster in Indiana.

5. A corn borer is an insect that eats corn stalks.

Science: How Does Popcorn Pop?

Instructions for Steps 2 and 3

If possible, use a microwave or electric hot-air popper to pop corn. Otherwise, pop corn in a heavy saucepan with a loose lid. Use 1/3 c oil for every cup of kernels. Heat oil to between 400–460°F. CAUTION: *If the oil smokes, it is too hot.* Carefully place one or two fresh kernels in the pan to test the oil. Add the rest of the popcorn when the first two kernels pop. Cover and shake the pan. Remove from heat when the sound of popping slows down.

2. Answers will vary. Sample: 40%

3. Answers will vary. Sample: 10%

4. The failure rate of the dried popcorn is much higher than the failure rate of fresh popcorn.

5. Popcorn that has dried out does not pop as well as fresh popcorn that contains moisture.

Mathematics: World Corn Production and Use

1. China

2. Accept all reasonable answers; most likely, extra corn was stored in previous years in case there was a shortage.

3. Hungary, Romania, United States, Yugoslavia

4. Romania's corn production increased 2,890 metric tons.

5. United States' corn consumption increased 16,018 metric tons.

6. 40%

7. 31%

8. 33%

9. It increased 2 percentage points.

Mathematics: Volume Increase of Popcorn

1. Answers will vary. Estimates must be more than 1/8 cup. The best estimates will be between 2 and 5 cups.

2. Answers will vary. Sample: 4 cups

3. Answers will vary. Sample: 3 7/8 cups

4. Answers will vary. Sample: 3,100%

5. Estimates will vary. Sample: 3/8 cup

Interdisciplinary Exploration

Name _____ Date _____ Class _____

From Bacteria to Plants

Multiple Choice
Write the letter of the correct answer on the line at the left.

_____ 1. All living things have the following traits except
   a. having identical cells.
   b. using energy.
   c. containing similar chemicals.
   d. reproducing.

_____ 2. All bacteria
   a. contain nuclei.
   b. improve the lives of people.
   c. are prokaryotes.
   d. cause sickness.

_____ 3. A virus produces its own proteins inside its
   a. nuclei.
   b. cytoplasm.
   c. prokaryotes.
   d. host's cells.

_____ 4. About 3.6 billion years ago, Earth's atmosphere contained little
   a. oxygen.
   b. water vapor.
   c. carbon dioxide.
   d. methane.

_____ 5. Viruses
   a. make their own food.
   b. use energy to grow and develop.
   c. produce wastes.
   d. are considered nonliving.

_____ 6. Animal-like protists include all of the following except
   a. sarcodines.
   b. diatoms.
   c. zooflagellates.
   d. ciliates.

_____ 7. All fungi
   a. cause disease.
   b. live in symbiotic relationships with other organisms.
   c. reproduce with seeds.
   d. are eukaryotes.

From Bacteria to Plants • *Book Test*

_____ 8. A major function of vascular tissue in plants is to
   a. strengthen the cell wall.
   b. transport nutrients.
   c. perform photosynthesis.
   d. attract pollinators.

_____ 9. Gymnosperms are characterized by
   a. seeds not enclosed by a fruit.
   b. wide, flat leaves.
   c. shallow root systems.
   d. growing close to the ground.

_____ 10. Plant leaves show a positive tropism toward
   a. light.
   b. water.
   c. touch.
   d. gravity.

Completion

Fill in the line to complete each statement.

11. A virus's _____ is contained in its inner core.

12. The cell wall of a plant is made up mostly of _____.

13. The process during which nutrients build up in a pond over time and increase the growth of algae is called _____.

14. In its _____ stage, a plant produces sperm cells and egg cells.

15. Carbon dioxide enters leaves through small pores called _____.

True or False

If the statement is true, write **true**. *If it is false, change the underlined word or words to make the statement true.*

_____ 16. Scientists hypothesize that small chemical units of life formed gradually over millions of years in Earth's waters.

_____ 17. The genetic material of a bacterium is found in its nucleus.

_____ 18. Animal-like protists are called protozoans.

_____ 19. In fertilization, carbon dioxide and water combine in light to produce sugar and oxygen.

_____ 20. The process by which water evaporates from a plant's leaves is called transpiration.

From Bacteria to Plants • *Book Test*

Using Science Skills

Use the diagram below to answer the following questions.

21. **Classify** In the boxes above, write the names of the eight levels of groups that biologists use to classify organisms. Arrange them in order from broadest at the top to most specific at the bottom.

22. **Applying Concepts** What is Linnaeus's naming system called? Which levels in the chart are included in this system?

_____

Essay

Write an answer for each of the following.

23. How can a vaccine help prevent disease?

_____

_____

24. Compare and contrast a bacterial cell with the cell of a vascular plant.

_____

_____

_____

25. How is symbiosis a form of mutualism?

_____

_____

_____

_____

Name _____ Date _____ Class _____

From Bacteria to Plants • *Book Test*

Using Science Skills

Use the table below to answer the following questions.

	Moss	Fern	Angiosperm
Vascular tissue present?	no		
Potential height		tall	
Internal method of water transport?	water moves cell to cell only		
Requires moist environment for growth?	yes		
Reproduces with seeds or spores?			seeds

26. Compare/Contrast Complete the table above.

27. Classifying To which of these three groups are gymnosperms most similar? Explain.

_____

_____

Essay

Write an answer for each of the following.

28. Name and give one fact about each of the four kingdoms within domain eukarya.

_____

_____

29. Explain how the properties of light and chlorophyll make a leaf appear green in sunlight.

_____

_____

30. Compare and contrast asexual reproduction in bacteria with sexual reproduction in bacteria.

_____

_____

_____

_____

Book Test

1. a
2. c
3. d
4. a
5. d
6. b
7. d
8. b
9. a
10. a
11. genetic material
12. cellulose
13. eutrophication
14. gametophyte
15. stomata
16. true
17. cytoplasm
18. true
19. photosynthesis
20. true
21. domain, kingdom, phylum, class, order, family, genus, species
22. Binomial nomenclature; genus and species
23. A vaccine stimulates the body to produce chemicals that destroy specific disease-causing organisms. If that organism ever enters the body, it is destroyed before it can cause disease.
24. The cell wall is the outermost structure of a bacterium cell. Inside that is the cell membrane, which controls the passage of material to and from the inside of the bacterium. Genetic material and ribosomes are in the cytoplasm. Some bacteria have flagella that extend out from the cell wall. A plant cell has a cell wall made of cellulose. Inside is the cell membrane, and inside that is cytoplasm, in which there are different structures such as chloroplasts that make food and oxygen, ribosomes that make proteins, and a nucleus, in which the genetic material is contained.
25. Symbiosis is a close relationship between two species where at least one of the species benefits. When both species benefit, the relationship is called mutualism.

26.

Moss	Fern	Angiosperm
no	yes	yes
short	tall	tall
water moves cell to cell only	vascular tissue	vascular tissue
yes	yes	no, can live in quite dry places
spores	spores	seeds

27. Gymnosperms are most like angiosperms. They are vascular plants that reproduce with seeds. They can live in fairly dry habitats and grow tall.
28. Facts about the kingdoms will vary. Samples:
The four kingdoms within domain Eukarya are: protist, fungus, plant, and animal.
The protist kingdom is sometimes called the "odds and ends" kingdom because its members are so different from one another. Some are autotrophs, while others are heterotrophs. Most are unicellular but some, such as seaweeds, are multicellular.
Most fungi are multicellular, though some are unicellular. All are heterotrophs.
Plants are multicellular autotrophs.
Animals are multicellular. They are heterotrophs. They have adaptations that allow them to locate, capture, eat, and digest food.
29. Sunlight is made of different colors of light. When sunlight strikes chlorophyll in a leaf, most of the green light is reflected. Most of the other colors are absorbed. When we see the reflected green light, the leaf appears green.
30. Bacteria reproduce asexually by binary fission. In binary fission one cell is the parent. The result is two cells exactly like the parent. Some bacteria can reproduce by a simple form of sexual reproduction called conjugation. In conjugation, two bacteria exchange genetic material. Conjugation doesn't increase the number of bacteria cells, but it results in cells that are different from the parents.

Living Things

Lab zone™ Chapter Project Mystery Object

The following steps will walk you through the Chapter Project. Use the hints as you guide your students through planning, object observations, and presentations.

Chapter Project Overview

Before introducing the project, bring organisms, such as a plant and a fish, into the classroom to show to the students. Talk about the characteristics that these organisms share with other living things.

Have students read the Chapter Project Overview. Review the project's rules, and hand out the Chapter Scoring Rubric that you will use for scoring students' work. Discuss with students what will be expected of them.

Set a deadline for the project presentation and interim dates for Keep Students on Track activities at the end of Section 1, Section 2, and Section 4. Encourage students to copy the dates in the Project Timeline.

Have students brainstorm a list of characteristics that living things possess. They should also think about some nonliving things that share one or more of these characteristics.

Distribute copies of Chapter Project Worksheet 1. Have students read over the questions they will need to answer in the preliminary stage of this project.

Give each student a mystery object (see Materials and Preparation section for suggestions) and an instruction sheet describing how they should care for their object. Stress to students that it is important that they care for their object even if they do not believe that their object is living.

To maintain students' interest, be sure each student observes at least one object that undergoes visible changes or responds positively to some tests.

Chapter Project Worksheet 2 will help students through collecting data and preparing for the presentation. Remind students to refer to the hints in the Chapter Project Overview as they plan and carry out the project.

Materials and Preparation

Some possibilities for living mystery objects include baker's yeast (mix one teaspoonful each of yeast and sugar to 250 mL warm water; observe under microscope), seeds (soak lentil seeds in water overnight, then wrap in wet paper towel; place towel in plastic bag and store in dark; observe daily), brine shrimp, slime mold, bread mold, insect larvae, goldfish, and plants.

Some possibilities for nonliving mystery objects include pebbles, vermiculite, lead shot (they look like seeds), artificial plants (they look real but don't grow or have cellular structure), soluble salts in a saturated solution (crystal gardens appear to "grow"), hair (it has cellular structure, but is no longer living), and toys with microchips (they are capable of complex responses).

Students will also need to use various materials to test their mystery objects for signs of life. Such items would include a microscope, glass slides and coverslips, scissors, a plastic dropper, and a ruler. You may need to show students how to use a microscope.

Consider organizing the class in groups to do the project. You may also have students observe several different objects in the classroom. This would allow you to care for the objects, preventing students from harming living mystery objects.

Keep Students on Track— Section 1

Before you give students their mystery objects, make sure they have completed Chapter Project Worksheet 1. They should have a clear concept of the characteristics that are used to describe living organisms. They should also have thought of reasonable tests that they could use to observe these characteristics. Be sure that these tests will not harm the mystery objects.

Once students have received their objects, they should examine them carefully. If necessary, they should revise their list of life characteristics and the tests that they plan to use.

Mystery Object *(continued)*

Keep Students on Track— Section 2

Give students time in class each day to care for their mystery objects. During this time, have them record their observations.

Check students' observation records on a regular basis. Be sure students include diagrams that depict changes in the size and appearance of their objects.

Periodically, check the health of the objects. If the student's mystery object is an organism, be sure that it is still alive.

Keep Students on Track— Section 4

Tell students that analyzing their data means looking at their observations, summarizing them, finding patterns, and deciding what these patterns tell about their mystery object. Living organisms should be classified as completely as possible, given students' knowledge.

Remind students they will be introducing their mystery objects to the class. Let them decide how they want to make their presentations. Encourage students to be creative.

Chapter Project Wrap Up

As students give their reports, ask their classmates to take brief notes, writing down the major characteristics of each mystery object. Have the class decide whether they agree with the living/nonliving decision that the presenter made. If necessary, some students may have to defend their choice. Have them discuss the specific characteristics that led them to their decision, and ask the class whether they would have used different characteristics.

After all presentations have been made, have students evaluate their projects. Ask them to explain which characteristics of life were difficult to observe. Determine whether there were any common characteristics that all of the students had a difficult time observing. Discuss why this may be so. Have them write down advice to give to other students who might want to study characteristics of life in different objects.

Tell students about their mystery objects, including the classification groups the objects belong to (if applicable) and whether they are classified as living or not. Describe the characteristics of life, and explain why some of these may be hard to observe (e.g., they may occur at a different life stage).

Extension

In the 1970s, NASA sent a lander named *Viking* to Mars. *Viking* sent back pictures and other information describing the planet's surface, and scientists used some of this data to look for signs of life. Have students find out what characteristics scientists were most interested in looking for, and what kinds of instruments they used in order to detect them.

Living Things • *Chapter Project*   **Overview**

Chapter Project Mystery Object

In this project you will be observing a mystery object to determine whether or not it is living. Sound easy? Maybe. But sometimes it is difficult to determine whether an object is indeed living. What characteristics distinguish living from nonliving? How do you test for these characteristics? What if an object has some of the distinguishing characteristics, but not others?

You will begin this project by identifying characteristics that distinguish living organisms from nonliving objects. You will then need to develop tests that will help you to observe these characteristics in your mystery object. Finally, you will spend about two weeks observing your mystery object to determine whether it is living. At the conclusion of this project, you will present your observations and conclusions in a class presentation.

Project Rules

- Write out a plan for testing your object to determine whether it is living or nonliving. Your teacher will approve your research plans before giving you your mystery object.

- Your teacher will give you an instruction sheet describing how you must care for your object. You are responsible for the well-being of your mystery object and should care for it in every possible way.

- You must observe your mystery object daily, sketching diagrams and recording observations in a data table.

- When you have finished making your observations, you will need to draw conclusions about your object. If you determine that your object is living, try to classify it into domain and kingdom.

Suggested Materials

- Your mystery object, which will be given to you by your teacher

- Some items will be required for proper care of your object. Your teacher should include these on your instruction sheet.

- Items that you can use to observe your object include a microscope, glass slides and coverslips, scissors, a plastic dropper, and a ruler.

Living Things · *Chapter Project*

Project Hints

- Brainstorm a list of characteristics that living organisms share. Make sure you consider that not all organisms share every specific characteristic. For example, many living organisms move, but this characteristic alone does not describe all organisms. Trees are alive, but they do not move around. Also, some nonliving objects may share a specific characteristic. For examples, clouds and vehicles show movement.

- Before you conduct tests of your mystery objects, predict what observations will help to classify your object as living.

- When you observe your object, describe what the object looks like, what and how much it is eating, what it does, and anything else you think is important. Also, list things that may affect your object's behavior, such as the time of day, the temperature, and the weather.

- Recall that organisms in different domains and kingdoms get their food in different ways. If you think your object is alive and also think you know what domain or kingdom it belongs in, this knowledge can help you to design tests about nutrition and growth.

- There are many ways to present what you have learned. You can write a report, give a speech, draw illustrations with captions, or record a summary on videotape.

Project Timeline

Task   **Date Due**

1. Complete list of characteristics of living things.   _____

2. Propose a list of ways to test for characteristics of life.

3. Receive mystery object.   _____

4. Revise test plans to fit specific mystery object.   _____

5. Complete observations of object.   _____

6. Make presentation of object, and describe analysis
   and conclusions.   _____

Living Things

Living Things · *Chapter Project*

Mystery Object

Part I

Complete the following tasks using a separate sheet of paper. When the tasks have been completed, you are ready to get your teacher's approval and obtain your mystery object.

1. What characteristics do all living things share? Write a few sentences describing these characteristics, and explain why you chose them.

2. How can you test for these characteristics? For each characteristic that you listed above, describe at least two ways in which you could test an object for the characteristic. Make sure that you predict the results of these tests. What results would classify this organism as living?

3. For the tests that you described above, create a list of materials that you would need. Are these materials available to you? Are there any tests that you described that you would be unable to do in the time allowed? Redesign your tests, if necessary.

Part II

Complete the following tasks using a separate sheet of paper. When the tasks have been completed, you are ready to begin your tests and observations.

4. Look at your mystery object, and make an initial hypothesis about whether or not it is living. Write a few sentences describing the observations that support your hypothesis.

5. Reconsider the tests that you designed, making any necessary modifications (you may need to use a microscope to observe your object).

6. Write out a plan for how you will proceed with this project. What tests will you use? How often will you conduct these tests?

Name _____ Date _____ Class _____

Mystery Object

Record your observations in a data table organized like the one below. Include a description of the test you conducted, how the object responded, and anything else you think is important, such as sketches of your object.

Date	Time	Test Used	Observation

Analyzing and Presenting

Complete the following tasks on a separate sheet of paper. When they have been completed, you are ready to put together your presentation.

1. Write several sentences summarizing your research. What tests did you conduct that were helpful in determining whether your object is living? What tests were not helpful? Why?

2. Write several sentences summarizing your observations from the data table. Do you think that your object is living? What leads you to this conclusion? If your object is living, to which classification group does it belong?

3. Decide how you want to communicate what you have learned to your classmates. Make a list of the things you will need to make this presentation.

Living Things • *Chapter Project* **Scoring Rubric**

Mystery Object

In evaluating how well you complete the Chapter Project, your teacher will judge your work in the following categories. In each, a score of 4 is the best rating.

	4	3	2	1
Development of Hypothesis Based on Characteristics of Living Things	Considers several different characteristics of living things, including all those described in the textbook.	Considers several different characteristics of living things, but the list is missing one or two characteristics described in the textbook.	Considers some characteristics of living things, but the list is missing many characteristics described in the textbook.	Considers few characteristics of living things, and the list is short.
Design of Methods to Test Characteristics	Develops many feasible methods to test characteristics.	Develops many methods to test characteristics, but some are impractical.	Develops a few methods to test characteristics, some of which are unrelated to the characteristics described.	Chooses largely unreasonable methods to test the characteristics chosen.
Testing the Object and Making Observations	Tests and observes the object daily. Makes 15 complete observation entries on the object's responses.	Tests and observes the object on most days. Makes at least 12 complete observation entries on the object's responses.	Tests and observes the object several times. Makes 9 to 11 observation entries, but some may be unorganized or incomplete.	Rarely tests and observes the object. Makes six or fewer entries, which may be unorganized or incomplete.
Presenting the Project	Makes a thorough, well-organized presentation. Communicates why particular tests were chosen. Able to justify living/nonliving decision and choice of domain/kingdom.	Makes an adequate presentation. Somewhat able to communicate why particular tests were chosen. Somewhat able to justify living/nonliving decision and choice of domain/kingdom.	Makes a presentation, but it is hard to follow. Unable to communicate why particular tests were chosen. Unable to justify living/nonliving decision or choice of domain/kingdom.	Gives only a brief presentation. Unable to communicate the experimental design or justify living/nonliving decision or choice of domain/kingdom.

What Is Life?

2–3 periods, 1–1 1/2 blocks

ABILITY LEVELS KEY
L1 Basic to Average
L2 For All Students
L3 Average to Advanced

Objectives

A.1.1.1 List the characteristics all living things share.
A.1.1.2 Explain where living things come from.
A.1.1.3 Identify what all living things need to survive.

Key Terms

• organism • cell • unicellular • multicellular
• stimulus • response • development
• spontaneous generation
• controlled experiment • autotroph
• heterotroph • homeostasis

Local Standards

PRETEACH

Build Background Knowledge
Invite students to describe the most unusual thing they have seen and describe it as a plant, animal, or other life form.

 *Is It Living or Nonliving?* **L1**

Targeted Resources

❏ **All in One Teaching Resources**
  L2 Reading Strategy Transparency A1: Using Prior Knowledge
❏ ⊙ **PresentationExpress™ CD-ROM**

INSTRUCT

The Characteristics of Living Things Use questions to link the lesson subheadings with the lesson Key Concept.
Life Comes From Life Use a figure to summarize Redi's experiment.
The Needs of Living Things Describe the basic needs of living things, and give examples.

 Please Pass the Bread! **L2**

Targeted Resources

❏ **All in One Teaching Resources**
  L2 Guided Reading, pp. 47–50
  L2 Transparencies A2, A3
  L2 Lab: *Please Pass the Bread!* pp. 53–54
❏ **PHSchool.com** Web Code: cep-1011
❏ 📼 **Lab Activity Video**
  Skills Lab: *Please Pass the Bread!*
❏ ⊙ **Student Edition on Audio CD**

ASSESS

Section Assessment Questions
↻ Have students use their completed Using Prior Knowledge graphic organizers to answer the questions.

Reteach
Use a concept map to identify characteristics of living things.

Targeted Resources

❏ **All in One Teaching Resources**
  Section Summary, p. 46
  L1 Review and Reinforce, p. 51
  L3 Enrich, p. 52

Living Things · *Section Summary*

What Is Life?

Key Concepts

■ What characteristics do all living things share?

■ Where do living things come from?

■ What do living things need to survive?

Organisms are living things. All living things share six important characteristics. **All living things have a cellular organization, contain similar chemicals, use energy, respond to their surroundings, grow and develop, and reproduce.**

A **cell** is the basic unit of structure and function in an organism. **Unicellular,** or single-celled, organisms include bacteria, the most numerous organisms on Earth. **Multicellular** organisms are composed of many cells. The cells of organisms use energy to grow and repair injured parts.

Cells are composed of chemicals. The most abundant chemical in cells is water. Another chemical called carbohydrate is a cell's energy source. Proteins and lipids are the building materials of cells. Nucleic acids are the genetic materials that direct the cell's activities.

A change in an organism's surroundings that causes the organism to react is called a **stimulus.** An organism reacts to a stimulus with a **response**—an action or change in behavior.

Living things grow and develop. Growth is the process of becoming larger. **Development** is the process of change that occurs during an organism's life to produce a more complex organism.

Another characteristic of organisms is the ability to reproduce, or produce offspring that are similar to the parents. **Living things arise from living things through reproduction.**

People once believed the mistaken idea that living things arise from nonliving sources—an idea called **spontaneous generation.** Controlled experiments helped disprove spontaneous generation. In a **controlled experiment,** a scientist carries out two tests that are identical in every respect except for one factor, called the variable.

All organisms need four things to stay alive. **All living things must satisfy their basic needs for food, water, living space, and stable internal conditions.**

Organisms that make their own food are called **autotrophs.** Organisms that cannot make their own food are called **heterotrophs.** Heterotrophs consume autotrophs or other heterotrophs. All organisms need food, water, and living space. Because space on Earth is limited, some organisms compete for food and space.

Because conditions in their surroundings can change, organisms must be able to keep the conditions inside their bodies constant. The maintenance of stable internal conditions despite changes in surroundings is called **homeostasis.**

Living Things · *Guided Reading and Study*

What Is Life? (pp. 6–14)

This section explains the characteristics of living things and what living things need to survive.

Use Target Reading Skills

Look at the section headings and visuals to see what this section is about. Then write what you already know about living things in the graphic organizer below. As you read, write what you learn.

What You Know
1. Living things grow.
2.

What You Learned
1.
2.

The Characteristics of Living Things (pp. 7–9)

1. What is an organism?

   _____

   _____

Living Things · *Guided Reading and Study*

What Is Life? *(continued)*

2. List six characteristics that all living things share.

    a. _____

    b. _____

    c. _____

    d. _____

    e. _____

    f. _____

3. The basic building blocks of all organisms are _____ .

4. Is the following sentence true or false? Most cells can be seen only with a microscope, a tool that magnifies small objects. _____

5. Is the following sentence true or false? An organism made of many cells is a unicellular organism. _____

6. Circle the letter of the most abundant chemical in cells.
    a. proteins
    b. carbohydrates
    c. water
    d. nucleic acids

7. Lipids and _____ are the building materials of cells.

8. Is the following sentence true or false? The cells of organisms use energy for growth and repair. _____

9. Circle the letter of a change in an organism's surroundings that causes the organism to react.
    a. growth
    b. response
    c. stimulus
    d. development

Living Things • *Guided Reading and Study*

10. Give one example of a stimulus and one example of a response.

Stimulus: _____

Response: _____

11. What is development?

_____

_____

_____

12. All organisms can _____, or produce offspring that are similar to the parents.

Life Comes From Life (pp. 10–11)

13. Is the following sentence true or false? Flies can arise from rotting meat.

_____

14. The idea that living things can come from nonliving sources is called

_____.

15. What did Francesco Redi show in his experiment?

_____

_____

_____

_____

16. The factor that a scientist changes in a controlled experiment is the _____

_____.

17. Is the following sentence true or false? Louis Pasteur used a controlled experiment to show that bacteria arise from spontaneous generation.

_____

Name _____ Date _____ Class _____

The Needs of Living Things (pp. 12–14)

18. Complete this concept map to show what living things need to survive.

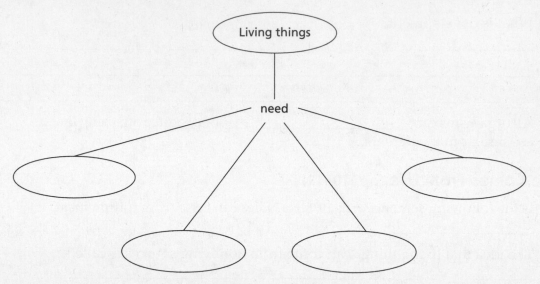

19. Is the following sentence true or false? Living things use food as their energy source to carry out their life functions. _____

20. Organisms that make their own food are called _____.
Organisms that cannot make their own food are called _____
_____.

21. Is the following sentence true or false? Living things can live without water for long periods of time. _____

22. Why do living things need water?

_____

_____

_____

23. Is the following sentence true or false? Organisms compete with each other for space to live. _____

24. Why must living things have homeostasis, or stable internal conditions?

_____

_____

Name _____ Date _____ Class _____

What Is Life?

Understanding Main Ideas

Answer the following questions on a separate sheet of paper.

1. What are six characteristics all living things share?
2. How did Redi's experiment help disprove the idea of spontaneous generation?
3. What are the four basic needs all living things must satisfy?
4. Describe the difference between growth and development.

Building Vocabulary

From the list below, choose the term that best completes each sentence.

autotrophs	heterotrophs	controlled experiment
unicellular	multicellular	organisms
spontaneous generation	homeostasis	stimulus
response	cell	reproduce
manipulated variable		

5. A change in an organism's environment that causes the organism to react is called a(n) _____.

6. Organisms that make their own food are _____.

7. _____ organisms are composed of many cells.

8. _____ is the mistaken idea that living organisms arise from nonliving sources.

9. Living things are also called _____.

10. The _____ is the basic unit of structure in an organism.

11. Organisms that get energy by consuming other organisms are _____.

12. An organism reacts to a stimulus with a(n) _____.

13. A(n) _____ is conducted by performing two tests that are identical except for one factor called the _____.

14. An organism's ability to maintain stable internal conditions is called _____.

15. To _____ is to produce offspring that are similar to the parents.

16. Bacteria, the most numerous organisms on Earth, are _____ organisms.

Name _____ Date _____ Class _____

Living Things · *Enrich*

Bacteria Counts

Many scientists use bacteria in the course of their research. They must provide the bacteria with the proper conditions for growth.

This is how one laboratory grows bacteria. A certain amount of bacteria are placed into a solution of water and nutrients the bacteria need as an energy source. After a period of a few days, a small amount of this solution is poured onto a *petri dish*, a shallow, round container with a cover, made from transparent plastic. Inside the petri dish is a layer of *agar*, usually a gelatin-like material that also contains nutrients and on which bacteria can grow. The petri dishes are then put in a warm, moist place for a week. After a week, the bacteria on each dish are counted. To do this, the scientist places each dish under a large magnifying glass that has a grid similar to graph paper drawn on it. She then counts the number of spots of bacteria growing on the agar in each of the squares on the grid. The individual bacterium is not counted; rather, each spot is actually a colony of bacteria. The scientist knows approximately how many bacteria are in a colony, so once she knows the number of colonies growing on a petri dish, she can calculate the number of bacteria present.

Here are the drawings one of the scientists made in her laboratory notebook of the petri dishes she examined. She has also noted the conditions the bacteria were grown in next to each drawing.

Study the drawings and the information next to each dish. On a separate sheet of paper, write a brief description of the conditions of each dish and explain why the bacteria appeared as they did.

1.
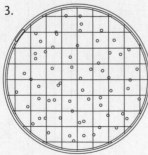

Growing conditions:
Fresh agar
37°C
moist environment
checked after 1 week

2.
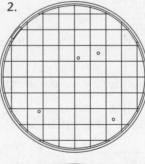

Growing conditions:
Fresh agar
0°C
moist environment
checked after 1 week

3.
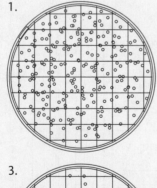

Growing conditions:
Old agar, past expiration date
37°C
moist environment
checked after 1 week

4.
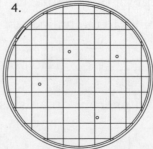

Growing conditions:
Fresh agar
37°C
moist environment
checked after 1 month

Name _____ Date _____ Class _____

Living Things · *Skills Lab*

Please Pass the Bread!

Problem

What factors are necessary for bread molds to grow?

Skills Focus

observing, controlling variables

Materials

paper plates

plastic dropper

bread without preservatives

sealable plastic bags

tap water

packing tape

Procedure

1. Brainstorm with others to predict which factors might affect the growth of bread mold. Record your ideas.

2. Place two slices of bread of the same size and thickness on separate, clean plates.

3. To test the effect of moisture on bread mold growth, add drops of tap water to one bread slice until the whole slice is moist. Keep the other slice dry. Expose both slices to the air for one hour.

4. Put each slice into its own sealable bag. Press the outside of each bag to remove the air. Seal the bags. Then use packing tape to seal the bags again. Store the bags in a warm, dark place.

5. Record your observations in the data table.

6. Every day for at least five days, briefly remove the sealed bags from their storage place. Record whether any mold has grown. Estimate the area of the bread where mold is present. **CAUTION:** *Do not unseal the bags. At the end of the experiment, give the sealed bags to your teacher.*

Living Things ▪ *Skills Lab*

Please Pass the Bread! *(continued)*

Data Table				
	Moistened Bread Slice		**Unmoistened Bread Slice**	
Day	**Mold Present?**	**Area with Mold**	**Mold Present?**	**Area with Mold**
1				
2				
3				
4				
5				

Analyze and Conclude

Write your answers on a separate sheet of paper.

1. **Observing** How did the appearance of the two slices of bread change over the course of the experiment?

2. **Inferring** How can you explain any differences in appearance between the two slices?

3. **Controlling Variables** What was the manipulated variable in this experiment? Why was it necessary to control all other variables except this one?

4. **Communicating** Suppose that you lived in Redi's time. A friend tells you that molds just suddenly appeared on bread. How would you explain to your friend about Redi's experiment and how it applies to molds and bread?

Design an Experiment

Choose another factor that may affect mold growth, such as temperature or the amount of light. Set up an experiment to test the factor you choose. Remember to keep all conditions the same except for the one you are testing. *Obtain your teacher's permission before carrying out your investigation.*

Classifying Organisms

🕐 *1–2 periods, 1/2–1 block*

ABILITY LEVELS KEY
L1 Basic to Average
L2 For All Students
L3 Average to Advanced

Objectives

A.1.2.1 Explain why biologists classify organisms.
A.1.2.2 Relate the levels of classification to the relationships between organisms.
A.1.2.3 Explain how taxonomic keys are useful.
A.1.2.4 Explain the relationship between classification and evolution.

Key Terms

• classification • taxonomy • binomial nomenclature • genus • species • evolution

Local Standards

PRETEACH

Build Background Knowledge
Invite students to describe how libraries are organized.

 Discover Activity *Can You Organize a Junk Drawer?* **L1**

Targeted Resources

❏ **All in One Teaching Resources**
　L2 Reading Strategy Transparency A4: Asking Questions
❏ 💿 **PresentationExpress™ CD-ROM**

INSTRUCT

Why Do Scientists Classify? Use an imaginary fish to discuss classification.
The Naming System of Linnaeus Define *genus* and *species* and apply to an example.
Level of Classification Use a drawing to discuss the levels of classification.
Taxonomic Keys Use a sample taxonomic key to discuss their usefulness.
Evolution and Classification Ask questions to help students relate evolution and classification.

 Skills Lab *Living Mysteries* **L2**

Targeted Resources

❏ **All in One Teaching Resources**
　L2 Guided Reading, pp. 57–60
　L2 Transparencies A5, A6
　L2 Lab: *Living Mysteries*, pp. 63–65
❏ 📼 **Lab Activity Video**
　Skills Lab: *Living Mysteries*
❏ **PHSchool.com** Web Code: ced-1012
❏ **Discovery SCHOOL Video Field Trip**
❏ 💿 **Student Edition on Audio CD**

ASSESS

Section Assessment Questions
🔄 Have students use their completed Asking Questions graphic organizers to answer the questions.

Reteach
Have students list the levels of classification from broad to specific.

Targeted Resources

❏ **All in One Teaching Resources**
　Section Summary, p. 56
　L1 Review and Reinforce, p. 61
　L3 Enrich, p. 62

Living Things · *Section Summary*

Classifying Organisms

Key Concepts

- Why do biologists organize living things into groups?
- What do the levels of classification indicate about the relationships among organisms?
- How are taxonomic keys useful?
- What is the relationship between classification and evolution?

Classification is the process of grouping things based on their similarities. **Biologists use classification to organize living things into groups so that the organisms are easier to study.** The scientific study of how living things are classified is called **taxonomy.**

The first scientist to develop a classification system for organisms was the Greek scholar Aristotle. Aristotle observed and divided animals into three groups: those that fly, those that swim, and those that walk, run, or crawl.

The Swedish scientist Carolus Linnaeus created a naming system for organisms called **binomial nomenclature,** in which each organism is given a two-part name. The first part of an organism's scientific name is its genus. A **genus** is a classification grouping that contains similar, closely related organisms. The second part of an organism's scientific name sets each species apart from one another in the genus. A **species** is a group of similar organisms that can mate and produce offspring that can also mate and reproduce.

Modern biologists classify organisms into eight levels. A domain is the broadest level of organization. Within a domain, there are kingdoms. Within a kingdom, there are phyla, and within each phylum there are classes. Each class is divided into orders. Each order contains families, and each family contains at least one genus. Within a genus, there are species. Organisms are grouped by their shared characteristics. **The more classification levels that two organisms share, the more characteristics they have in common.**

You can identify organisms with field guides and taxonomic keys. Field guides are books with illustrations that highlight differences between similar-looking organisms. **Taxonomic keys are useful tools for determining the identity of organisms.** A taxonomic key is a series of paired statements that describe the physical characteristics of different organisms.

The British scientist Charles Darwin published a theory about how species can change over time. He observed that two groups of the same species can accumulate enough differences over a long time to become two separate species. This process by which species gradually change over time is called **evolution.**

The theory of evolution changed the way biologists think about classification. Scientists understand that certain organisms are similar because they share a common ancestor. **Species with similar evolutionary histories are classified more closely together.** Scientists get information about the evolutionary history of species primarily by examining the chemical makeup of the organisms' cells.

Name _____ Date _____ Class _____

Living Things ▪ *Guided Reading and Study*

Classifying Organisms (pp. 16–24)

This section tells how scientists divide living things into groups. It also describes the first classification systems and how the theory of evolution changed classification systems.

Use Target Reading Skills

Before you read, preview the red headings. In the graphic organizer below, ask a what, why, *or* how *question for each heading. As you read, write the answers to your questions.*

Classifying Organisms

Question	Answer
Why do scientists classify?	Scientists classify because...

Name _____ Date _____ Class _____

Classifying Organisms (continued)

Why Do Scientists Classify? (p. 17)

1. The process of grouping things based on their similarities is

   _____.

2. Why do biologists use classification?

   _____

   _____

   _____

3. The scientific study of how living things are classified is called

   _____.

4. Is the following sentence true or false? Once an organism is classified, a scientist knows a lot about that organism. _____

The Naming System of Linnaeus (pp. 18–19)

5. Is the following sentence true or false? Linnaeus placed organisms into groups based on their features that he could observe.

   _____

6. In Linnaeus's naming system, called _____, each organism is given a two-part name.

7. Is the following sentence true or false? A species is a group of similar organisms that can mate with each other and produce offspring that can also mate and reproduce. _____

8. *Felis concolor* is the scientific name for mountain lions. To which genus do mountain lions belong? What is the species?

   Genus: _____ Species: _____

9. Circle the letter of each sentence that is true about binomial nomenclature.

   a. A scientific name is written in italics.
   b. Many scientific names are in Latin because Latin was the language of scientists during Linnaeus's time.
   c. The genus name begins with a small letter.
   d. Binomial nomenclature makes it easy for scientists to talk about an organism.

Name _____ Date _____ Class _____

Levels of Classification (pp. 20–21)

10. List the eight levels of classification used by modern biologists in order from the broadest level to the most specific level.

_____

_____

_____

11. Is the following sentence true or false? The more classification levels that two organisms share, the more characteristics they have in common.
_____

12. Look carefully at the figure, *Levels of Classification*, in your textbook. What order does the great horned owl belong to?

_____

_____

Taxonomic Keys (p. 22)

13. Name two tools you could use to learn the identity of an organism.

    a. _____

    b. _____

14. Is the following sentence true or false? A taxonomic key is a book with illustrations that highlight the differences between organisms that look similar. _____

15. Look at the taxonomic key in the figure, *Identifying Organisms*, in your textbook. How many legs does a tick have? _____

Living Things • *Guided Reading and Study*

Evolution and Classification (pp. 23–24)

16. Is the following sentence true or false? Darwin's theory of evolution did not affect the way in which species were classified. _____

17. What is evolution?

_____

_____

_____

18. Is the following sentence true or false? Species with shared ancestors are classified more closely together. _____

19. What do scientists today rely on primarily to determine evolutionary history?

_____

_____

Living Things ▪ *Review and Reinforce*

Classifying Organisms

Understanding Main Ideas

Complete the table below.

Scientist	Contributions to Modern Classification
Carolus Linnaeus	
Charles Darwin	

1. Describe the modern system of classification.

   _____

   _____

   _____

Building Vocabulary

Match each term with its definition by writing the letter of the correct definition in the right column on the line beside the term in the left column.

____ 2. classification

____ 3. binomial nomenclature

____ 4. evolution

____ 5. genus

____ 6. species

____ 7. taxonomy

a. naming system developed by Carolus Linnaeus

b. process of grouping things based on their similarities

c. first word in an organism's scientific name

d. process by which species gradually change over time

e. a group of organisms that can mate and produce offspring that can also mate and reproduce

f. the scientific study of how things are classified

Living Things • *Enrich*

How Many Species of Animals Are There?

There are more species of insects than any other type of animal on Earth. The majority of animals, including insects, live in the tropics. If you can estimate how many species of insects there are in the tropics, you can get a pretty good estimate of the number of species of animals on Earth.

Over the years, entomologists (scientists who study insects) have been discovering and naming new kinds (species) of insects, and now over a million kinds of insects are known. Dr. Terry Erwin, an entomologist at the Smithsonian Institution, studies beetles. Beetles make up a large percentage of insects and related animals. By estimating the number of species of beetles in the tropics, Dr. Erwin was able to estimate the total number of species of animals in the world. Dr. Erwin used the following information to arrive at his estimate:

- Dr. Erwin found 1,200 species of beetles living in *Luehea seemannii* trees.

- Of those 1,200 species of beetles, he estimated that 163 are found only in the *Luehea seemannii* tree, and not in other species of trees.

- There are about 50,000 species of trees in the tropics.

- Beetles make up about 40% of insects and related animals.

- Dr. Erwin estimated that there are about twice as many species of insects and related animals in tropical trees as there are on the ground of the forest.

Answer the following questions on a separate sheet of paper. Use a calculator to make the calculations.

1. If each kind of tree has 163 species of beetles that are found only on that type of tree but no others, how many kinds of beetles are there in tropical trees?

2. Using your answer from question 1, estimate how many species of insects and related animals there are in tropical trees.

3. Using your answer from question 2, estimate how many species of insects and related animals are on the forest floor in the tropics.

4. Using your answer from questions 2 and 3, estimate how many species of insects and related animals there might be in the trees and the forest floor together in the tropics.

5. Why did Dr. Erwin focus on tropical forests to estimate the total number of animal species in the world?

6. What are some likely sources of error in Dr. Erwin's estimation method?

Name _____ Date _____ Class _____

Living Things · *Skills Lab*

Living Mysteries

Problem

How can you create a taxonomic key to help identify tree leaves?

Skills Focus

observing, classifying, inferring

Materials

a variety of leaves
hand lens
metric ruler

Procedure

1. Your teacher will give you five different tree leaves. Handle the leaves carefully.

2. Use a hand lens to examine each of the leaves. Look for characteristics such as those described in the table. Make a list of five or more identifying characteristics for each leaf.

3. Use your observations to create a taxonomic key for the leaves. In creating your taxonomic key, use the characteristics you listed, along with any others that you observe. Remember that your taxonomic key should consist of paired statements, similar to the one shown in the chapter.

4. Exchange your leaves and taxonomic key with a partner. If your partner cannot identify all of the leaves using your key, revise your key as necessary.

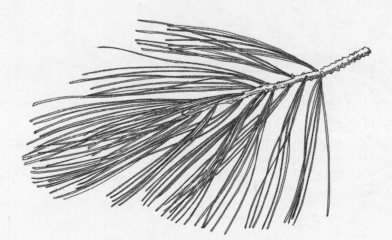

Living Things · *Skills Lab*

Living Mysteries (continued)

Leaf Characteristics to Consider	
Characteristic	**Observations**
Overall Shape	Is the leaf needlelike and narrow, or is it flat and wide? For a flat leaf, is it rounded, oblong, heart-shaped, or some other shape?
Simple vs. Compound	Is the leaf a single unit, or is it made up of individual leaflets? If it is made up of leaflets, how are they arranged on the leaf stalk?
Pattern of Veins	Do the leaf's veins run parallel from the central vein or do they form a branching pattern?
Leaf Edges	Are the edges of the leaf jagged or smooth?
Leaf Texture	Is the leaf's surface fuzzy, shiny, or another texture?

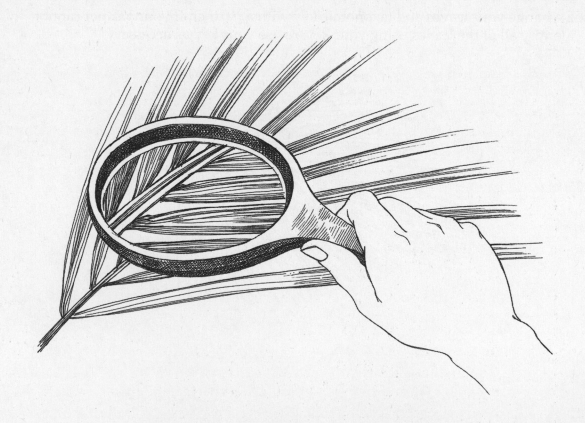

Name _____ Date _____ Class _____

Living Things ▪ *Skills Lab*

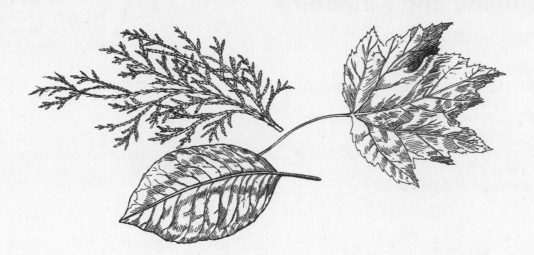

Analyze and Conclude

Write your answers on a separate sheet of paper.

1. **Observing** How are your leaves similar or different from one another?
2. **Classifying** How did you decide which characteristics to use in your taxonomic key?
3. **Inferring** Choose one of your leaves and look back over the list of characteristics you used to classify it. Do you think every single leaf of the same type would share those characteristics? Explain.
4. **Communicating** Explain in your own words why a taxonomic key is helpful. Include in your explanation why it is important that the paired statements in a taxonomic key be contrasting statements.

More to Explore

Suppose you are hiking through the woods and see many flowers of different colors, shapes, and sizes. You decide to create a taxonomic key to help identify the flowers. What characteristics would you include in the key?

Domains and Kingdoms

3–4 periods, 1 1/2–2 blocks

Objectives

A.1.3.1 List the characteristics used to classify organisms.

A.1.3.2 Compare and contrast bacteria and archaea.

A.1.3.3 Name the kingdoms within Eukarya.

Key Terms

• prokaryote • nucleus • eukaryote

Local Standards

PRETEACH

Build Background Knowledge
Have students name kinds of movies and discuss how the categories help them describe and compare organisms.

 **Discover Activity** *Which Organism Goes Where?* L1

Targeted Resources

❏ **All in One Teaching Resources**
   L2 Reading Strategy Transparency A7: Comparing and Contrasting
❏ 💿 **PresentationExpress™ CD-ROM**

INSTRUCT

Domain Bacteria Use an example of a common bacterial disease, strep throat, to discuss bacteria.
Domain Archaea Discuss the differences between bacteria and archaea.
Domain Eukarya Discuss characteristics of the kingdoms that make up Eukarya.

Targeted Resources

❏ **All in One Teaching Resources**
   L2 Guided Reading, pp. 68–69
❏ **www.SciLinks.org** Web Code: scn-0113
❏ 💿 **Student Edition on Audio CD**

ASSESS

Section Assessment Questions
Have students use their Comparing and Contrasting graphic organizers to answer the questions.

Reteach
As a class, summarize the characteristics of each domain and the kingdoms of Eukarya.

Targeted Resources

❏ **All in One Teaching Resources**
   Section Summary, p. 67
   L1 Review and Reinforce, p. 70
   L3 Enrich, p. 71

Living Things • *Section Summary*

Domains and Kingdoms

Key Concepts

■ What characteristics are used to classify organisms?

■ How do bacteria and archaea differ?

■ What are the kingdoms within the domain Eukarya?

Today, a three-domain system of classification is commonly used. The three domains are Bacteria, Archaea, and Eukarya. Within the domains are kingdoms. **Organisms are placed into domains and kingdoms based on their cell type, their ability to make food, and the number of cells in their bodies.**

Members of the domain Bacteria are prokaryotes. **Prokaryotes** are organisms whose cells lack a nucleus. A **nucleus** is a dense area in a cell that contains nucleic acids—the chemical instructions that direct the cell's activities. In prokaryotes, nucleic acids are scattered throughout the cell.

Members of the domain Archaea, whose name comes from the Greek word for "ancient," can be found in some of the most extreme environments on Earth, including hot springs, very salty water, swamps, and the intestines of cows! Scientists think that the harsh conditions in which archaea live are similar to those of ancient Earth. Like bacteria, archaea are unicellular prokaryotes. And like bacteria, some archaea are autotrophs while others are heterotrophs. **Although bacteria and archaea are similar in some ways, there are important differences in the structure and chemical makeup of their cells.**

Members of the domain Eukarya are **eukaryotes**—organisms with cells that contain nuclei. **Scientists classify organisms in the domain Eukarya into one of four kingdoms: protists, fungi, plants, or animals.**

Slime molds are protists. The protist kingdom is sometimes called the "odds and ends" kingdom because its members are so different from one another. Protists can be autotrophs or heterotrophs. Although many protists are unicellular, some, such as seaweeds, are multicellular.

Mushrooms, molds, mildew, and yeast are all fungi. Most fungi are multicellular eukaryotes. A few, such as yeast, are unicellular eukaryotes. Fungi are found almost everywhere on land, but only a few live in fresh water. All fungi are heterotrophs. Most fungi feed by absorbing nutrients from dead or decaying organisms.

Plants are all multicellular eukaryotes. The plant kingdom includes a variety of organisms. In general, plants are autotrophs and feed almost all of the heterotrophs on land.

All animals are multicellular eukaryotes. All animals are heterotrophs. Animals have different adaptations that allow them to find food, capture it, eat it, and digest it. Members of the animal kingdom are found in diverse environments on Earth.

Living Things ▪ *Guided Reading and Study*

Domains and Kingdoms (pp. 26–29)

This section describes each of the domains and kingdoms into which all living things are grouped.

Use Target Reading Skills

As you read, compare and contrast the characteristics of organisms in domains Bacteria, Archaea, and Eukarya by completing the table below.

Domain or Kingdom	Cell Type and Number	Able to Make Food?
Bacteria	Prokaryote; unicellular	
Archaea		
Eukarya: Protists		
Fungi		
Plants		
Animals		

1. List the three domains of living things.

   a. _____ b. _____

   c. _____

2. Complete the concept map to show how organisms are placed into domains and kingdoms.

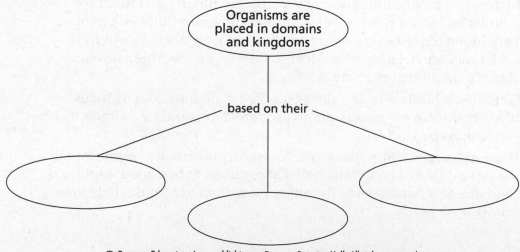

© Pearson Education, Inc., publishing as Pearson Prentice Hall. All rights reserved.

Name _____ Date _____ Class _____

Living Things • *Guided Reading and Study*

Domain Bacteria (p. 27)

3. Circle the letter of each sentence that is true about bacteria.

   a. Bacteria can be either autotrophic or heterotrophic.
   b. Bacteria are prokaryotes.
   c. Bacteria have a cell nucleus.
   d. Bacteria do not have nucleic acids.

4. A dense area in a cell that contains nucleic acids is a(n)
   _____.

Domain Archaea (p. 27)

5. Is the following sentence true or false? Archaea have a similar chemical makeup to bacteria. _____

6. Why are members of this domain called archaea, which comes from the Greek word for "ancient"?

   _____

   _____

   _____

Domain Eukarya (pp. 28–29)

7. Is the following sentence true or false? Protists can be either unicellular or multicellular. _____

8. How do protists differ from bacteria and archaea?

   _____

   _____

   _____

9. Is the following sentence true or false? Mushrooms, molds, mildew, and yeast are all fungi. _____

10. Circle the letter of each characteristic of fungi.

    a. eukaryotes   c. autotrophs
    b. prokaryotes   d. heterotrophs

11. Plants are _____; they can make their own food.

12. Is the following true or false? Plants provide food for all the heterotrophs on Earth. _____

13. Circle the letter of each characteristic of animals.

    a. unicellular   c. eukaryotes
    b. heterotrophs   d. autotrophs

14. Is the following sentence true or false? All animals are multicellular.

    _____

Living Things • *Review and Reinforce*

Domains and Kingdoms

Understanding Main Ideas

Match the following organisms to the kingdom to which they belong.

protist   fungi   plant   animal

1. mushroom_____

2. horse _____

3. redwood tree_____

4. seaweed _____

5. yeast _____

6. dog _____

7. dandelion _____

Building Vocabulary

Write a definition for each of the following terms on the lines below or on a separate sheet of paper.

8. nucleus

_____

_____

_____

9. prokaryote

_____

_____

_____

10. eukaryote

_____

_____

_____

Name _____ Date _____ Class _____

A New Phylum

In 1995, scientists discovered a new species of organism, which they named *Symbion pandora*. It is not very unusual for new species to be identified. However, the discovery of *S. pandora* drew attention from around the world because this strange animal did not seem to belong to any of the phyla into which scientists classify organisms. As a result, a new phylum called Cycliophora was created for *S. pandora*. So far, *S. pandora* is the only species belonging to this phylum. (Contrast this with the phylum Chordata, which includes all species of reptiles, amphibians, birds, and mammals.)

S. pandora was discovered living on bristles that surround the mouths of Norway lobsters. It has a very complex life cycle with several different stages. One stage consists of a female that stays attached to the lobster's bristles. This stage is about 0.35 mm in length and is shown in the figure below. A tiny male clings to this female feeding stage. There are also stages of *S. pandora* that swim freely; these stages do not feed.

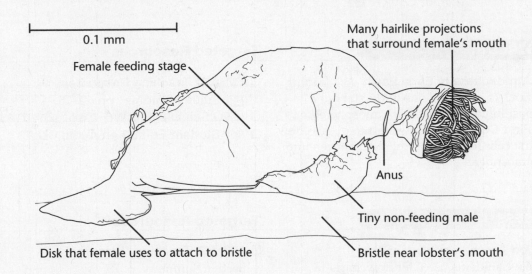

0.1 mm

Female feeding stage

Many hairlike projections that surround female's mouth

Anus

Tiny non-feeding male

Disk that female uses to attach to bristle

Bristle near lobster's mouth

Answer the following questions on a separate sheet of paper.

1. *S. pandora* is a member of the animal kingdom. What are three things that you can conclude about *S. pandora* from this statement?

2. Why do you think *S. pandora* was not discovered earlier?

3. What genus does *S. pandora* belong to? How many species are in this genus?

4. How do you think *S. pandora* gets food?

The Origin of Life

1–2 periods, 1/2–1 block

Objectives
A.1.4.1 Contrast the atmosphere of early Earth with today's atmosphere.
A.1.4.2 Describe some hypotheses about how life arose on Earth.

Key Term
• fossil

Local Standards

PRETEACH

Build Background Knowledge
Discuss the gases found in air.

 **Discover Activity** *How Can the Composition of Air Change?* L2

Targeted Resources

❑ **All in One** Teaching Resources
L2 Reading Strategy Transparency A8: Identifying Supporting Evidence
❑ **PresentationExpress™ CD-ROM**

INSTRUCT

The Atmosphere of Early Earth Ask leading questions to help students understand the composition of Earth's early atmosphere.
The First Cells Use a flowchart to discuss how the first cells formed and released oxygen into the atmosphere.

Targeted Resources

❑ **All in One** Teaching Resources
L2 Guided Reading, pp. 74–76
❑ **www.SciLinks.org** Web Code: scn-0114
❑ **Student Edition on Audio CD**

ASSESS

Section Assessment Questions
Have students use their flowcharts sequencing the steps in protein synthesis to answer the questions.

Reteach
Use a chart to reteach the sequence of main events that scientists associate with the origin of life.

Targeted Resources

❑ **All in One** Teaching Resources
Section Summary, p. 73
L1 Review and Reinforce, p. 77
L3 Enrich, p. 78

Living Things • *Section Summary*

The Origin of Life

Key Concepts

■ How was the atmosphere of early Earth different from today's atmosphere?

■ How do scientists hypothesize that life arose on early Earth?

Scientists think that early Earth had a different atmosphere than it has today. **On ancient Earth, nitrogen, water vapor, carbon dioxide, and methane were probably the most abundant gases in the atmosphere.** Although all these gases still make up a small part of the atmosphere today, the major gases are nitrogen and oxygen.

Scientists have formed hypotheses about what the first life forms were like. First, early life forms did not need oxygen to survive. Second, they were probably unicellular organisms. Third, they probably lived in the oceans.

In 1953, Miller and Urey designed an experiment that recreated the conditions of early Earth in their laboratory. They placed water and a mixture of the gases that probably made up early Earth's atmosphere into a flask. Then, they sent an electric current through the mixture to act as lightning. Within a week, the mixture in the flask contained some small chemical units that could form proteins. In similar experiments, other scientists succeeded in producing carbohydrates and nucleic acids.

Scientists hypothesize that the small chemical units of life formed gradually over millions of years in Earth's waters. Some of these chemical units joined to form the large chemical building blocks found in cells. Eventually, some of these large chemicals joined together and became the forerunners of the first cells.

This hypothesis is supported by evidence from fossils. **Fossils** are traces of ancient organisms that have been preserved in rock or other substances. Fossils of bacteria-like organisms have been found that are between 3.4 and 3.5 billion years old. Scientists think that these ancient cells may be evidence of Earth's earliest forms of life.

The first cells were probably heterotrophs that used the chemicals in their surroundings for energy. As they grew and reproduced, their numbers increased. As their numbers increased, the amount of chemicals available to them decreased. At some point, some of the cells may have developed the ability to make their own food. As they made their own food, they produced oxygen as a waste product. Oxygen accumulated in Earth's atmosphere. Over hundreds of millions of years, the amount of oxygen increased to its current level.

Name _____ Date _____ Class _____

The Origin of Life (pp. 30–33)

This section describes how Earth's atmosphere formed and how scientists think life first appeared on Earth.

Use Target Reading Skills

As you read, identify the evidence that supports scientists' hypothesis of how life arose on Earth. Write the evidence in the graphic organizer below.

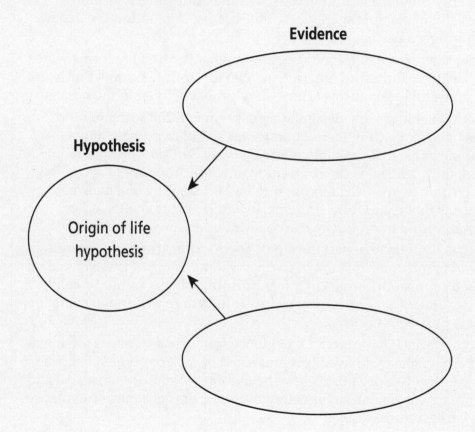

Living Things · *Guided Reading and Study*

The Atmosphere of Early Earth (pp. 30–31)

1. Complete this Venn diagram to compare the major gases that made up early Earth's atmosphere and Earth's atmosphere today.

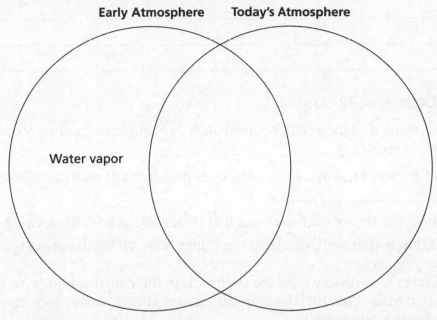

Early Atmosphere   **Today's Atmosphere**

Water vapor

2. Circle the letter of each sentence that is true about the characteristics of Earth's early life forms.

   a. Early life forms needed oxygen to survive.

   b. Early life forms were probably unicellular.

   c. The first life forms probably lived in the oceans.

   d. The first organisms were very different from archaea that live today in extreme conditions.

3. Is the following sentence true or false? Scientists think that the first life forms on Earth probably did arise from nonliving materials. _____

4. What materials did Stanley Miller and Harold Urey use to recreate the conditions of early Earth in their laboratory?

   _____

   _____

   _____

5. Miller and Urey used an electric current in their experiment to simulate

   _____.

Living Things ▪ *Guided Reading and Study*

The Origin of Life *(continued)*

6. What were the results of Miller and Urey's experiment?

_____

_____

_____

_____

The First Cells (pp. 32–33)

7. Scientists think that the small chemical units of life formed gradually over millions of years in Earth's _____.

8. Traces of ancient organisms that have been preserved in rock or other substances are _____.

9. Circle the letter before each sentence that is true about how life formed on Earth.

   a. Fossils show that archaea-like living things were on Earth between 3.4 and 3.5 billion years ago.

   b. The first cells probably used the chemicals in their surroundings for energy.

   c. Cells that made their own food produced oxygen as a waste product, which built up in Earth's atmosphere.

   d. Scientists know for certain how life first appeared on Earth.

Living Things ▪ *Review and Reinforce*

The Origin of Life

Understanding Main Ideas

Answer the following questions in the space provided.

1. A geologist claims to have found a sealed chamber below Earth's surface. The chamber reportedly contains air that is over 3.6 billion years old. How would such air be different from the air you breathe today? How would it be similar?

   _____

   _____

   _____

2. Scientists think that the first life forms probably arose from nonliving materials. Explain how Miller and Urey's experiment supports this theory.

   _____

   _____

   _____

3. What do scientists think were the characteristics of the first life forms?

   _____

   _____

   _____

4. Explain how scientists think that oxygen accumulated in Earth's atmosphere.

   _____

   _____

   _____

Building Vocabulary

Write an answer for the following question in the space provided.

5. What are fossils? How is the hypothesis about Earth's earliest life forms consistent with fossil evidence?

   _____

   _____

   _____

Living Things · *Enrich*

Is This Life?

For many years, people on Earth have wondered whether there is life on other planets. And if life does exist, what form of life would that be? In 1984, researchers found a 2-kg potato-shaped rock in the ice fields of Antarctica that they think is a meteorite that originated on Mars. In 1996, NASA scientists released the results of their experiments on the rock. What they did or did not find within that meteorite has been the topic of debate among scientists ever since.

Imagine that you are part of the research team assigned to analyze the data collected from the Martian meteorite. You are given the following summary, listing observations and test results from the rock.

Chemical building blocks present	Chemical compounds similar to proteins were found. Also, other chemicals that form from these building blocks when microorganisms die were found.
Chemicals from the atmosphere present	Mineral deposits formed from the carbon and oxygen in the Martian atmosphere were found. It is believed they were dissolved in the water present at the planet surface, and carried into the rock through tiny cracks.
Fossil-like formations present	Possible structures of tiny, ancient bacteria were found. However, they are also similar to other structures not related to living organisms.
Appearance of fossil-like structures	The largest structures are less than 1/100 the diameter of a human hair. Some are egg-shaped, while others are tubular.
Approximate date of the meteorite	The sample was dated at about 4.5 billion years. This is about the time that Mars formed.
Other important observations	The fossil-like structures, the mineral deposits, and the chemical building blocks were all found near the center of the rock, within a few hundred thousandths of an inch of one another.

After studying the data, write a brief paragraph on a separate sheet of paper, explaining whether or not you think the Martian meteorite contains evidence of life.

Name _____ Date _____ Class _____

Key Terms

Use the clues to identify Key Terms from the chapter. Write the terms on the lines. Then find the words hidden in the puzzle and circle them. Words are across or up-and-down.

Clues	Key Terms
Change that produces a more complex organism	_____
A trace of an ancient organism that has been preserved in rock	_____
The maintenance of stable internal conditions	_____
A dense area in a cell that contains nucleic acids	_____
An organism whose cell lacks a nucleus	_____
A group of organisms that can mate and produce offspring that can also mate and reproduce	_____
Change in the surroundings that causes an organism to react	_____
The scientific study of how living things are classified	_____
The basic unit of structure and function in an organism	_____

```
e h p r o k a r y o t e j d e y v t a o
h s j i l f b t e h o m e o s t a s i s
d t l s k e t u h g d s m a e t b p u f
o i b p d e v e l o p m e n t f i n r f
a m p e o r d y w o v a r l t o c n y o
r u a c p j i o l g e r x d a v e m u s
p l n i s t w t a x o n o m y p l h r s
a u p e k t u o e d a s p u f c l v r i
h s i s h r a c v n u c l e u s m p r l
```

Connecting Concepts

Develop a concept map that uses the Key Concepts and Key Terms from this chapter. Keep in mind the big idea of this chapter. The concept map shown is one way to organize how the information in this chapter is related. You may use an extra sheet of paper.

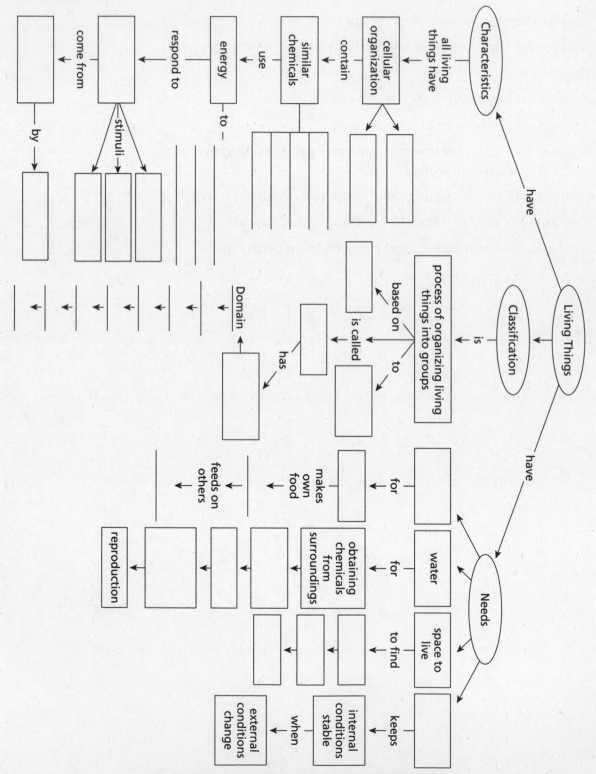

Developing a Classification System for Seeds

Key Concept

Classification is a tool used to organize and study living things.

Skills Focus

observing, classifying, communicating

Time

40 minutes

Materials *(per group)*

paper cup containing seeds

2 hand lenses

tray

metric ruler

scrap paper

Alternate Materials: Any available seeds or beans can be used. Pictures of flowers and other plants, pictures of different animals, or even common items such as miscellaneous buttons can be used in place of seeds.

Advance Preparation

To prepare a mixture of seeds for each group, put eight of each of the following seeds in a small paper cup: pinto bean, kidney bean, lima bean, black-eyed pea, navy bean, and split pea.

Teaching Tips

- Encourage students to use the hand lens for closer inspection of the seeds.

- Students need to keep clear records of the characteristics they used for classification. In addition to describing these characteristics, students could illustrate them for clarification.

- The diagram students make might be a flowchart or a concept map.

- Have groups of students make different lists of five common items. Possible subjects could include video or movie titles, local vegetation, lab equipment, types of clothing, and so forth. Encourage the different groups to compare the characteristics for classification.

Living Things

Living Things ▪ *Laboratory Investigation*

Developing a Classification System for Seeds (continued)

Pre-Lab Discussion

Suppose you discovered a plant or an animal that no one had ever seen. What would you call it? Where would you even begin?

To simplify the identification and naming of organisms, scientists have developed a system of classification. The classification system groups similar animals, plants, and other organisms. There are eight major levels of classification. The broadest group is a domain. Within a domain are kingdoms. Kingdoms contain phyla (singular *phylum*), classes, orders, families, genera (singular *genus*), and species. Organisms of the same species have the most characteristics in common.

In this investigation, you will develop a system of classification for seeds.

1. Why do scientists classify organisms into groups?

   _____

   _____

   _____

2. What can you infer if organism A shares three classification levels with organism B and five levels with organism C?

   _____

   _____

Problem

What characteristics can be used to classify seeds?

Materials *(per group)*

paper cup containing seeds   metric ruler

2 hand lenses   scrap paper

tray

Safety

Review the safety guidelines in Appendix A of your textbook.

Keep seeds in containers at all times to prevent accidents. Do not eat the seeds.

Procedure

1. Get a cup containing seeds. Carefully pour the seeds onto the tray. **CAUTION:** *Immediately pick up any seeds that drop on the floor.* Use a hand lens to examine the seeds carefully. Answer question 1 in Observations.

2. Think about what characteristic you could use to divide all the seeds into two large groups. Remember, each group must contain seeds with similar characteristics.

3. Sort the seeds into two piles, based on the characteristic that you selected. On scrap paper, note the characteristics that you choose.

4. Working with one of the two large groups, divide the seeds in that group into two smaller groups based on another characteristic. Record the characteristic as in Step 3.

Living Things · *Laboratory Investigation*

5. Continue to divide the seeds into smaller groups by choosing and recording new characteristics. Eventually, you should have only one seed left in each group.

6. Repeat steps 4 and 5 with the other large group.

7. In Observations, draw a diagram that shows how your classification system works.

8. Compare your classification system with those of other groups in your class. Answer questions 2–4 in Observations.

Observations

Diagram of Seed Classification

1. What are some of the characteristics of your seeds?

   _____

   _____

2. How many groups are in your classification system?

   _____

3. Compare the final classification system you have with those of other groups using different characteristics. Do they differ or are they the same? What different characteristics did they use?

   _____

   _____

Analyze and Conclude

1. What characteristics did you find most useful for classifying the seeds?

   _____

   _____

2. Explain why your final classification groups differed or were the same as those of other groups.

   _____

   _____

Living Things ▪ *Laboratory Investigation*

Developing a Classification System for Seeds (continued)

3. How does a classification system help you understand organisms?

_____

_____

_____

4. How is this investigation similar to the way in which scientists classify organisms?

_____

_____

_____

_____

Critical Thinking and Applications

1. Could you have classified your seeds using another system? Give a reason for your answer.

_____

_____

2. Could you have classified each characteristic in groups of three or more types at each step? Do you think more groups would make choices harder or easier? Give a reason for your answer.

_____

_____

_____

3. Suppose you wanted to classify all the birds that came to a particular area of a pond during a spring day. What are some of the characteristics that you would use to classify the birds?

_____

_____

4. When classifying organisms, do you think that it is better to go from general characteristics to specific characteristics or from specific characteristics to general characteristics? Give a reason for your answer.

_____

_____

_____

More to Explore

Make a list of five or more household appliances. Combine your list with a classmate's. Then separately devise classification systems for the combined list of appliances. What characteristics did you use to classify these items into groups? Did your classmate come up with the same classification system?

Classifying Cerealites

Students are presented with the problem of creating a classification system for 10 types of Cerealites (actually pieces of cereal). They must include at least three levels of classification in their system and present their system on a poster. To solve this problem, students must apply the concepts they have learned about shared characteristics and classification systems.

Expected Outcome

Students' systems will vary. However, students should base their classification systems on several characteristics of the cereal such as color, shape, size, flake versus not flake, and so on. Each characteristic should be used to classify a larger group of cereal pieces into two or more smaller groups. For example, students may choose to divide the group of all cereal pieces into two smaller groups of yellow pieces and brown pieces based on the characteristic of color. Then they may choose to divide the group of yellow pieces into two smaller group of round yellow pieces and square yellow pieces based on the characteristic of shape. Students should keep subdividing their groups until each piece of cereal is by itself in its own group. Students' posters should clearly show their system's levels of classification and the shared characteristics of each group.

Content Assessed

The Performance Assessment tests students' understanding of shared characteristics and classification systems.

Skills Assessed

observing, applying concepts, classifying

Materials

Give each student 10 different types of cereal pieces. Include a wide variety of shapes, colors, sizes, and textures.

Provide poster board, glue, colored pencils or markers, and any other materials students will need to make their posters.

Advance Preparation

■ Encourage students to bring small plastic bags full of their favorite cereal to class on the day of the activity.

Time

■ 40 minutes

Monitoring the Task

■ Have several visual representations of classification systems on hand for students to look at and to use for ideas.

■ Suggest that students glue their cereal pieces onto their posters so that people looking at the poster will be able to see what the "Cerealites" look like.

■ To save time, you may want to have students diagram their systems on sheets of notebook paper rather than having them create posters.

■ As an extension, suggest that students create a taxonomic key for their classification system.

Classifying Cerealites

In assessing students' performance, use the following rubric.

	4	3	2	1
Developing a Classification System	Student's system is clearly based on shared characteristics. System has at least three levels of classification. Larger, more general groups are divided into smaller, more specific groups.	Student's system is based on shared characteristics. System has three levels of classification. Larger, more general groups are divided into smaller, more specific groups.	Student's system is only partially based on shared characteristics. System has only two levels of classification. Larger, more general groups are not always divided into smaller, more specific groups.	Student's system is not based on shared characteristics. System has two or fewer levels of classification. Student fails to divide larger, more general groups into smaller, more specific groups.
Presenting the Classification System	Student's poster makes the classification system easy to understand. The shared characteristics of each group in each level are clearly labeled. The progression from general to specific is indicated.	Student's poster makes the classification system clear. The shared characteristics of each group in each level are labeled. The progression from general to specific is indicated.	Student's poster describes the classification system. The shared characteristics of each group in each level are mostly labeled. The progression from general to specific is indicated.	Student's poster makes the classification system difficult to understand. The shared characteristics of each group in each level are sometimes labeled. The progression from general to specific is not indicated.
Concept Understanding	Student demonstrates a mastery of the concepts of shared characteristics and classification systems.	Student demonstrates a good understanding of the concepts of shared characteristics and classification systems.	Student demonstrates partial understanding of the concepts of shared characteristics and classification systems.	Student demonstrates minimal understanding of the concepts of shared characteristics and classification systems.

Name _____ Date _____ Class _____

Living Things ▪ *Performance Assessment*

Classifying Cerealites

Problem

Suppose that you are both a space explorer and a scientist. You have recently arrived on the planet Cereal. The organisms on this planet are called Cerealites. How can you create a classification system for Cerealites?

Suggested Materials

> 10 different types of Cerealites
> poster board
> glue
> colored pencils or markers

Devise a Plan

1. Examine the Cerealites and begin to think of a way that you could classify them. Notice their similarities and their differences. Do not eat the Cerealites.

2. Decide which characteristics of the Cerealites will be the most important in your system. Use these characteristics to classify your organisms into at least three levels.

3. Make a poster that explains your system of classification. You will probably want to outline your system on a separate sheet of paper before you begin work on your poster.

Analyze and Conclude

After completing your poster, answer the following questions on a separate sheet of paper.

1. What characteristics did you use to classify the Cerealites? Why did you choose these characteristics?

2. Look at the posters of other students in your class. Is there more than one correct way to classify the Cerealites? Explain.

3. Suppose one of your Cerealites suddenly changed from yellow to red. How would this affect your classification system?

4. Like the animals of Earth, Cerealites have also undergone millions of years of evolution. Which types of Cerealites seem to be most closely related? Explain.

Living Things

Multiple Choice

Write the letter of the correct answer on the line at the left.

_____ 1. An organism's ability to maintain stable internal conditions is called

    a. taxonomy.   **b.** evolution.

    c. development.   **d.** homeostasis.

_____ 2. The two kingdoms that contain only heterotrophs are animals and

    a. archaea.   **b.** fungi.

    c. protists.   **d.** bacteria.

_____ 3. The process of change that occurs during an organism's life to produce a more complex organism is called

    a. response.   **b.** evolution.

    c. development.   **d.** growth.

_____ 4. Which scientist organized animals into groups according to observable features?

    a. Stanley Miller   **b.** Louis Pasteur

    c. Harold Urey   **d.** Carolus Linnaeus

_____ 5. Which of the following is not one of the four kingdoms of eukaryotes?

    a. fungi   **b.** archaea

    c. protists   **d.** plants

_____ 6. The dense portion of some cells containing nucleic acids is called the

    a. nucleus.   **b.** prokaryote.

    c. protein.   **d.** eukaryote.

_____ 7. The most abundant chemical in cells is

    a. carbohydrates.   **b.** nucleic acids.

    c. proteins.   **d.** water.

_____ 8. A group of organisms that can mate with each other and produce offspring that can also mate and reproduce is called a(n)

    a. genus.   **b.** phylum.

    c. kingdom.   **d.** species.

_____ 9. Experiments that involve two tests that are identical except for one factor are called

    a. supervised experiments.   **b.** organized experiments.

    c. controlled experiments.   **d.** spontaneous experiments.

_____ 10. A change in an organism's environment that causes a reaction is called a(n)

    a. response.   **b.** classification.

    c. stimulus.   **d.** variable.

Living Things ▪ *Chapter Test (continued)*

Completion

Fill in the line to complete each statement.

11. An organism is a(n) _____ if it can make its own food.

12. A belief in _____ was disproved when Francesco Redi performed experiments to show that flies do not arise from meat.

13. _____ are traces of ancient organisms preserved in rocks.

14. The scientific study of how things are classified is called _____.

15. The first word of an organism's scientific name indicates the _____.

True or False

Determine whether each statement is true or false. If it is true, write true. *If it is false, change the underlined word or words to make the statement true.*

_____ **16.** The major gases present in the atmosphere today are <u>methane</u> and oxygen.

_____ **17.** An organism that is made up of many cells is <u>unicellular</u>.

_____ **18.** An organism whose cells contain nuclei is called a <u>eukaryote</u>.

_____ **19.** The domains of bacteria and <u>protists</u> contain only prokaryotes.

_____ **20.** Food, <u>water</u>, living space, and stable internal conditions are basic needs of living things.

Living Things · *Chapter Test (continued)*

Using Science Skills

Use the taxonomic key in the textbook and the figures below to answer the following questions. Write your answers on a separate sheet of paper.

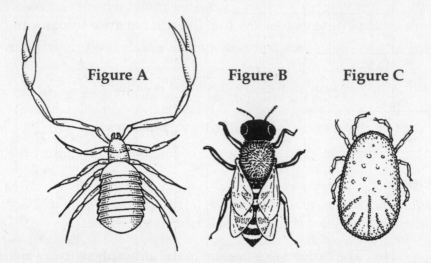

Figure A   **Figure B**   **Figure C**

21. **Interpreting Diagrams** Can this taxonomic key be used to classify all of the organisms shown? Explain why or why not.

22. **Classifying** Name the organism in Figure A. Which key statements helped you identify this organism?

23. **Drawing Conclusions** Based on the key, how can you tell the difference between a centipede and a millipede?

Essay

On a separate sheet of paper, write a brief paragraph to answer each of the following questions.

24. How do organisms differ from nonliving things?

25. A group of scientists is planning a space mission to a new planet with unknown conditions. What basic human needs must the scientists consider before they decide which supplies to take with them?

Living Things • *Chapter Test (continued)*

Using Science Skills

The experiment shown below is intended to test how temperature affects the growth of Phaseolus *bean seedlings. Use the figure to answer the following questions. Write your answers on a separate sheet of paper.*

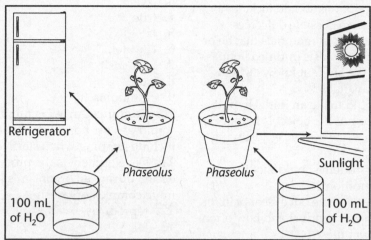

Science Fair Poster

26. **Interpreting Diagrams** Your friend plans to conduct this experiment to test how temperature affects plant growth. Explain why this is not a controlled experiment.

27. **Drawing Conclusions** What change(s) need to be made so that the experiment would test only for differences in temperature?

Essay

On a separate sheet of paper, write a brief paragraph to answer each of the following questions.

28. Scientists are beginning to understand what the first organisms were like. Compare these early life forms to organisms in the bacteria kingdom. How are they similar? How are they different?

29. You have discovered an organism that is multicellular and autotrophic. Upon examining its cells, you discover that they each have a nucleus. To which kingdom(s) could this organism belong? Explain how you know.

30. Which of the following birds are more closely related: *Parus bicolor, Tachycineta bicolor, Parus atricapillus*? How do you know?

Chapter Project Worksheet 1

1. The students should write a few sentences that describe characteristics of living organisms. This list should touch on characteristics covered in section, *What Is Life?* of the text.
2. The student should come up with two different tests to examine characteristics described in question 1. The descriptions should include how he or she would analyze possible outcomes.
3. The students should list materials that he or she needs to conduct the tests outlined in question 2. Be sure that the student knows whether such materials are available.
4. The student should make an initial hypothesis about whether or not the object is living. He or she should write a few sentences justifying the hypothesis.
5. If necessary, the student should modify any tests described in question 2.
6. The student should write out a clear plan for what tests he or she will conduct and how often he or she will conduct these tests.

Chapter Project Worksheet 2

The student's data table should be well organized and show a regular schedule of observations.
1. The student should write several sentences describing the research, including a description of why some tests worked better than others did.
2. The student should write several sentences summarizing observations and drawing a conclusion as to whether the object is living. If the mystery object is living, the student should try to classify the object into a domain and kingdom.
3. This paragraph should include the student's plan for how to present his or her project to the class.

What Is Life?
Guided Reading and Study

Use Target Reading Skills
Possible answers include:
What You Know
1. Living things grow.
2. Living things are made of cells.
What You Learned
1. Unicellular organisms are composed of only one cell.
2. The cells of living things are composed of chemicals.
3. The cells of organisms use energy to do things they must do.

1. An organism is a living thing.
2. a. Have cellular organization
   b. Contain similar chemicals
   c. Use energy
   d. Grow and develop
   e. Respond to their surroundings
   f. Reproduce
3. cells
4. true
5. false
6. c. water.
7. proteins
8. true
9. c. stimulus
10. Stimulus: Answers might include the sound of a car horn. **Response:** Answers might include jumping when startled.
11. Development is the process of change that occurs during an organism's life to produce a more complex organism.
12. reproduce
13. false
14. spontaneous generation
15. He showed that flies do not spontaneously arise from decaying meat.
16. manipulated variable
17. false
18. Food; Water; Living space; Stable internal conditions
19. true
20. autotrophs; heterotrophs
21. false
22. Organisms need water to obtain chemicals from their surroundings, break down food, grow, move substances within their bodies, and reproduce.
23. true
24. Conditions must be just right for the cells to function.

What Is Life?
Review and Reinforce

1. All living things have cellular organization, contain similar chemicals, use energy, grow and develop, respond to their surroundings, and reproduce.
2. Redi's experiment showed that flies do not spontaneously arise from rotting meat but are produced from the eggs of other flies.
3. Living things must satisfy basic needs for food, water, living space, and stable internal conditions.
4. Growth is the process of becoming larger, where development is the process of becoming more complex.

5. stimulus
6. autotrophs
7. Multicellular
8. Spontaneous generation
9. organisms
10. cell
11. heterotrophs
12. response
13. controlled experiment, manipulated variable
14. homeostasis
15. reproduce
16. unicellular

What Is Life?
Enrich

1. The bacteria showed the best growth. They had all their basic needs satisfied: food, water, living space, and a temperature that helped maintain stable internal conditions.
2. Bacterial growth was poor because the freezing temperature did not provide stable internal conditions.
3. Only some colonies grew. Because the agar was old, it probably did not have as many nutrients available to the growing bacteria.
4. Since one month passed before the bacteria were checked, the scientist cannot be sure what happened. Perhaps the living space became overcrowded and the food source was insufficient.

Please Pass the Bread!
Skills Lab

For answers, see the Teacher's Edition.

Classifying Organisms
Guided Reading and Study

Use Target Reading Skills
Possible questions and answers include: **Why do scientists classify?** (*Scientists classify because they want to organize living things into groups so they are easier to study.*)
What system did Linnaeus use to name organisms? (*He used a system called binomial nomenclature.*)
What are the levels of classification? (*Domain, kingdom, phylum, class, order, family, genus, species.*)

1. classification
2. Biologists organize living things into groups so that the organisms are easier to study.
3. taxonomy
4. true
5. true

6. binomial nomenclature
7. true
8. Genus: *Felis*; Species: *Felis concolor*
9. a, b, d
10. domain, kingdom, phylum, class, order, family, genus, species
11. true
12. It belongs to the order Strigiformes.
13. **a.** field guide, **b.** taxonomic key
14. false
15. A tick has eight legs.
16. false
17. Evolution is the process by which species gradually change over time.
18. true
19. They rely primarily on information about the chemical makeup of cells.

Classifying Organisms
Review and Reinforce

Carolus Linnaeus: devised a naming system called binomial nomenclature that indicates organism's genus and species
Charles Darwin: published the theory about how species can change over time; provided evidence that certain organisms are similar because they share similar evolutionary histories
1. The modern system classifies organisms into eight levels: domain, kingdom, phyla, class, order, family, genus, and species. The scientific name given to an organism is based on binomial nomenclature. Species with similar evolutionary histories are classified more closely together.
2. b
3. a
4. d
5. c
6. e
7. f

Classifying Organisms
Enrich

1. $50,000 \times 163 = 8,150,000$
2. $40\% \times$ number of insects and related animals $= 8,150,000$; insects and related animals $= 20,375,000$
3. $20,375,000 \times 1/2 = 10,187,500$
4. $10,187,500 + 20,375,000 = 30,562,500$
5. More species of animals live in the tropics than anywhere else. If Dr. Erwin could estimate how many species of animals there are in the tropics, that number would be closer to the maximum number of animals on Earth.

6. Answers may vary. Samples: At several steps in his method, Dr. Erwin estimated numbers that were used in calculations. These include the number of beetles living in *Luehea seemannii* trees and no other kind of tree, the number of kinds of trees in the tropics, the percentage of insects and related animals that are beetles, the percentage of insects and related animals that are found in tropical trees compared to on the forest floor. The actual numbers were probably different from his estimations. Also, he estimated that each of the 50,000 kinds of tropical trees had 163 beetles species found in no other kind of tree. This might not be true.

Living Mysteries
Skills Lab

For answers, see the Teacher's Edition.

Domains and Kingdoms
Guided Reading and Study

Use Target Reading Skills
Bacteria: Prokaryotes; unicellular; Some are able to make food
Archaea: Prokaryotes; unicellular; Some are able to make food
Eukarya: Protists: Eukaryotes; unicellular or multicellular; Some are able to make food
Fungi: Eukaryotes; unicellular or multicellular; No
Plants: Eukaryotes; multicellular; Yes
Animals: Eukaryotes; multicellular; No
1. a. Bacteria
   b. Archaea
   c. Eukarya
2. Types of cells; Ability to make food; Number of cells in their bodies
3. a, b
4. nucleus
5. false
6. Scientists think that the harsh conditions in which archaea live are similar to those of ancient Earth.
7. true
8. Protists are eukaryotes—their cells contain nuclei.
9. true
10. a, d
11. autotrophs
12. false
13. b, c
14. true

Domains and Kingdoms
Review and Reinforce

1. fungi
2. animal
3. plant
4. protist
5. fungi
6. animal
7. plant
8. A nucleus is a dense area in a cell that contains nucleic acids.
9. Prokaryotes are organisms whose cells lack nuclei. Their nucleic acids are not contained in nuclei.
10. Eukaryotes are organisms with cells that have nuclei containing their nucleic acids.

Domains and Kingdoms
Enrich

1. All animals, including *S. pandora*, are multi-cellular, eukaryotic, and heterotrophic.
2. Answers may vary. Sample: I think it wasn't discovered earlier because it is so small.
3. Genus *Symbion*; there is only one known species, *Symbion pandora*, in this genus.
4. Answers may vary. In fact, *S. pandora* feeds by sweeping food into its mouth with its hair-like projections.

The Origin of Life
Guided Reading and Study

Use Target Reading Skills
Possible answer: fossil evidence of archaea-like organisms; fossils dated to be between 3.4 and 3.5 billion years old.
1. Left circle: Carbon dioxide, Methane; Center: Nitrogen; Right circle: Oxygen
2. b, c
3. true
4. They used water and a mixture of gases thought to make up Earth's early atmosphere.
5. lightning
6. They found that the dark fluid in the flask contained small chemicals that could form proteins.
7. waters or oceans
8. fossils
9. a, b, c

The Origin of Life Review and Reinforce

1. The air in the chamber is different from the air today because it does not contain any oxygen. Both the air in the chamber and the air we breathe today have large amounts of nitrogen. Both also contain water vapor, carbon dioxide, and methane, although they make up a smaller portion of the air we breathe today.

2. Miller and Urey's experiment simulated how lightning affected the ocean and the gases in the atmosphere of early Earth. They ran an electric current through a flask of gases and water. The current represented lightning in the atmosphere. A week later they found some small chemical units that could form the building blocks of life called proteins.

3. Scientists believe that the first organisms did not need oxygen, were unicellular and heterotrophic, and lived in the oceans.

4. Scientists think that early heterotrophs used chemicals in their surroundings for energy. As the number of heterotrophs increased, the amount of chemicals available to them decreased. Some of these heterotrophs may have developed the ability to make their own food. These early autotrophs released oxygen as a waste product. As the autotrophs thrived, oxygen accumulated in Earth's atmosphere.

5. Fossils are traces of ancient organisms that have been preserved in rock or other substances. The earliest known fossils contain archaea-like life forms. Hypotheses about the earliest forms of life on Earth suggest that the earliest life forms were very similar to archaea today.

The Origin of Life
Enrich

Answers will vary. Answers supporting the evidence of life should include the presence of chemical building blocks; the presence of carbon and oxygen in the Martian atmosphere, and the presence of water on the Martian surface when the rock was on Mars; and the shape of the fossil-like evidence is similar to cell-like fossil remains on Earth. The fact that the fossil-like structures, the mineral deposits, and the chemical building blocks were found so close together in the rock, indicate that an organism could have formed the structure, left behind some of its chemical makeup, and also some material that formed from that makeup once the organism died.

Answers that refute the evidence of life might include that all the chemicals present could have come from nonliving sources; the structures might not be fossils but rather are artificial structures; and the fact that the rock is about as old as Mars suggests that life might have formed quickly after Mars' formation, which is not likely.

Key Terms

development
fossil
homeostasis
nucleus
prokaryote
species
stimulus
taxonomy
cell

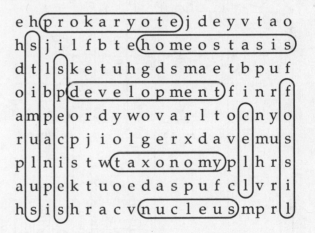

Connecting Concepts

This concept map is only one way to represent the main ideas and relationships in this chapter. Accept other logical answers from students.

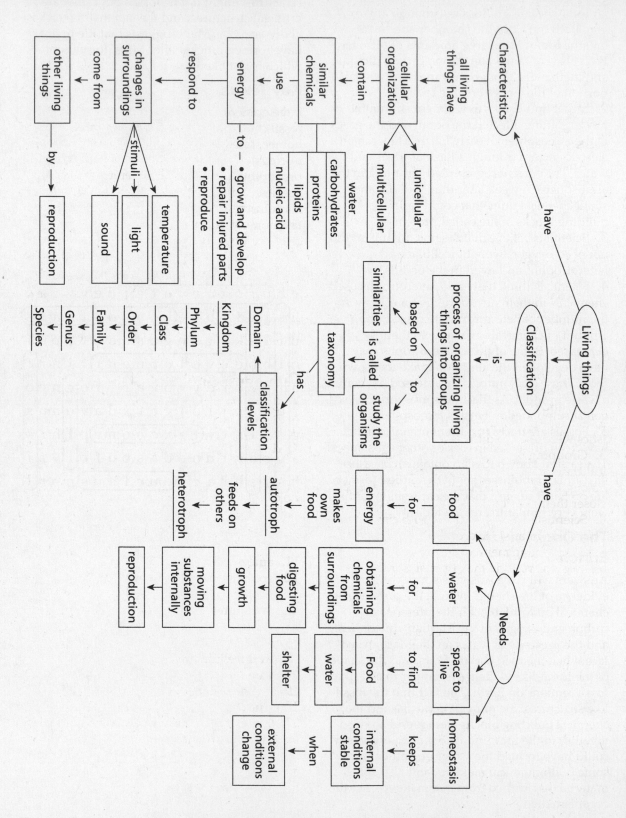

Laboratory Investigation

Developing a Classification System for Seeds

1. Scientists classify organisms into groups so that they are easier to study and so that the relationships among organisms can be better understood.

2. Organism A has more characteristics in common with organism C than it does with organism B.

Observations

1. Answers may vary. Characteristics may include size, color, shape, and texture.

2. Answers may vary. If students are able to classify so specifically that they have only one seed in each group, then they should have as many groups as there are seeds.

3. Answers will vary. Classification systems will likely have similar divisions based on obvious characteristics such as size and color. More subtle characteristics, such as texture, may not be used by all groups.

Analyze and Conclude

1. Answers will vary. Students will probably mention specific physical traits such as color, shape, and size.

2. Final groups may vary if different characteristics were used to differentiate the seeds.

3. Grouping organisms that have similar physical traits lets you see possible relationships among them. The more similar their traits, the closer their relationships are likely to be.

4. Scientists place organisms with similar characteristics in the same group. On the basis of differences among members of the group, scientists subdivide the organisms into subgroups and so on.

Critical Thinking and Applications

1. Answers will vary. Students should be aware of the possibility of using other characteristics.

2. Answers will vary. Sample answer: Yes. But because of the complexity or similarity of some organisms, a greater number of choices could lead to confusion. Even with two choices, it is sometimes difficult to decide which characteristic best describes the organism.

3. Characteristics may include color or specific markings, body form, type of bill and feet, and song.

4. Answers will vary. Sample answer: from specific to general. That way you base classifications on specific characteristics, rather than trying to force characteristics to fit a broad category. Alternative answer: from general to specific. That way it is easier to observe general patterns.

Chapter Performance Assessment

Analyze and Conclude

1. Answers may vary. Sample: The Cerealites were classified by shape, color, and size. I chose these characteristics because they are easy to see.

2. Yes, there is more than one correct classification system. Explanations may vary. Sample: Some students looked at different characteristics than I did. Some students used the same characteristics that I did, but at different levels of their system.

3. Answers may vary. Sample: I would have to add a new group to my system. The first level of classification would now divide the Cerealites into three groups: yellow, brown, and yellow that later changes to red.

4. Answers may vary. Students should say that the types of Cerealites that seem to be most closely related share the most characteristics.

Chapter Test

1. d
2. b
3. c
4. d
5. b
6. a
7. d
8. d
9. c
10. c
11. autotroph
12. spontaneous generation
13. Fossils
14. taxonomy
15. genus
16. nitrogen
17. multicellular
18. true
19. archaea
20. true
21. You cannot use the given key to classify figure B because it has fewer than eight legs.
22. Figure A is a pseudoscorpion; 1a, 2b, 5a, 6b

23. A centipede only has one pair of legs on each body segment. A millipede has two pairs on each body segment.

24. Living organisms differ from nonliving things in a number of ways. Living organisms are composed of cells. Living organisms also differ from nonliving things in that they use energy to grow, develop, and reproduce. Living organisms are also able to respond to their surroundings.

25. Humans, like all organisms, need energy, water, living space, and stable internal conditions. In addition, humans need oxygen to survive. Since the scientists do not know what the planet's conditions are like, they must make sure that they have enough food, water, oxygen, shelter, and clothing to survive any possible conditions.

26. There is more than one variable factor. The plant inside the refrigerator is not only colder, but also has less light than the plant on the windowsill.

27. Answers may vary. Both seedlings should receive the same amount of light. You could put both seedlings inside boxes that contain comparable light sources. The only difference between the seedlings should be temperature.

28. Both the first organisms and bacteria were unicellular prokaryotes. Like some bacteria, the first organisms were probably heterotrophs that did not need oxygen to survive.

29. The organism could be a member of the protist kingdom or the plant kingdom. It could not be either bacteria or archaea, which are all unicellular, and it could not be a member of the animal kingdom or fungi kingdom because these organisms are heterotrophs.

30. The *Parus bicolor* and the *Parus atricapillus* are more closely related because they share the same genus. Using binomial nomenclature, the genus is the first word of the name and is a group of closely related organisms.

Viruses and Bacteria

▲ Lab zone Chapter Project Be a Disease Detective

The following steps will walk you through the Chapter Project. Use the hints as you guide your students through research, survey preparation, analysis and interpretation of survey results, and written report and presentation.

Chapter Project Overview

To introduce the project, discuss the vaccinations received by most students in the class. Ask students to describe the symptoms of each of the diseases against which they were vaccinated. They will probably have difficulty describing the symptoms because these diseases are now quite rare, due in large part to the use of vaccines.

Have students read the Chapter Project Overview. Review the project's rules and hand out the Chapter Project Scoring Rubric you will use for scoring students' work. Discuss with students what will be expected of them.

Set a deadline for the project presentation and interim dates for Keep Students on Track at the end of Section 2 and Section 3. Encourage students to copy the dates in the Project Timeline.

This project is limited to typical infectious childhood diseases. Do not approve other research topics, such as sexually transmitted diseases. In addition, it is best to assign diseases for which a vaccine became widely used between ten and fifty years ago.

You may want to assign a particular disease to each student or group. This prevents too many students from choosing the same disease.

Distribute copies of the Chapter Project Worksheets. Have students read over the questions in Worksheet 1 that they will need to answer in the research stage of this project.

Worksheet 2 will help students prepare data for the presentation. Remind students to refer to the hints in the Chapter Project Overview as they plan and carry out the project.

Materials and Preparation

Below are diseases that are routinely vaccinated against in the United States and the approximate time of vaccine introduction.

- Diphtheria (bacterial) 1920s
- Pertussis (bacterial) early 1940s
- Tetanus (bacterial) early 1940s
- Polio (viral) 1950s
- Measles (viral) early 1960s
- Mumps (viral) late 1960s
- Rubella (viral) late 1960s
- H. influenza type b (bacterial) 1980s
- Varicella (viral) 1995

The Centers for Disease Control and Prevention (www.cdc.gov) of the U.S. Department of Health and Human Services is a good resource for more information on these diseases and on immunizations.

Check with the librarian and the school nurse to determine if they can locate relevant research material for students.

Discuss the information in Worksheet 1 that a student should gather during the research phase.

Discuss in class the kinds of information students will need to survey as outlined in Worksheet 2. The goal of the project is to determine if the occurrence and public knowledge of childhood diseases has changed over the years.

Keep Students on Track— Section 2

Survey questions should allow straightforward recording of answers to be used in data analysis. Have students ask questions requiring yes/no or numerical responses. In addition, students could ask multiple choice questions.

Make sure that each student's questions will obtain the desired information. For example: Have you had the disease? What causes the disease? Are you familiar with the symptoms? How is the disease transmitted? How is the disease treated? Are vaccinations available?

Ask the student whom he or she intends to survey. Make sure that the student will survey people of all ages. Also, be sure that the same individuals are not surveyed repeatedly by different students.

Keep Students on Track— Section 3

Check that students have almost finished giving the survey.

Check students' records and manner of tabulating the data. Review with the class some of the ways (bar graphs, circle graphs) in which data can be visually presented. Students can find information on data tables and graphics in the Skills Handbook.

Chapter Project Wrap Up

Help students prepare their presentations. Make sure their graphs represent the data accurately.

After all presentations have been made, lead a class discussion on the results. Encourage students to note similarities and differences between the results obtained by different groups.

Extension

Suggest that students do an in-depth interview of a parent or grandparent to learn anecdotes about childhood diseases. How were childhood diseases treated when the subject was a child?

Invite the school nurse to speak to the class about the vaccinations that are required before a child can attend school.

Viruses and Bacteria ▪ *Chapter Project*   **Overview**

Lab zone Chapter Project **Be a Disease Detective**

For this project, you will investigate an infectious childhood disease. First, you will research the disease using the library, Internet, and other sources. Then, you will prepare a survey that you will give to 30 people of different ages. The purpose of the survey is to determine if the occurrence and public knowledge of the disease has changed since the introduction of a vaccine for the disease.

   After you have researched the disease and conducted your survey, you will describe what you have found in a report to the rest of the class.

Project Rules

- Select a childhood disease to research and obtain your teacher's approval.

- Research the disease using the library, Internet, and other sources suggested by your teacher.

- Prepare a draft of your survey, show it to your teacher, and revise the survey as needed.

- Give your survey to at least 30 people of various ages.

- Analyze the results of your survey. Determine whether the incidence of and public knowledge about the disease has changed over time.

- Present the results of your project to the class.

Project Hints

- After your teacher has approved your disease topic, you need to do some initial research. In your research, try to answer the following questions: What causes the disease? (bacterium, virus, other) What are the symptoms of the disease? What is the treatment for the disease? Is there a vaccine for the disease and, if so, when was it developed and introduced on a large scale? You should gather any other information you feel will be helpful.

- Libraries, the Internet, and local health professionals are good places to find information about the disease you choose.

- Your survey questions should be written in a way that the answers can be easily counted, such as questions requiring yes/no or numerical responses. In addition, you could ask multiple choice questions.

Viruses and Bacteria • *Chapter Project*   **Overview**

- Decide what information you want to obtain in your survey. For example: Have you had the disease? (yes, no, or don't know) What causes the disease? (bacteria, virus, other organism, or don't know) Are you familiar with the symptoms? (yes or no) If so, what are the symptoms? (Decide how you will tabulate answers to this question.) How is the disease transmitted? (through air, food, water, direct contact, other, or don't know) How is the disease treated? (antibiotics, other drugs, no treatment, or don't know) Are vaccinations available? (yes, no, or don't know)

- Before giving your survey, come up with ways to analyze and present the data. For example, you could count the number of individuals above and below a certain age who are familiar with the symptoms of the disease. You could then present this information on a bar graph.

- An important date that you will discover in your research is the first year that a vaccine was widely administered. It will probably be useful to compare survey answers for individuals who were children before this date, and those who were children after this date.

Project Timeline

Task   **Date Due**

1. Disease topic approved.   _____

2. Research on disease completed.   _____

3. First draft of survey written and presented
   to teacher; plan for survey approved.   _____

4. Final draft of survey written and presented
   to teacher.   _____

5. Surveys of 30 individuals finished.

6. Presentation given to class.   _____

Viruses and Bacteria ▪ *Chapter Project*   **Worksheet 1**

Prepare Your Survey

Use the following suggestions to guide you during the research phase of your project.

The Survey

1. After your teacher has approved your disease topic, try to find the scientific name for that disease. Also determine whether the organism responsible for the disease is a virus, bacterium, or other organism.

   Common Name: _____

   Scientific Name: _____

   Organism Type: _____

2. Determine the symptoms of the disease and any treatments that are available to treat it. Can the disease result in death of the patient? If so, your survey may have to ask whether they know anyone else who has had the disease, rather than asking if they have had the disease themselves.

3. Find out if there is a vaccine for the disease and when it was first widely administered. What is the immunization schedule for the vaccine? How effective is the vaccine at preventing the disease? Are there any side effects to the vaccine? If so, how often do these side effects occur?

4. Given the time when the vaccine was first widely administered, infer when the occurrence of the disease was expected to decline. This will help you determine how to group individuals of different ages in your survey.

5. Decide what questions will be on the survey questionnaire (see Project Hints). What exactly do you want to know? What specific answers do you need to conclude that the occurrence of a disease or public knowledge about a disease has changed? How will you record individual answers? How will you analyze the answers?

6. Record additional information that you wish to include in your report such as the type of vaccine, the scientists who discovered the vaccine, the changes that have been made in the vaccine over the years, and so on.

Viruses and Bacteria • *Chapter Project*   **Worksheet 2**

Conduct the Survey

This worksheet will help you conduct your survey and analyze the results.

Conducting the Survey

1. You must decide who will be in your survey group. You should choose individuals from all age groups.

2. You need to decide how, where, and when you will give each person the survey. Could you conduct the survey in person? Could you give the survey by phone or using e-mail? Could you drop a copy of the survey off at a person's house and pick it up the next day?

3. You must decide what you will need to say to introduce yourself politely and explain your desire to obtain the information for your project. You need to decide what you will do if a person does not want to answer a particular question. How will you conclude the interview? Be sure to thank people for their participation.

Analyzing and Presenting the Data

1. Divide the answers to your survey into two age groups. Use the timing of the introduction of the vaccine to determine the age groups you will use, for example, below age 35 and above age 35 (see Project Hints).

2. Record the answers to your survey questions into tables, one for each age group.

3. Compare the numbers in each of your tables to one another. Graphing the numbers may make a comparison easier. Do the two tables differ from one another? If they do, is the difference between them what you expected? For example, are more of the people from the older age group able to describe the symptoms of the disease?

4. Decide what you are able to conclude from the results of your survey. Did you discover any information during the research phase of the project that agrees or disagrees with your survey results? Keep in mind that 30 individuals is a relatively small sample size.

Viruses and Bacteria ▪ *Chapter Project* 　　　　　　　　　　**Scoring Rubric**

Lab zone Chapter Project Be a Disease Detective

In evaluating how well you complete the Chapter Project, your teacher will judge your work in four categories. In each, a score of 4 is the best rating.

	4	3	2	1
Research	Thoroughly researches the disease. Presents a complete and correct account of what is already known about the disease.	Adequately researches the disease. Presents a correct account of what is already known about the disease.	Does some research into the disease. Presents an incomplete account of what is already known about the disease.	Does little research into the disease. Presents an incorrect account of what is already known about the disease.
Planning and Conducting the Survey	Survey is complete and asks for all the relevant information about the disease. Student gives survey to at least 30 individuals of different ages.	Survey is adequate and asks for most of the relevant information about the disease. Student gives survey to at least 30 individuals.	Survey is only partly adequate and asks for little of the relevant information about the disease. Student gives survey to fewer than 30 individuals.	Survey does not address relevant information. Student gives survey to only a few individuals.
Analysis of Survey Results	Survey results are analyzed in a thorough and methodical manner. Written report is complete.	Survey results are analyzed adequately. Written report is clear and covers much of the relevant information.	Data analysis is incomplete. Written report is incomplete.	Data not analyzed, no conclusions drawn. Written report is poorly organized.
Class Presentation and Evaluation of Evidence	Evidence supporting all conclusions is well communicated in a clear, accurate manner.	Evidence supporting all conclusions is communicated in an adequate manner.	Presentation hard to follow and not communicated well. Some evidence presented to support conclusions about the disease.	Presentation lacking in information and not communicated well. Little evidence presented.

Viruses

🕐 *2–3 periods, 1–1 1/2 blocks*

ABILITY LEVELS KEY
L1 Basic to Average
L2 For All Students
L3 Average to Advanced

Objectives

A.2.1.1 List characteristics of viruses and state reasons why viruses are considered to be nonliving.

A.2.1.2 Describe the components of the basic structure of a virus.

A.2.1.3 Explain how both active and hidden viruses multiply.

A.2.1.4 Discuss both positive and negative ways that viruses affect living things.

Key Terms

• virus • host • parasite • bacteriophage

Local Standards

Viruses and Bacteria

PRETEACH

Targeted Resources

Build Background Knowledge
Invite students to name diseases, as you list them on the board. Ask them to identify any they know are caused by viruses. *(Sample: cold, flu, smallpox, measles, mumps, polio)*

 Discover Activity *Which Lock Does the Key Fit?* **L1**

❑ **All in One Teaching Resources**
  L2 Reading Strategy Transparency A10: Sequencing

❑ 💿 **PresentationExpress™ CD-ROM**

INSTRUCT

Targeted Resources

What Is a Virus? Students discuss the characteristics, shapes, and sizes of viruses. They learn how names are chosen for them.
The Structure of Viruses Students compare the similarities and differences in viral structures.
How Viruses Multiply Students learn how a virus takes over a host cell to reproduce viruses.
Viruses and the Living World Students learn both the diseases caused by some viruses and the usefulness of other viruses.

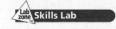 Skills Lab *How Many Viruses Fit on a Pin?* **L2**

❑ **All in One Teaching Resources**
  L2 Guided Reading, pp. 109–112
  L2 Transparencies A11, A12, A13, A14
  L2 Lab: *How Many Viruses Fit on a Pin?* pp. 115–116

❑ 💿 **Lab Activity Video/DVD**
Skills Lab: *How Many Viruses Fit on a Pin?*

❑ **PHSchool.com** Web Code: cep-1021

❑ 💿 **Student Edition on Audio CD**

ASSESS

Targeted Resources

Section Assessment Questions
🔄 Have students use their Sequencing graphic organizers to answer the questions.

Reteach
Students review flowchart about viruses with a partner, adding any necessary information.

❑ **All in One Teaching Resources**
Section Summary, p. 108
  L1 Review and Reinforce, p. 113
  L3 Enrich, p. 114

Viruses and Bacteria ▪ *Section Summary*

Viruses

Key Concepts

■ How do viruses differ from living things?

■ What is the basic structure of a virus?

■ How do viruses multiply?

A **virus** is a tiny, nonliving particle that enters and then reproduces inside a living cell. Biologists consider viruses to be nonliving because viruses are not cells. Viruses do not use energy to grow or to respond to their surroundings.

Although viruses can multiply, they do so differently than organisms. Viruses can only multiply when they are inside a living cell. The organism that a virus enters and multiplies inside is called a host. A **host** is an organism that provides a source of energy for a virus or another organism. Organisms that live on or in a host and cause harm to the host are called **parasites.** Most viruses are like parasites because they destroy the cells in which they multiply.

Viruses vary in shape and size. Viruses can be round, or rod-shaped, or shaped like bricks, threads, or bullets. Some viruses, including bacteriophages, have complex, robotlike shapes. A **bacteriophage** is a virus that infects bacteria. Viruses are much smaller than cells.

Scientists may name a virus after the disease it causes, the organisms they infect, the place where it was first found, or the scientists who first identified it.

All viruses have two basic parts: a protein coat that protects the virus and an inner core made of genetic material. Some viruses are surrounded by an additional membrane envelope. Each virus contains unique proteins on its outer surface. The shape of these proteins allows the virus to attach to, or lock onto, only certain host cells.

After a virus attaches to a host cell, it enters the cell. **Once inside a cell, a virus's genetic material takes over many of the cell's functions. It instructs the cell to produce the virus's proteins and genetic material. These proteins and genetic material then assemble into new viruses.**

An active virus immediately takes over the cell's functions, and the cell quickly begins to produce the virus's proteins and genetic material. These parts are assembled into new viruses. When it is full of new viruses, the host cell bursts open and releases the new viruses.

When a hidden virus enters a host cell, the virus's genetic material becomes part of the cell's genetic material. The virus's genetic material may stay inactive for a long time. Then, the virus's genetic material suddenly becomes active and takes over the cell's functions and replicates. Once the host cell is full of new viruses, it bursts open to release them.

Viruses and Bacteria · *Guided Reading and Study*

Viruses (pp. 40–46)

This section describes what viruses are, what they look like, and how they multiply.

Use Target Reading Skills

As you read, make two flowcharts that show how active and hidden viruses multiply. Put the steps in the process in separate boxes in the flowchart in the order in which they occur.

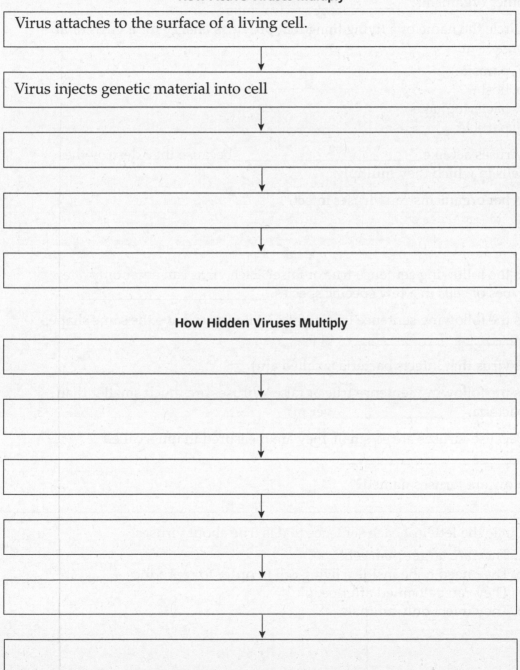

How Active Viruses Multiply

| Virus attaches to the surface of a living cell. |

↓

| Virus injects genetic material into cell |

↓

| |

↓

| |

↓

| |

How Hidden Viruses Multiply

| |

↓

| |

↓

| |

↓

| |

↓

| |

↓

| |

Viruses and Bacteria • *Guided Reading and Study*

Viruses (continued)

What Is a Virus? (pp. 41–42)

1. Why do biologists consider viruses to be nonliving?

_____

_____

_____

2. Is the following sentence true or false? Viruses multiply the same way as other organisms. _____

3. Circle the name of a living thing that provides energy for a virus or an organism.

   a. parasite
   b. host
   c. bacteriophage
   d. particle

4. Viruses act like _____ because they destroy the cells in which they multiply.

5. What organisms can viruses infect?

_____

_____

6. Is the following sentence true or false? Each virus can enter only a few types of cells in a few specific species. _____

7. Is the following sentence true or false? All viruses have the same shape. _____

8. A virus that infects bacteria is called a(n) _____.

9. Is the following sentence true or false? Viruses are much smaller than bacteria. _____

10. Because viruses are so small, they are measured in units called _____.

11. How are viruses named?

_____

12. Circle the letter of each sentence that is true about viruses.

   a. They are larger than cells.
   b. They need to be inside a living cell in order to reproduce.
   c. They can be named after people.
   d. They infect only animals.

Viruses and Bacteria • *Guided Reading and Study*

The Structure of Viruses (p. 43)

13. Label the two basic parts of a virus in this diagram.

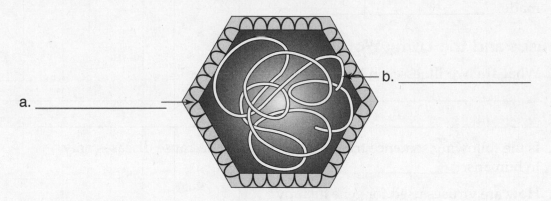

a. _____

b. _____

14. What are two functions of a virus's protein coat?

a. _____

b. _____

15. Is the following sentence true or false? The shape of the proteins allows the virus's coat to attach to only certain cells in the host.

_____

How Viruses Multiply (pp. 44–45)

Match the kind of virus with the way it multiplies in a cell. Viruses may be used more than once.

How It Multiplies

_____ **16.** The virus's genetic material becomes part of the cell's genetic material.

_____ **17.** The virus immediately begins to multiply after entering the cell.

_____ **18.** The virus stays inactive for a long time.

Viruses

a. active virus

b. hidden virus

Viruses and Bacteria ▪ *Guided Reading and Study*

Viruses (continued)

19. Is the following sentence true or false? When the virus is active, the cell makes the virus's proteins and genetic material and new viruses are made. _____

Viruses and the Living World (p. 46)

20. What are two illnesses in humans caused by viruses?

_____

_____

21. Is the following sentence true or false? Viruses can cause diseases only in humans. _____

22. How are viruses used for gene therapy?

_____

_____

_____

Viruses and Bacteria • *Review and Reinforce*

Viruses

Understanding Main Ideas

Answer the following questions on a separate sheet of paper.

1. Viruses are considered to be nonliving. How are viruses similar to living organisms? How are they different?

2. How are viruses similar to parasites?

3. How do hidden viruses differ from active viruses?

4. In the diagram below, identify the two structural parts of the virus. Explain the function of each part.

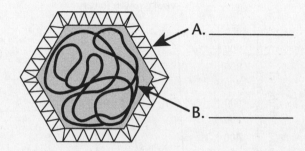

A. _____

B. _____

Building Vocabulary

Write a definition for each of the following terms on the lines below.

5. virus

_____

_____

_____

6. bacteriophage

_____

_____

_____

7. parasite

_____

_____

_____

8. host

_____

_____

_____

Name _____ Date _____ Class _____

Viral Multiplication

Different kinds of viruses not only look different and infect different kinds of cells, they also multiply at different rates. The rate at which a virus multiplies and when and how this multiplication takes place can help to identify the virus.

The graph below shows the rate of growth of four groups of animal viruses, that is, viruses that infect animal cells. Some herpesviruses cause skin blisters such as "cold sores." The diseases smallpox and cowpox are caused by different pox-viruses. Certain adenoviruses produce upper respiratory infections. The viruses called polyomaviruses can trigger the growth of tumors.

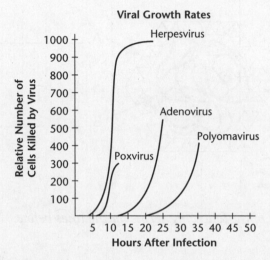

To collect the data for the graph above, scientists grew viruses in the laboratory. Counting viruses is very difficult because they are so small. It's much easier to measure how effective a virus is at killing cells. So in the graph, the *y*-axis of the graph shows the number of places where cells have been destroyed because of viral activity. For each kind of virus, a higher number of cells killed by the virus means a higher number of virus particles.

Answer the following questions on a separate sheet of paper.

1. Which kind of virus begins multiplying first? How soon after infection does this happen?

2. Which kind of virus begins multiplying last? How soon after infection does this happen?

3. What is similar about the four lines on the graph? What does this mean about the growth rates of the four kinds of virus groups?

4. The upper part of the line representing the growth curve of herpesvirus is nearly horizontal. What does this mean about the rate of multiplication of the herpesvirus from 15 to 20 hours after infection?

Name _____ Date _____ Class _____

Viruses and Bacteria · *Skills Lab*

How Many Viruses Fit on a Pin?

Problem

How can a model help you understand how small viruses are?

Skills Focus

calculating, making models

Materials

straight pin   long strips of paper   pencil

meter stick   scissors   tape

calculator (optional)

Procedure

1. Examine the head of a straight pin. Write a prediction about the number of viruses that could fit on the pinhead. **CAUTION:** *Avoid pushing the pin against anyone's skin.*

2. Assume that the pinhead has a diameter of about 1 mm. If the pinhead were enlarged 10,000 times, its diameter would measure 10 m. Create a model of the pinhead by cutting and taping together narrow strips of paper to make a strip that is 10 m long. The strip of paper represents the diameter of the enlarged pinhead.

3. Lay the 10-m strip of paper on the floor of your classroom or in the hall. Imagine creating a large circle that had the strip as its diameter. The circle would be the pinhead at the enlarged size. Calculate the area of the enlarged pinhead using this formula:

$$\text{Area} = \pi \times \text{radius}^2$$

   Remember that you can find the radius by dividing the diameter by 2.

4. A virus particle may measure 200 nm on each side (1 nm equals a billionth of a meter). If the virus were enlarged 10,000 times, each side would measure 0.002 m. Cut out a square 0.002 m by 0.002 m to serve as a model for a virus. (*Hint:* 0.002 m = 2 mm.)

5. Next, find the area in meters of one virus particle at the enlarged size. Remember that the area of a square equals side × side.

6. Now divide the area of the pinhead that you calculated in Step 3 by the area of one virus particle to find out how many viruses could fit on the pinhead.

7. Exchange your work with a partner, and check each other's calculations.

Viruses and Bacteria ▪ *Skills Lab*

How Many Viruses Fit on a Pin *(continued)*

Analyze and Conclude

Write your answers on a separate sheet of paper.

1. **Calculating** Approximately how many viruses can fit on the head of a pin?

2. **Predicting** How does your calculation compare with the prediction you made? If the two numbers are very different, explain why your prediction may have been inaccurate.

3. **Making Models** What did you learn about the size of viruses by magnifying both the viruses and pinheads to 10,000 times their actual size?

4. **Communicating** In a paragraph, explain why scientists sometimes make and use enlarged models of very small things, such as viruses.

More to Explore

Think of another everyday object that you could use to model some other facts about viruses, such as their shapes or how they infect cells. Describe your model and explain why the object would be a good choice.

Bacteria

3–4 periods, 1 1/2–2 blocks

ABILITY LEVELS KEY
L1 Basic to Average
L2 For All Students
L3 Average to Advanced

Objectives

A.2.2.1 Name and describe structures, shapes, and sizes of a bacterial cell.

A.2.2.2 Compare autotrophs to heterotrophs, and explain how energy is released through respiration.

A.2.2.3 Contrast asexual and sexual methods of bacterial reproduction.

A.2.2.4 Explain the roles of bacteria in the production of oxygen and food, in environmental recycling and cleanup, and in health and medicine.

Key Terms

• bacteria • cytoplasm • ribosome • flagellum
• respiration • binary fission
• asexual reproduction • sexual reproduction
• conjugation • endospore • pasteurization
• decomposer

Local Standards

PRETEACH

Build Background Knowledge
Students discuss samples of yogurt and Swiss cheese. Students infer that they are produced with the help of certain kinds of bacteria.

 **Discover Activity** *How Quickly Can Bacteria Multiply?* **L1**

Targeted Resources

❏ **All in One Teaching Resources**
  L2 Reading Strategy: Building Vocabulary

❏ **PresentationExpress™ CD-ROM**

INSTRUCT

The Bacterial Cell Students discuss structures, shapes, and sizes of bacteria.
Obtaining Food and Energy Students compare autotrophs to heterotrophs and then discuss energy released through respiration.
Reproduction Students study the conditions needed for bacteria to reproduce, comparing and contrasting asexual and sexual reproduction.
The Role of Bacteria in Nature Students discuss roles of bacteria in the production of oxygen and food, in environmental recycling and clean up, and in health and medicine.

 **Consumer Lab** *Comparing Disinfectants* **L2**

Targeted Resources

❏ **All in One Teaching Resources**
  L2 Guided Reading, pp. 119–121
  L2 Transparency A15
  L2 Lab: *Comparing Disinfectants*, pp. 124–126

❏ **Lab Activity Video/DVD**
Consumer Lab: *Comparing Disinfectants*

❏ **PHSchool.com** Web Code: ced-1022

❏ **Student Edition on Audio CD**

ASSESS

Section Assessment Questions
Have students use their Building Vocabulary definitions to write sentences about Key Terms.
Reteach
Students answer the assessment questions using their Building Vocabulary definitions.

Targeted Resources

❏ **All in One Teaching Resources**
Section Summary, p. 118
L1 Review and Reinforce, p. 122
L3 Enrich, p. 123

Viruses and Bacteria ▪ *Section Summary*

Bacteria

Key Concepts

- How do the cells of bacteria differ from those of eukaryotes?

- What do bacteria need to survive?

- Under what conditions do bacteria thrive and reproduce?

- What positive roles do bacteria play in people's lives?

Bacteria are single-celled organisms. **Bacteria are prokaryotes. The genetic material in their cells is not contained in a nucleus.** Bacterial cells have one of three basic shapes: spherical, rodlike, or spiral.

Most bacterial cells are surrounded by a rigid cell wall that helps to protect the cell. Inside the cell wall is the cell membrane that controls what materials pass into and out of the cell. **Cytoplasm** is the gel-like material inside the cell membrane. Inside the cytoplasm are tiny structures called **ribosomes** that are the chemical factories where proteins are produced. The cell's genetic material is also located in the cytoplasm, and contains the instructions for all the cell's functions. Some bacteria have flagella. A **flagellum** is a long, whiplike structure that extends from the cell membrane and out through the cell wall. A flagellum helps a cell to move.

All bacteria need certain things to survive. **Bacteria must have a source of food and a way of breaking down the food to release its energy.** Some bacteria are autotrophs and make their own food. Others are heterotrophs that obtain food by consuming autotrophs or other heterotrophs. The process of breaking down food to release its energy is called **respiration.**

When bacteria have plenty of food, the right temperature, and other suitable conditions, they thrive and reproduce frequently. Bacteria reproduce by **binary fission**, a process in which one cell divides to form two identical cells. Binary fission is a form of asexual reproduction. **Asexual reproduction** is a reproductive process that involves only one parent and produces offspring that are identical to the parent. Some bacteria perform a simple form of sexual reproduction called conjugation. **Sexual reproduction** involves two parents who combine their genetic material to produce a new organism that differs from both parents. During **conjugation,** one bacterium transfers some of its genetic material into another. After the transfer the cells separate.

Many bacteria can survive harsh conditions by forming endospores. An **endospore** is a small, rounded, thick-walled, resting cell that forms inside a bacterial cell.

Some bacteria cause diseases and other harmful conditions. However, most bacteria are either harmless or helpful to people. **Bacteria are involved in oxygen and food production, environmental recycling and cleanup, and health maintainance and medicine production.** Helpful bacteria produce foods such as cheese and pickles. However, some bacteria cause food to spoil. One method to slow down food spoilage is **pasteurization,** where food is heated to a temperature that is high enough to kill most harmful bacteria without changing the taste of the food. Heterotrophic bacteria in the soil break down materials for reuse. These bacteria are **decomposers**— organisms that break down large chemicals in dead organisms into small chemicals.

Viruses and Bacteria • *Guided Reading and Study*

Bacteria (pp. 48–57)

This section explains what bacteria are, their positive roles, and how they reproduce.

Use Target Reading Skills

After you read the section, reread the paragraphs that contain definitions of Key Terms. Use all the information you have learned to write a definition of each Key Term in your own words.

The Bacterial Cell (pp. 48–49)

1. Bacteria are _____. The genetic material in their cells is not contained in a nucleus.

2. Is the following sentence true or false? Bacteria are living organisms because they use energy, grow, and respond to their surroundings. _____

3. What three shapes can bacterial cells have?

   a. _____ b. _____

   c. _____

4. Circle the letter of the cell structures where proteins are made.

       a. cell wall   **b.** cytoplasm

       c. ribosomes   **d.** flagellum

5. Label the parts of a bacterial cell in this diagram.

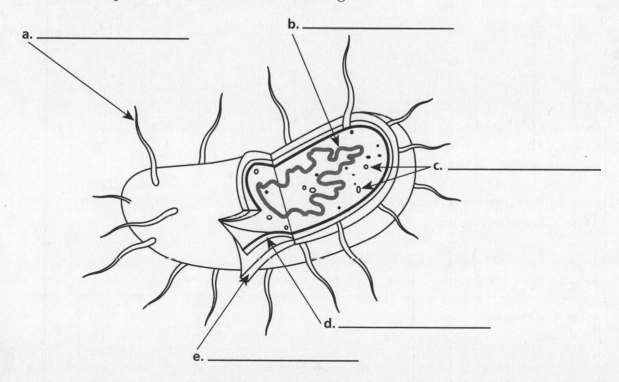

a. _____

b. _____

c. _____

d. _____

e. _____

Viruses and Bacteria ▪ *Guided Reading and Study*

Bacteria *(continued)*

6. Is the following sentence true or false? Bacteria that do not have flagella are never moved from one place to another. _____

Obtaining Food and Energy (pp. 50–51)

7. List the two ways in which autotrophic bacteria make food.

   a. _____

   b. _____

8. How do heterotrophic bacteria get food?

   _____

   _____

9. Is the following sentence true or false? All bacteria must use oxygen to break down food for energy. _____

Reproduction (pp. 52–53)

10. Complete the table below about reproduction in bacteria.

Reproduction in Bacteria

	Asexual Reproduction	Sexual Reproduction
Name of Process		
Number of Parents		
What Occurs in Process		
Result of Process		

Viruses and Bacteria · *Guided Reading and Study*

11. When do bacteria form endospores?

_____

_____

The Role of Bacteria in Nature (pp. 59–57)

12. Circle the letter of each sentence that is true about bacteria.

     a. All bacteria are harmful and cause disease.

     b. Some bacteria can use the sun's energy to make their own food.

     c. Bacteria help produce foods such as cheese, apple cider, and sauerkraut.

     d. Bacteria do not cause food to spoil.

13. Soil bacteria that break down large chemicals in dead organisms into small chemicals are called _____.

14. Is the following sentence true or false? Bacteria can be used to clean up oil spills and gasoline leaks. _____

15. List three ways that bacteria in your digestive system are helpful to you.

     a. _____

     b. _____

     c. _____

16. How do bacteria help people with diabetes?

_____

_____

_____

Viruses and Bacteria ▪ *Review and Reinforce*

Bacteria

Understanding Main Ideas
Answer the following questions on a separate sheet of paper.

1. How are bacterial cells different from the cells of eukaryotes?
2. List four ways that bacteria are helpful to people.

Building Vocabulary
Match each term with its definition by writing the letter of the correct definition on the line beside the term.

_____ 3. cytoplasm

_____ 4. endospore

_____ 5. binary fission

_____ 6. decomposer

_____ 7. sexual reproduction

_____ 8. flagellum

_____ 9. asexual reproduction

_____ 10. conjugation

_____ 11. respiration

_____ 12. ribosome

a. a process in which two parents combine their genetic material to produce a new organism that differs from both parents

b. one bacterium divides to form two identical bacterial cells

c. a small, thick-walled resting cell that forms inside a bacterial cell

d. the region inside the cell membrane

e. organism that breaks down the large chemicals in dead organisms into small chemicals

f. a process in which one bacterium transfers genetic material into another bacterial cell

g. the cell's chemical factories where proteins are produced

h. the process of breaking down food to release energy

i. whiplike structure that helps a cell to move

j. a process in which one parent reproduces offspring identical to that parent

Name _____ Date _____ Class _____

Identifying Bacteria

Thousands of different kinds of bacteria inhabit Earth. Each kind can be distinguished from the others by its characteristics. In addition to shape, these characteristics include: whether it will grow in water hotter than 45°C; whether it will grow in very salty water; whether it will grow in the presence of air; whether it will grow without air; and whether it forms endospores.

Scientists who study viruses use these and about 15 other characteristics to identify a bacterium. The chart below shows some of the characteristics of six common bacteria. A plus (+) sign means the bacterium has the characteristic. A minus (−) sign means the bacterium does not have the characteristic.

Bacterium	Rod	Sphere	Grows at 45°C	Grows in 6.5% Salt Water	Grows in Air	Grows Without Air	Endospores
1	+	−	+	unknown	+	+	+
2	+	−	+	unknown	−	+	+
3	−	+	−	+	+	+	−
4	+	−	+	−	−	+	−
5	−	+	−	−	+	+	−
6	−	+	+	−	+	+	−

Answer the following questions on a separate sheet of paper.

1. What characteristic do all of the bacteria have in common?
2. How could you distinguish bacterium 1 from bacterium 2?
3. Which bacteria might be found in hot springs?
4. What characteristic(s) can you use to distinguish the spherical bacteria from one another?
5. Sea water is about 3.5% salt. In some places, sea water gets trapped when the tide goes out. The heat of the sun will cause some of this water to evaporate. Which bacteria are most likely to survive in such water? Explain your answer.

Viruses and Bacteria • *Consumer Lab*

Comparing Disinfectants

Problem

How well do disinfectants control the growth of bacteria?

Skills Focus

observing, controlling variables

Materials

clock

wax pencil

2 plastic droppers

transparent tape

2 household disinfectants

3 plastic petri dishes with sterile nutrient agar

Procedure

1. Enter your results into the data table as you proceed.

2. Work with a partner. Obtain 3 petri dishes containing sterile nutrient agar. Without opening them, use a wax pencil to label the bottoms A, B, and C. Write your initials on each plate.

3. Wash your hands thoroughly with soap, and then run a fingertip across the surface of your worktable. Your partner should hold open the cover of petri dish A, while you run that fingertip gently across the agar in a zig-zag motion. Close the dish immediately.

4. Repeat Step 3 for dishes B and C.

5. Use a plastic dropper to transfer 2 drops of one disinfectant to the center of petri dish A. Open the cover just long enough to add the disinfectant to the dish. Close the cover immediately. Record the name of the disinfectant in your data table. **CAUTION:** *Do not inhale vapors from the disinfectant.*

6. Repeat Step 5 for dish B but add 2 drops of the second disinfectant. **CAUTION:** *Do not mix any disinfectants together.*

7. Do not add any disinfectant to dish C.

Viruses and Bacteria · *Consumer Lab*

8. Tape down the covers of all 3 petri dishes so that they will remain tightly closed. Allow the 3 dishes to sit upright on your work surface for at least 5 minutes. **CAUTION:** *Do not open the petri dishes again. Wash your hands with soap and water.*

9. As directed by your teacher, store the petri dishes in a warm, dark place where they can remain for at least 3 days. Remove them only to make a brief examination each day.

10. After one day, observe the contents of each dish without removing the covers. Estimate the percentage of the agar surface that shows any changes. Record your observations. Return the dishes to their storage place when you have finished making your observations. Wash your hands with soap.

11. Repeat Step 10 after the second day and again after the third day.

12. After you and your partner have made your last observations, return the petri dishes to your teacher unopened.

Data Table				
Petri Dish	**Disinfectant**	**Day 1**	**Day 2**	**Day 3**
A				
B				
C				

Viruses and Bacteria

Viruses and Bacteria · *Consumer Lab*

Comparing Disinfectants (continued)

Analyze and Conclude

Write your answers on a separate sheet of paper.

1. **Observing** How did the appearance of dish C change during the lab?
2. **Comparing and Contrasting** How did the appearance of dishes A and B compare with dish C?
3. **Drawing Conclusions** How did the appearance of dishes A and B compare with each other? What can you conclude about the two disinfectants from your observations?
4. **Controlling Variables** Why was it important to set aside one petri dish that did not contain any disinfectant?
5. **Communicating** Based on the results of this lab, what recommendation would you make to your family about the use of disinfectants? Explain where in the house these products would be needed most and why.

Design an Experiment

Go to a store and look at soap products that claim to be "antibacterial" soaps. How do their ingredients differ from other soaps? Design an experiment to test how well these products control the growth of bacteria. *Obtain your teacher's permission before carrying out your investigation.*

Viruses, Bacteria, and Your Health

2–3 periods, 1–1 1/2 blocks

Objectives
A.2.3.1 List four ways that infectious diseases can spread.
A.2.3.2 Describe treatments available for bacterial and viral diseases.
A.2.3.3 Describe how to protect themselves against infectious diseases.

Key Terms
• infectious disease • toxin • antibiotic
• antibiotic resistance • vaccine

Local Standards

PRETEACH

Build Background Knowledge
Students recall a time when they were ill. They make inferences about how they think they contracted the disease. Write their responses on the board to use later in class period.

 **Discover Activity** *How Can You Become "Infected"?* **L1**

Targeted Resources

❑ **All in One Teaching Resources**
   L2 Reading Strategy Transparency A16: Using Prior Knowledge
❑ ⊙ **PresentationExpress™ CD-ROM**

INSTRUCT

How Infectious Diseases Spread Students learn about sources of infectious diseases. Students discuss that infectious diseases spread through contact with persons, contaminated objects, infected animals, and other environmental sources of disease.
Treating Infectious Diseases Students learn about antibiotics and antibiotic resistance. They learn that no medication exists that can cure viral infections.
Preventing Infectious Diseases Students learn how vaccines work and their role in preventing infectious diseases.

Targeted Resources

❑ **All in One Teaching Resources**
   L2 Guided Reading, pp. 129–131
❑ **www.SciLinks.org** Web Code: scn-0123
❑ **Discovery SCHOOL** Video Field Trip
❑ ⊙ **Student Edition on Audio CD**

ASSESS

Section Assessment Questions
Students use their Using Prior Knowledge graphic organizers to answer assessment questions.
Reteach
Students review graphic organizers and revise them based on what they have learned.

Targeted Resources

❑ **All in One Teaching Resources**
   Section Summary, p. 128
   L1 Review and Reinforce, p. 132
   L3 Enrich, p. 133

Viruses and Bacteria • *Section Summary*

Viruses, Bacteria, and Your Health

Key Concepts

- How do infectious diseases spread?

- What treatments are effective for bacterial and viral diseases?

- How can you protect yourself against infectious diseases?

Many diseases are **infectious diseases**—illnesses that pass from one organism to another. **Infectious diseases can spread through contact with either an infected person, a contaminated object, an infected animal, or an environmental source.** Other infectious diseases can be spread by inhaling the tiny drops of moisture that an infected person sneezes or coughs into the air. This is because the drops of moisture contain organisms that cause the disease.

Some viruses and bacteria can survive outside a person's body. They can then be spread by objects or in contaminated food or water. If you touch an object that an infected person has sneezed or coughed on, you may transfer some viruses or bacteria to yourself when you touch your mouth or eyes. If you drink water or eat food that an infected person has contaminated, you may get sick.

Animal bites can transmit some serious infectious diseases to humans. Rabies can be spread through the bite of an infected animal. Bites from ticks can spread the bacteria that cause Lyme disease. Bites from mosquitoes can spread the virus that causes encephalitis.

Some viruses and bacteria live in food, water, and soil, or on the surface of objects. The places where they are naturally found are environmental sources of disease. A soil bacterium called *Clostridium tetani,* a soil-dwelling bacterium, can enter a person's body through a wound. It produces a poison known as a **toxin,** which can cause the deadly disease tetanus.

Fortunately, many bacterial diseases can be cured with medications known as antibiotics. An **antibiotic** is a chemical that can kill bacteria without harming a person's cells. Antibiotics are less effective today than they once were because many bacteria have become resistant to antibiotics. **Antibiotic resistance** results when some bacteria are able to survive in the presence of an antibiotic. **Unlike bacterial diseases, there are currently no medications that can cure viral infections.** For most infectious diseases, however, the best treatment is bed rest. However, there are many over-the-counter medications that treat the disease's symptoms.

One way to prevent the spread of infectious diseases is vaccines. **Vaccines are important tools that help prevent the spread of infectious diseases.** A **vaccine** is a substance introduced into the body to stimulate the production of chemicals that destroy specific viruses or bacteria. It may be made from dead or altered viruses or bacteria. The altered viruses or bacteria put the body "on alert." If the virus or bacterium ever enters the body, it is destroyed before it can produce disease.

The best way to protect against infectious diseases is to stay healthy. You should eat nutritious food and get plenty of rest, fluids, and exercise.

Viruses and Bacteria · *Guided Reading and Study*

Viruses, Bacteria, and Your Health (pp. 60–65)

This section explains how diseases are passed from person to person and how these diseases can be treated or prevented.

Use Target Reading Skills

Look at the section headings and visuals to see what this section is about. Then write what you already know about diseases caused by viruses and bacteria in the graphic organizer below. As you read, write what you learn.

What You Know
1. You can catch a cold from somebody who has one.
2.
3.

What You Learned
1.
2.
3.

How Infectious Diseases Spread (pp. 60–61)

1. What is an infectious disease?

_____

_____

_____

Name _____ Date _____ Class _____

Viruses, Bacteria, and your Health (continued)

2. Complete this concept map to show how infectious diseases can spread.

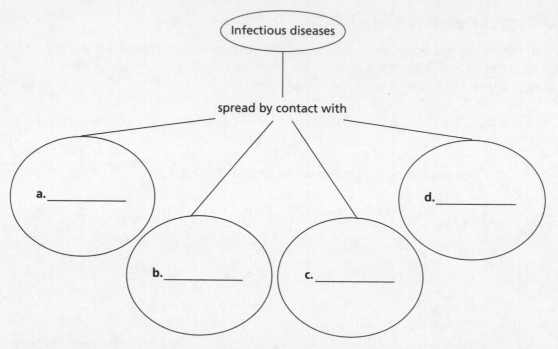

3. How do disease-causing agents enter the body?

_____

_____

_____

4. Is the following sentence true or false? The flu is spread only by direct contact, such as kissing a person with the flu. _____

5. Give one example of how objects can spread diseases.

_____

_____

_____

Match the animal with the disease that it spreads.

Disease	Animal
____ 6. rabies	a. ticks
____ 7. Lyme disease	b. raccoons
____ 8. encephalitis	c. mosquitoes

9. Is the following sentence true or false? Some viruses and bacteria that live in food, water, and soil can cause disease. _____

Viruses and Bacteria · *Guided Reading and Study*

10. Circle the letter of the bacteria that produces a toxin that can cause tetanus.

   a. salmonella

   b. *Clostridium botulinum*

   c. *Clostridium tetani*

   d. encephalitis

Treating Infectious Diseases (pp. 62–64)

11. What is an antibiotic?

_____

_____

12. Why are antibiotics less effective now than they once were?

_____

_____

_____

13. Is the following sentence true or false? Diseases caused by viruses can be cured with antibiotics. _____

Preventing Infectious Diseases (p. 65)

14. Is the following sentence true or false? A vaccine activates the body's natural defenses so that the body is ready to destroy an invading virus or bacterium. _____

15. What are three diseases that vaccines can protect you from?

_____

_____

16. Circle the letter of each sentence that is true about protecting yourself from infectious diseases.

   a. Eat nutritious food.

   b. Get plenty of rest, fluids, and exercise.

   c. Share eating utensils or cups.

   d. Get vaccinated.

17. What should you do if you get ill?

_____

_____

Viruses and Bacteria ▪ *Review and Reinforce*

Viruses, Bacteria, and Your Health

Understanding Main Ideas

Complete the table below by naming examples of behaviors to avoid, and behaviors to practice in order to prevent the spread of infectious diseases.

What Can You Do to Prevent Catching an Infectious Disease?		
How Disease Is Spread	**DO NOT**	**DO**
Contact with Infected Person		
Contact with Infected Object		
Contact with Infected Animal		
Environmental Source		

Answer the following questions on a separate sheet of paper.

1. Why is it important to know whether your sore throat is caused by a virus or bacteria?
2. How do antibiotics work, and why are they becoming less effective?
3. How can a vaccine help prevent an infectious disease?

Building Vocabulary

From the list below, choose the term that best completes each sentence.

infectious diseases   vaccine   antibiotic
antibiotic resistance   toxin

4. Dead or altered viruses or bacteria that are used to stimulate the body to be "on alert" are called a(n) _____.
5. Illnesses that pass from one organism to another are called _____.
6. Chemicals made by microorganisms that are used to kill bacteria are called a(n) _____.
7. A poisonous substance produced by bacteria is called a(n) _____.
8. _____ results when some bacteria are able to survive in the presence of an antibiotic.

Name _____ Date _____ Class _____

Fighting a Viral Disease

Before the 1960s, severe outbreaks of the disease *poliomyelitis* occurred in many parts of the world. This disease, also known as "infantile paralysis" or simply "polio," infected mostly children. However, it was capable of attacking adults as well. One of the most famous victims of polio was United States President Franklin Delano Roosevelt, who got the disease as an adult.

Polio is transmitted from person to person, usually by inhaling droplets infected with the virus. It can paralyze the arms or legs of a person or the muscles that control breathing and can even cause death.

The graph shows the history of polio in South America, Central America, and North America from 1954 to 1973. In the 1990s, polio was eliminated in the Americas.

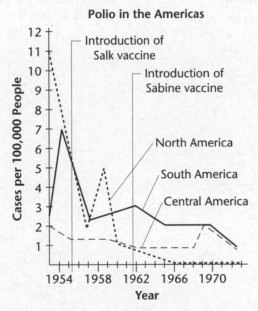

Polio in the Americas

Answer the following questions on a separate sheet of paper.

1. What was used in an attempt to fight the spread of polio?

2. In 1954, about how many cases of polio per 100,000 people were there in South America? Central America? North America?

3. In 1972, about how many cases of polio per 100,000 people were there in South America? Central America? North America?

4. Compare the three lines of the graph. What is the most obvious difference among them? Write a hypothesis to explain the difference.

Viruses and Bacteria ▪ *Key Terms*

Key Terms

Use the clues below to identify Key Terms from the chapter. Write the terms on the lines, putting one letter in each blank. When you finish, the word enclosed in the diagonal lines will reveal the way in which bacteria multiply by asexual reproduction.

Clues

1. A virus that infects bacteria
2. Nonliving particle that invades cells
3. Two bacteria exchange genetic material
4. Harmful organism that lives on a host
5. Breaking down food to release energy
6. Region inside the cell membrane
7. Long, whiplike structure on bacteria

8. Chemical that kills only bacteria
9. Small, rounded, thick-walled, resting cell
10. Energy source for a parasite
11. Poison produced by bacteria
12. Cell part in which proteins are made
13. Stimulates the body to produce chemicals that destroy viruses and bacteria

1. __ __ __ __ __ __ __ __ __ __ __ __
2. __ __ __ __ __ __ __
3. __ __ __ __ __ __ __ __ __ __
4. __ __ __ __ __ __ __ __
5. __ __ __ __ __ __ __ __ __ __
6. __ __ __ __ __ __
7. __ __ __ __ __ __ __ __ __
8. __ __ __ __ __ __ __ __ __
9. __ __ __ __ __
10. __ __ __ __ __
11. __ __ __ __ __ __
12. __ __ __ __ __ __ __ __
13. __ __ __ __ __ __ __

Connecting Concepts

Develop a concept map that uses the Key Concepts and Key Terms from this chapter. Keep in mind the big idea of this chapter. The concept map shown is one way to organize how the information in this chapter is related. You may use an extra sheet of paper.

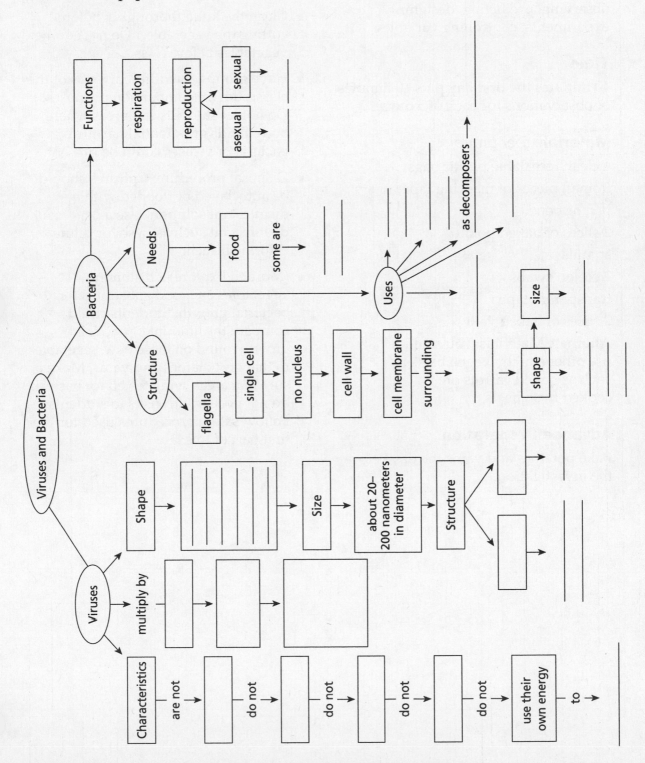

Bacteria That Dine on Vegetables

Key Concept

Bacteria grow nearly everywhere.

Skills Focus

observing, predicting, designing experiments, controlling variables

Time

40 minutes the first day plus 10 minutes of observations for each of 5 days

Materials (*per group*)

4 clear, resealable plastic bags

8 small pieces of masking tape

pen or pencil

2 slices of baked potato

spatula

2 cotton swabs

transparent tape

2 slices of baked yam

Alternate Materials: You could use other starchy vegetables, such as boiled carrots or cooked fresh beets.

Advance Preparation

Bake potatoes and yams the day before the investigation.

Teaching Tips

- You may want to wash and rinse the plastic bags yourself to prevent contamination problems.

- Clean the knife thoroughly before cutting the vegetables. Do not cut the vegetables before class.

- Have groups test different areas of the classroom for comparison purposes. Do not let students test areas where body fluids or potential harmful bacteria or viruses could be present.

- Disposal procedure: Cultures should be autoclaved or flooded with a disinfectant solution. Use a disinfectant such as Lysol or dilute chlorine bleach.

- (More to Explore) All starchy vegetables are good substrates for bacterial growth. Students could compare the amount of bacterial growth found on these new vegetables to that on potatoes and yams. Make sure that areas being tested for bacteria do not pose health risks to students. Follow safety procedures used for the first part of this lab.

Name _____ Date _____ Class _____

Viruses and Bacteria ▪ *Laboratory Investigation*

Bacteria That Dine on Vegetables

Bacteria are among the most numerous organisms on Earth. If a bacterium is in the right temperature range and has enough moisture and food, it can reproduce rapidly. In 24 to 48 hours, it can multiply so often that its offspring form a visible colony.

In this investigation, you will witness this explosive growth as you grow bacteria on common vegetables.

Pre-Lab Discussion

1. How are the cells of bacteria different from those of eukaryotes?

_____

_____

Problem

What conditions do bacteria need for growth?

Materials *(per group)*

4 clear, resealable plastic bags

8 small pieces of masking tape

pen or pencil

2 slices of baked potato

spatula

2 cotton swabs

transparent tape

2 slices of baked yam

Safety *Review the safety guidelines in Appendix A of your textbook.*

Do not open the plastic bags after placing the vegetables inside. Wash your hands thoroughly after handling the vegetables and plastic bags. Have the teacher dispose of the specimens at the end of the experiment.

Viruses and Bacteria ▪ *Laboratory Investigation*

Bacteria That Dine on Vegetables (continued)

Procedure

1. Thoroughly wash four plastic bags with soap and water and rinse them thoroughly.

2. Put a masking-tape label on the outside of each bag. Write the following words on the four different labels: "A-Potato," "A-Yam," "B-Potato," and "B-Yam."

3. Predict where bacteria might be living in your classroom. Give a reason for your predictions. Record your predictions in Observations. Compare your predictions with those of your classmates, and choose an area of your classroom that you will test for bacteria. Have the teacher approve your choice before you continue.

4. Get two slices of baked potato. Wash the spatula with soap and water and use it to pick up the slices. Take care that each slice has one side that touches nothing but the knife that cut it.

5. Put a potato slice with its untouched side facing up in a bag labeled "A-Potato." Seal the bag securely and tape the sealed edge shut.

6. Put the other potato slice with its untouched side facing up in a plastic bag labeled "B-Potato."

7. Rub a cotton swab on the area in your classroom where you think bacteria might live. Then rub the cotton swab on the untouched side of the potato in bag B.

8. Seal the bag securely and tape the sealed edge shut. Set both potato bags in a warm place. Do not open them again. Your teacher will tell you where to dispose of the used cotton swab.

9. Repeat steps 4–8, using two baked yam slices.

10. Wash your hands when you're finished with the lab.

11. Observe the potato and yam slices daily for 5 days. DO NOT OPEN THE BAGS. Each day, draw both slices of each vegetable in the appropriate spaces in Observations and record your observations in the Data Table.

12. At the end of the fifth day, ask the teacher to dispose of the plastic bags and their contents.

Observations

1. Predict where bacteria might be living in your classroom. Give a reason for your prediction.

_____

_____

2. What area of your classroom will you test for bacteria?

_____

Name _____ Date _____ Class _____

Viruses and Bacteria ▪ *Laboratory Investigation*

Vegetable 1: _____

Day 1

Day 2

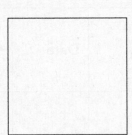
Day 3

Day 4

Day 5

Vegetable 2: _____

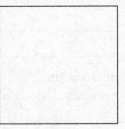
Day 1

Day 2

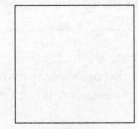
Day 3

Day 4

Day 5

Viruses and Bacteria • *Laboratory Investigation*

Bacteria That Dine on Vegetables (continued)

Data Table

Day	Date	Potato		Yam	
		A-Potato	**B-Potato**	**A-Yam**	**B-Yam**
1					
2					
3					
4					
5					

Analyze and Conclude

1. Large colonies of bacteria may look shiny or like mucus. Which bag(s) had the greatest growth of bacteria? The least growth?

   _____

   _____

2. Do the organisms growing on the potato appear to be different from the organisms growing on the yam? Give a plausible reason for your results.

   _____

   _____

3. Why did you leave the slices untouched in the plastic bags labeled "A"?

   _____

   _____

Viruses and Bacteria ▪ *Laboratory Investigation*

Critical Thinking and Applications

1. Early biologists grew bacteria on freshly cut slices of vegetables. They considered the inside of a vegetable to be sterile, or free of microorganisms. How did the bacteria get on your vegetables?

_____

_____

_____

2. Why was it important to thoroughly wash and rinse the plastic bags before placing the vegetable slices in them?

_____

_____

_____

3. Why did you use a spatula instead of your hand to transfer the vegetable slices into the plastic bags?

_____

_____

_____

4. Suppose you repeated this investigation, but this time you left the plastic bags labeled "A" open for a few minutes before sealing them. What do you think you might observe? Why?

_____

_____

_____

_____

5. What methods can you suggest for keeping vegetables unspoiled for a long time?

_____

_____

_____

_____

More to Explore

Try this activity with other vegetables, such as boiled carrots or cooked fresh beets. Sample other areas of your classroom where you think bacteria might be living. Have the teacher approve your procedure before you carry out the investigation. Do your results resemble results found in this lab?

What Are Viruses and Bacteria?

Students are presented with the problem of creating a question-and-answer game about viruses and bacteria. To solve this problem, students will apply the concepts they have learned about these particles and organisms.

Expected Outcome

Students will work in pairs to write at least 20 questions and answers about bacteria and viruses. These questions will form the basis of their game. They will gather or make the necessary playing materials for the game, such as a board or cards. They will also write a list of rules. Finally, pairs will switch games, and partners will play against each other. Expect a variety of game formats. Descriptions of some sample games follow.

Students could base their game on a television game show. For instance, a question could be written on one side of a card and the answer on the other. A player would read the answer, and respond with the question that goes with this answer. For example, for the answer "a virus that infects bacteria," the question would be "What is a bacteriophage?" If the student responds with the correct question, he or she would get a point.

Some students could choose to make a board game. For instance, players might have to answer a question correctly in order to move their game piece forward on the board. The first player to move his or her game piece around the board would win.

Students could also make a card game. For example, players could take turns drawing cards with a question written on them. If a player answers correctly, he or she would get a point. If the player answers incorrectly, he or she would lose a point and the second player would get a chance to answer.

Content Assessed

This activity assesses students' understanding of concepts related to viruses and bacteria.

Skills Assessed

communicating, applying concepts

Materials

- Provide students with materials for constructing their games, such as index cards, colored pens or pencils, cardboard (for making game boards), small bells (for signaling devices), number cubes, and pennies or buttons (for game pieces).

Time

40 minutes

Monitoring the Task

- Discuss with students the kinds of questions they should use in their games. Ask students: **Suppose you were asked, "What is your favorite color?" How would you answer?** *(Answers may vary. Samples: blue, red)* **Why wouldn't this be a very good question for your game?** *(There is more than one correct answer for this question. The answer is subjective.)* **How could you change this question so that it has only one correct answer?** *(Answers may vary. Sample: If you changed the question to "What color is the sky?" the only correct answer would be "blue.")*

- As an alternative to having students play their games in pairs, you may want to play at least some of the games as an entire class.

What Are Viruses and Bacteria?

In assessing students' performance, use the following rubric

Viruses and Bacteria

	4	3	1
Creating Game	Student and partner write at least 20 highly relevant questions and answers about bacteria and viruses. Information in questions and answers is accurate and complete.	Student and partner write 18–20 mostly relevant questions and answers about bacteria and viruses. One or two questions and answers contain minor errors.	Student and partner write 16–18 fairly relevant questions and answers about bacteria and viruses. Three or four questions and answers contain minor errors.
			Student and partner write fewer than 16 questions and answers about bacteria and viruses, many of which are not relevant. More than four questions and answers contain errors.
Applying Concepts	Student demonstrates a mastery of concepts related to bacteria and viruses.	Student demonstrates a good understanding of concepts related to bacteria and viruses.	Student demonstrates only a partial understanding of concepts related to bacteria and viruses.
			Student demonstrates a minimal understanding of concepts related to bacteria and viruses.
Working Cooperatively	Student takes a lead in designing and establishing rules for designing and establishing rules for the game as well as in playing a game designed by other students.	Student actively participates in designing and establishing rules for designing and establishing rules for the game as well as in playing a game designed by other students.	Student participates in most aspects of designing and establishing rules for the game as well as in playing a game designed by other students.
			Student participates in only a few aspects of designing and establishing rules for the game as well as in playing a game designed by other students.

Viruses and Bacteria ▪ *Performance Assessment*

What Are Viruses and Bacteria?

You work for a toy company. Your boss wants you to design a new game. The only requirement is that the game involves questions and answers about viruses and bacteria.

Problem

How can you help to create a game about viruses and bacteria?

Suggested Materials

index cards

colored pens and pencils

cardboard

2 small bells

number cubes

game pieces (such as pennies or buttons)

Devise a Plan

1. Work with a partner to write at least 20 questions and answers about bacteria and viruses on a separate sheet of paper.

2. Think of a way you could use these questions to develop a game. Types of games you might consider include a board game, a card game, or a home-version of a television game show. Gather or construct the necessary materials for your game. Write a set of rules on a separate sheet of paper. Consider how the players will keep score and how they will check their answers.

3. Switch games with another pair of students. Read the rules of that game, and then play it with your partner.

Analyze and Conclude

After following the plan you devised, answer the following questions on a separate sheet of paper.

1. Did you write any questions for the game that could have more than one correct answer? If so, what were they? How could you change these questions so that they have only one correct answer?

2. Did you write any questions that the players couldn't answer? If so, what were they? How could you make these questions easier for the players to answer correctly?

3. What did you learn about viruses and bacteria by creating the game?

Viruses and Bacteria

Multiple Choice

Write the letter of the correct answer on the line at the left.

_____ 1. A substance that stimulates the body to produce chemicals that destroy viruses or bacteria is called a(n)
    a. endospore.   **b.** vaccine.
    c. cytoplasm.   **d.** antibiotic.

_____ 2. Organisms that live in or on a host organism and cause harm to the host are called
    a. parasites.   **b.** bacteriophages.
    c. viruses.   **d.** flagellum.

_____ 3. Conjugation is a form of
    a. respiration.   **b.** producing energy.
    c. sexual reproduction.   **d.** asexual reproduction.

_____ 4. The chemical factories in cells that produce proteins are called
    a. cytoplasm.   **b.** cell walls.
    c. nuclei.   **d.** ribosomes.

_____ 5. To survive in unfavorable conditions, some bacteria form
    a. flagella.   **b.** vaccines.
    c. cytoplasm.   **d.** endospores.

_____ 6. Which of the following is not a characteristic of an active virus?
    a. multiplies quickly   **b.** has an outer coat made
    c. uses energy to grow   of proteins
                            d. destroys its host cell

_____ 7. The area inside the cell membrane of a bacterium is called the
    a. cytoplasm.   **b.** flagellum.
    c. protein coat.   **d.** nucleus.

_____ 8. The best treatment for an unknown viral disease is
    a. an antibiotic.   **b.** exercise.
    c. bed rest.   **d.** a vaccine.

_____ 9. A chemical that can kill bacteria without harming the human body is called a(n)
    a. virus.   **b.** vaccine.
    c. antibiotic.   **d.** ribosome.

_____ 10. In order to multiply, a virus must
    a. conjugate with another virus.   **b.** invade a host cell.
    c. manufacture extra food.   **d.** remain hidden.

Viruses and Bacteria

Viruses and Bacteria ▪ *Chapter Test*

Completion

Fill in the blank to complete each statement.

11. Bacteria that break down large chemicals in dead organisms into small chemicals are called _____.

12. The process of breaking down food to release its energy is called _____.

13. A(n) _____ is a whiplike structure that helps a bacterial cell move.

14. A virus that attacks and destroys bacteria is called a(n) _____.

15. The bacterium *Clostridium tetani* produces a poison called a(n) _____, which can cause tetanus.

True or False

Determine whether each statement is true or false. If it is true, write true. *If it is false, change the underlined word or words to make the statement true.*

_____ 16. Bacteria reproduce by <u>binary fission</u>.

_____ 17. <u>Hidden</u> viruses immediately take over a host cell's functions.

_____ 18. Some infectious diseases can be prevented with <u>vaccines</u>.

_____ 19. Bacteria are prokaryotes. Their cells <u>have nuclei</u> that contain the cell's genetic materials.

_____ 20. <u>Asexual reproduction</u> is the process by which two parents combine their genetic material to produce a new organism that differs from both parents.

Name _____ Date _____ Class _____

Viruses and Bacteria ▪ *Chapter Test*

Using Science Skills

21. Classifying Use what you know about viruses and bacteria to complete the following table. Mark an **X** in the box if the characteristic applies. A characteristic may apply to both. When you have finished, add one characteristic that applies to viruses and one that applies to bacteria.

Characteristics	Viruses	Bacteria
Surrounded by a cell wall		
Contains genetic material		
Requires a host organism to reproduce		
Microscopic		
Causes infectious diseases		
Add your Own:		
Add your Own:		

22. Interpreting Data Use the information in the table above to explain how viruses and bacteria are similar, and how they are different. Write your answer below.

_____

_____

_____

Essay

On a separate sheet of paper, write a brief paragraph to answer each of the following questions.

23. Give three examples of ways bacteria can be helpful to humans.

24. Name the four ways infectious diseases are spread and give an example of each.

25. Describe the structure of viruses and explain how active viruses reproduce.

Name _____ Date _____ Class _____

Viruses and Bacteria ▪ *Chapter Test*

Using Science Skills

Study the graph below and answer questions 26 and 27 in the space provided.

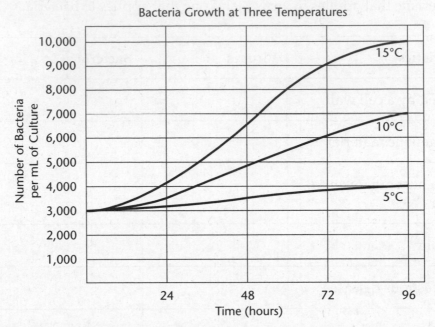

Bacteria Growth at Three Temperatures

26. **Interpreting Graph** What was the increase in number of bacteria per mL of culture after four days at each temperature?

_____

_____

27. **Writing Hypotheses** Write a hypothesis regarding rate of bacteria growth and temperature that explains the graphed results.

_____

_____

Essay

On a separate sheet of paper, answer each of the following questions with a brief paragraph.

28. You are looking at a cell under a microscope. How can you tell if you are looking at a bacterium or the cell of a different type of organism?

29. The symptoms of a viral flu are high fever, sore throat, and headache. What treatments would you recommend? Explain your answer.

30. One bacterium is placed on a dish with nutrients. Six days later, a colony of bacteria all genetically identical to the original bacterium are on the same dish. By what method did the bacteria reproduce? How do you know?

Chapter Project Worksheet 1

1.–5. All answers will vary and depend on the disease chosen.

Chapter Project Worksheet 2

1.–4. All answers will vary and depend on the disease chosen.

Viruses
Guided Reading and Study

Use Target Reading Skills

One way students might organize the information is: How Active Viruses Multiply — **1.** Virus attaches to surface of living cell **2.** Virus injects genetic material into cell **3.** Cell produces viral proteins and genetic material **4.** Viruses assemble. **5.** Cell bursts, releasing viruses.
How Hidden Viruses Multiply — **1.** Virus attaches to cell **2.** Virus injects its genetic material **3.** Virus's genetic material becomes part of cell's genetic material **4.** Later, virus's genetic material becomes active **5.** Cell produces viral proteins and genetic material; viruses are assembled **6.** Cell bursts, releasing viruses

1. Viruses are not cells. They do not use energy to grow or to respond to their surroundings. They cannot make or take in food or produce wastes.
2. false
3. **b.** host
4. parasites
5. Viruses can infect all organisms.
6. true
7. false
8. bacteriophage
9. true
10. nanometers
11. A virus can be named after the disease it causes, the location where it was first found, or after people who first identified the virus.
12. **b.** They need to be inside a living cell in order to reproduce. **c.** They can be named after people.
13. **a.** Protein coat, **b.** Genetic material
14. **a.** It protects the virus. **b.** It allows the virus to attach to certain cells in the host.
15. true
16. b
17. a
18. b
19. true
20. cold, flu, AIDS
21. false
22. Viruses are used as a "messenger service" to deliver genetic materials to cells that need it.

Viruses
Review and Reinforce

1. Viruses resemble organisms because they can multiply. They are different because they are not alive: they are not cells, they do not use energy to grow, and they do not respond to their surroundings.
2. A parasite is an organism that causes harm to its host. Although nonliving, a virus also destroys the invaded host cell by multiplying until the cell bursts.
3. An active virus's genetic material immediately takes over the cell's functions. The cell quickly begins to produce the virus's proteins and genetic material. Then, these parts assemble into new viruses. A hidden virus's genetic material becomes part of the cell's genetic material. The hidden virus does not appear to affect the cell's functions and may stay hidden for quite some time. Then suddenly the virus's genetic material becomes active. From that point, it takes control of the cell's functions the same way an active virus does.
4. Part A is the protein coat. The protein coat protects the virus and enables it to attach to a host cell by fitting into specific proteins on the host cell's surface. Part B is the genetic material. The genetic material contains instructions for making new viruses. It takes over the host cell's functions and directs the cell to produce the virus's proteins and genetic material.
5. A small, nonliving particle that invades a living cell and then reproduces inside it
6. A virus that infects bacteria
7. An organism that causes harm by living on or inside another organism
8. A living thing that provides a source of energy for a virus or organism

Viruses
Enrich

1. Herpesvirus. A little less than 5 hours after infection
2. Polyomavirus, 20 hours
3. The first part of each line rises steeply. This means that each viral group multiplies very rapidly at first.
4. It means the virus' rate of multiplication has slowed down to the point that it is nearly zero.

How Many Viruses Fit on a Pin?
Skills Lab

For answers, see the Teacher's Edition.

Bacteria
Guided Reading and Study

Use Target Reading Skills.
One way students might organize the information is: Students may write one or two descriptive phrases to help them remember the key term. Call on students to share their definitions.
1. prokaryotes
2. true
3. a. spherical, **b.** rodlike, **c.** spiral
4. c. ribosomes
5. a. Flagellum, **b.** Genetic material, **c.** Ribosomes, **d.** Cell wall, **e.** Cell membrane
6. false
7. a. Capture and use the sun's energy, **b.** Use the energy from chemical substances in their environment
8. Heterotrophic bacteria eat other organisms or the food that other organisms make.
9. false
10.

Reproduction in Bacteria

	Asexual Reproduction	Sexual Reproduction
Name of Process	Binary fission	Conjugation
Number of Parents	One	Two
What Occurs in Process	The cell duplicates its genetic material. Then the cell divides into two separate cells.	One bacterium transfers some of its genetic material into another though a thin, threadlike bridge that joins the cells.
Result of Process	New cells identical to parents	Bacteria that are genetically different from parents

11. Bacteria form endospores when conditions in the environment become unfavorable for growth.
12. b, c
13. decomposers
14. true
15. a. Digest food, **b.** Make vitamins, **c.** Prevent harmful bacteria from attaching to the intestines

16. People with some types of diabetes cannot make their own insulin. Bacteria can be engineered to produce human insulin. Insulin-making bacteria are grown and the insulin they produce is then purified and made into medicine.

Bacteria
Review and Reinforce

1. Bacteria are prokaryotes. Their genetic material is not contained within nuclei. Eukaryotes have their genetic material in the nuclei.
2. Bacteria provide oxygen, food products, environmental recycling, and medicines.
3. d
4. c
5. b
6. e
7. a
8. i
9. j
10. f
11. h
12. g

Bacteria
Enrich

1. All can grow without air.
2. Bacterium 1 can grow in air. Bacterium 2 cannot grow in air.
3. 1, 2, 4, 6
4. Growth at 45°C and growth in 6.5% salt water
5. Bacterium 3 is most likely to survive since it can grow in 6.5% salt water. Evaporation will increase the saltiness of the water to a concentration above which bacteria 4, 5, and 6 cannot survive. However, the sun might warm the water to a temperature that bacteria 3 and 5 could not tolerate.

Comparing Disinfectants
Consumer Lab

For answers, see the Teacher's Edition.

Viruses, Bacteria, and Your Health
Guided Reading and Study

Use Target Reading Skills
Possible answers include:
What You Know
1. You can catch a cold from somebody who has one.
2. Some diseases can be treated with medicines.

What You Learned

1. You can catch diseases through contact with an infected person, a contaminated object, an infected animal, or an environmental source.
2. Antibiotic resistance results when some bacteria are able to survive in the presence of an antibiotic.
1. An illness that can pass from one organism to another is an infectious disease.
2. a. Infected person, **b.** Contaminated object, **c.** Infected animal, **d.** Environmental source
3. They can enter through breaks in the skin, moist linings in the eyes, ears, nose, mouth, or other body openings. They can also be inhaled or swallowed.
4. false
5. Examples include drinking from a cup used by an infected person, touching an object that an infected person sneezed or coughed on, or eating food contaminated by an infected person.
6. b
7. a
8. c
9. true
10. c. *Clostridium tetani*
11. It is a chemical that can kill bacteria without harming a person's cells.
12. Many bacteria have become resistant to antibiotics. They can survive and reproduce in the presence of antibiotics.
13. false
14. true
15. Diseases include tetanus, measles, polio, and chickenpox.
16. a, b, d
17. Answers include get plenty of rest, follow the doctor's recommendations, and try not to infect others.

Viruses, Bacteria, and Your Health Review and Reinforce

Contact with Infected Person

DO NOT: touch, hug, or kiss infected people
DO: wash hands after contact, cover mouth and nose when sneezing, get vaccinated for diseases like chicken pox

Contact with Infected Object

DO NOT: eat the same food or drink the same drinks an infected person has contaminated
DO: use your own eating utensils, wash your hands often

Contact with Infected Animal

DO NOT: play with strange animals
DO: monitor your pets outside, wear long sleeves and pants when hiking

Environmental Source

DO NOT: eat food that has not been properly cooked, eat food in rusted or swollen cans, walk outside with unprotected feet
DO: properly cook and store foods, get vaccinated against tetanus

1. If a sore throat is caused by a virus, you can only treat the symptoms with over-the-counter medications. You can use an antibiotic to cure a sore throat caused by bacteria.
2. Antibiotics are chemicals that attack and kill bacteria. However, antibiotics are becoming less effective because many bacteria have adapted over the years and now are able to survive in their presence
3. A vaccine puts the body on alert for a particular virus or bacterium. It stimulates the body to produce chemicals that will destroy that virus or bacterium if it ever enters the body.
4. vaccine
5. infectious diseases
6. antibiotic
7. toxin
8. Antibiotic resistance

Viruses, Bacteria, and Your Health Enrich

1. The Salk and Sabin vaccines
2. 7; about 1.5; about 8
3. about 1; 1; close to 0
4. The number of cases per 100,000 people in North America has declined to almost zero. The number of cases per 100,000 people has not declined as much in South and Central America. More people have probably been vaccinated against polio in North America than in either South or Central America.

Key Terms

1. bacteriophage
2. virus
3. conjugation
4. parasite
5. respiration
6. cytoplasm
7. flagellum
8. antibiotic
9. endospore
10. host
11. toxin
12. ribosome
13. vaccine
 Answer: binary fission

Connecting Concepts

This concept map is only one way to represent the main ideas and relationships in this chapter. Accept oth
logical answers from students.

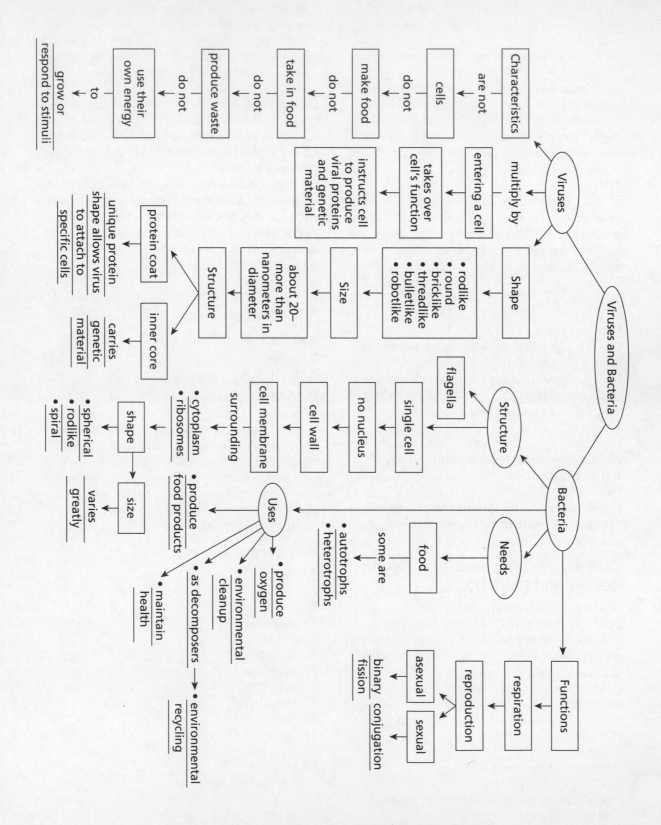

Laboratory Investigation
Bacteria That Dine on Vegetables
Pre-Lab Discussion

1. Bacteria are prokaryotes. Their cells do not have nuclei to contain the cell's genetic material.

Observations

1. Answers will vary. Students may predict noticeably "dirty" areas such as the floor or desktops.
2. Answers may vary. Encourage groups to pick different areas to test.

Analyze and Conclude

1. The plastic bags labeled "B-Potato" and "B-Yam" usually have the greatest growth of bacteria and the plastic bags labeled "A-Potato" and "A-Yam" have the least.
2. The bacterial growths are likely to appear similar. Depending on the choice of vegetables, different types of bacteria may be observed.
3. The untouched slices are a control for the experiment.

Critical Thinking and Applications

1. In the plastic bags labeled "B," the cotton swab carried bacteria from the test area to the vegetables. Also, airborne bacteria may have landed on the vegetables.
2. to prevent contamination of the vegetable slices by an unclean plastic bag
3. to prevent contamination of the vegetable slices by your hand
4. The vegetable slices in the plastic bags labeled "A" would probably have more bacterial growth than if the bags were sealed immediately. "B." This is because bacteria are in the air as well as in the areas tested by students.
5. Suggestions should include refrigerating and covering vegetables, to slow down bacterial growth. Students may suggest drying the food, so that the bacteria do not have the moisture they need to grow.

Chapter Performance Assessment
Analyze and Conclude

1. Answers will vary. Sample: One of my questions was "What is a disease spread by animal bites?" The answer I intended was "Lyme disease." Because someone could also answer "rabies" and be correct, I should change my question to be more specific. I could change my question to ask, "What is a disease caused by bacteria and spread by the bite of an infected deer tick?"
2. Answers will vary. Sample: One of my questions was "What happened in the 1970s?" The answer I intended was "the date that the first medicine-producing bacteria was made by scientists." Because the answer could be too many things, I should change my question to ask, "What was the first medicine-producing bacteria engineered by scientists, in the 1970s?"
3. Answers will vary.

Chapter Test

1. b
2. a
3. c
4. d
5. d
6. c
7. a
8. c
9. c
10. b
11. decomposers
12. respiration
13. flagellum
14. bacteriophage
15. toxin
16. true
17. Active
18. true
19. do not have nuclei
20. Sexual reproduction

21. Answers will vary for last two rows. See samples in chart below.

Characteristics	Viruses	Bacteria
Surrounded by a cell wall		X
Contains genetic material	X	X
Requires a host organism	X	
Microscopic	X	X
Causes infectious diseases	X	X
Add your Own: Nonliving	X	
Add your Own: Prokaryotes		X

22. Both viruses and bacteria are microscopic, contain genetic material, and are known to cause infectious diseases. However, viruses are nonliving and require a host to multiply. Bacteria are living prokaryotes that are surrounded by a cell wall.

23. Answers will vary. Sample: Bacteria are used in the production of medicines such as insulin. Yogurt is an example of how bacteria can be helpful in the production of food. Bacteria break down dead leaves into useful nutrients for other living things.

24. Students' answers may vary. Samples: Infectious diseases can be spread through contact with an infected person, such as by kissing. They can be spread through contact with an infected object, such as by using the cup of an infected person. They can also be spread through contact with an animal, such as by a dog bite. They can be spread through environmental sources such as soil and water.

25. All viruses have a protein coat that protects the virus, and all viruses have an inner core of genetic material. A virus attaches to its host. Its genetic material enters the cell and takes over the cell's functions. The virus instructs the cell to produce the virus's proteins and genetic material. These are assembled into new viruses until the cell is so full that it bursts.

26. The increases in bacteria per mL are 1,000 at 5°C, 4,000 at 10°C, and 7,000 at 15°C.

27. The higher the temperature, the greater is the rate of growth of bacteria.

28. If the cell contains a nucleus, it is not a bacterium.

29. There is no cure for a viral infection but you can treat the symptoms with over-the-counter medicines like aspirin, cough syrup, and throat lozenges. You should also drink lots of fluids and get plenty of bed rest.

30. The bacteria reproduced by binary fission because the offspring are genetically identical to the parent cell.

Protists and Fungi

Lab zone Chapter Project ▷ A Mushroom Farm

The following steps will walk you through the Chapter Project. Use the hints as you guide your students through choosing a variable, making a hypothesis, designing an experiment, analyzing the results, and preparing a poster.

Chapter Project Overview

Students often think of mushrooms as "green" plants that can get their energy from the sun. In reality, fungi such as mushrooms get their energy from decaying material. Like plants, they require certain conditions for optimal growth. In this project, students will test variables that affect mushroom growth. They will also look at the typical structures that make up a common mushroom.

To introduce the project, have students brainstorm variables they think would affect mushroom growth. List students' ideas on the chalkboard.

Have students read the Chapter Project Overview. Review the project's rules and hand out the Chapter Scoring Rubric that you will use for scoring students' work. Discuss with students what will be expected of them.

Set a deadline for the project poster to be completed and interim dates for the Keep Students on Track activities at the end of Section 2 and Section 3. Encourage students to copy the dates in the Project Timeline. It will take one class period to introduce the project. Allow students a day or two to design their experiments. The experiment itself will take between two and four weeks, depending on the conditions being tested. Allow one week following the end of the experiment for data analysis and poster preparation.

Discuss with students the different kinds of variables. Explain that the variable they choose to test is the manipulated variable. The results they get are represented by the responding variable. All other variables should be kept constant, and these are controlled variables. Ask students: **Suppose you hypothesized that mushrooms need fertilizer to grow. What variable could you manipulate?** (*You could grow a container of mushrooms without fertilizer.*)

Divide the class into small groups. Have

each group decide on a variable to test. In order to prevent too many groups from investigating the same variable, you may choose to assign a variable to each group. Variables that can be tested easily include light, heat, amount of water, and availability of nutrients.

Be aware that it is difficult to grow mushrooms from spores you collect. Use a mushroom growing kit for best results. If students' mushrooms fail to grow, have them join another group that has had more success.

Encourage students to examine their mushrooms frequently for signs of trouble. Make sure that students do not overwater their mushrooms. Be aware that the warmer the temperature, the faster the growth. Avoid temperatures below 5°C.

Distribute copies of Chapter Project Worksheet 1. Have students read over the questions they will need to answer in the experimental design stage of this project. Chapter Project Worksheet 2 will help students set up their experiment and collect data. Remind students to refer to the hints in the Chapter Project Overview as they plan and carry out the project.

Materials and Preparation

Mushroom growing kits are available from most biological supply companies. They provide all the materials necessary to complete a project. Read the instructions completely. You may want to make copies of the instructions for students or read aloud portions to the class.

You will probably need additional pots and peat moss. As an alternative to pots, you can use the bottoms of milk cartons, two-liter plastic bottles, or other such containers with holes cut in the bottom. A spray bottle works well for watering the containers.

For testing different variables you will need a dark location, a constant light source, a thermometer, a warm location or a source of heat, a cool location, and a substrate lacking nutrients, such as vermiculite.

If possible, provide students with the materials they will need for making their posters.

Keep Students on Track— Section 2

Students should complete Worksheet 1 and have you approve their hypothesis and experimental design. Make sure that students' experimental designs show that they know the difference between a manipulated variable and a responding variable. Students' experimental setups should also include a control, where all the variables are carefully controlled (controlled variables). In containers with a manipulated variable, make sure all variables are controlled except the one they are testing.

Encourage students to check their experiments and record data every day.

Keep Students on Track— Section 3

Students may need help analyzing their data. Explain that they should use a graph to organize and display their data. Tell students that they do not have to use all of their data in a single graph. Ask students: **If you were making a line graph, what variable could you plot on the *x*-axis?** (*Sample: time in days*) **What variable could you plot on the *y*-axis?** (*Samples: average height of mushrooms, average diameter of mushroom caps*)

Suggest that students show you a rough draft of their poster several days before it is due so that they can get feedback.

Chapter Project Wrap Up

Make sure that students understand the grading criteria for the poster. It is important that they include the hypothesis being tested, a description or diagram of the experimental design, and a graph of their data. They must then draw a conclusion from their results about the validity of their hypothesis. Students should also illustrate the anatomy of a common mushroom.

Have poster preparation occur during class. You may want to allow students to look at each other's posters to exchange ideas. You could also draw a poster plan on the chalkboard to help students get started. Be sure to mention that your drawing is only a plan and that students do not have to follow it as long as their poster meets all of the requirements.

Extension

At the end of the project, have a discussion about what would be the best combination of conditions for growing mushrooms. Then take your students to a local mushroom grower to learn what conditions are used to grow mushrooms commercially.

Protists and Fungi ▪ *Chapter Project*   **Overview**

◁Lab zone Chapter Project▷ A Mushroom Farm

Mushrooms, like all organisms, can grow only under certain conditions. In this project, you will determine how a single variable affects mushroom growth. You will also look at the typical structures that make up a common mushroom.

First, decide on a variable that you wish to test, or your teacher may assign a variable to you. Next, you will make a hypothesis about the effect that changing the variable will have on mushroom growth. Then you will plan and perform an experiment to test your hypothesis. Finally, you will analyze your observations by making a graph, infer the effect of the variable on the growth of mushrooms, and prepare a poster summarizing your experiment.

Project Rules

- If you are able to choose a variable, have your teacher approve your choice before proceeding.

- Make a hypothesis concerning the effect of the variable on mushroom growth.

- Design an experiment to test your hypothesis. Your experimental design should include two containers for growing mushrooms: one will test the manipulated variable and the other will represent the controlled variables. Complete Worksheet 1 and get your teacher's approval before beginning the experiment.

- Read the instructions that came with the mushroom kit or listen to your teacher read them aloud. Keep these instructions in mind when designing and setting up your experiment.

- Use Worksheet 2 to help you perform your experiment. Make observations of mushroom growth and record data every day of the experiment.

- Prepare a poster to summarize your findings. Your poster should include your hypothesis, a description or diagram of your experimental design, at least one graph of your results, and your conclusion. Be sure to include a labeled diagram of the parts of a mushroom as well.

- Follow the safety guidelines in Appendix A of your textbook. Always wash your hands thoroughly after handling soil.

Protists and Fungi • *Chapter Project*   **Overview**

Suggested Materials

■ Available materials may include a mushroom growing kit, containers that can be used as pots, a spray bottle for watering, a dark location, a light source, a heat source, a cool location, a thermometer, peat moss, and vermiculite. Peat moss contains nutrients, but vermiculite does not.

■ You may be provided with materials for making your poster, or you may bring your own materials from home.

Project Hints

■ Think about the growing requirements of other organisms to get ideas about what variable to test.

■ To make a hypothesis, think about where you see mushrooms growing in nature. Use these observations to make a prediction about whether changing your variable in a specific way will increase or decrease mushroom growth.

■ When getting ready to design an experiment, review what you know about controlling variables. Decide what variables need to be controlled in your experiment.

■ Decide what observations you will record during the experiment, and how you will analyze the results. See Worksheet 2.

■ Do not overwater your mushrooms. The substrate, or the substance in which the mushrooms are growing, should be moist but not soaked. Avoid temperatures below 5°C.

■ You can find books about mushrooms in the library or information about mushrooms on the Internet to help you draw and label your diagram of a mushroom.

Project Timeline

Task	Date Due
1. Variable selected and hypothesis proposed.	_____
2. Experimental design approved by teacher.	_____
3. Experiment and data table set up.	_____
4. Experiment completed.	_____
5. Final draft of survey written and presented to teacher.	_____
6. Poster completed.	_____

Protists and Fungi

Protists and Fungi · *Chapter Project*

A Mushroom Farm

Answer the following questions in the space provided. When you have completed this worksheet, you will be ready to get your teacher's approval and begin your experiment.

1. What variable will you test?

_____

2. Record a hypothesis that predicts what will happen to the growth of mushrooms when that variable is changed.

_____

_____

_____

3. What treatment will you use to test your manipulated variable in the experiment? What treatment will you use with the controlled variables?

_____

_____

_____

_____

4. How will you keep other variables controlled in your experiment?

_____

_____

_____

_____

5. What results from your experiment would support your hypothesis?

_____

_____

_____

6. What results from your experiment would show your hypothesis was not correct?

_____

_____

_____

Protists and Fungi • *Chapter Project*   **Worksheet 2**

A Mushroom Farm

Use this sheet to help set up your experiment and record your data.

1. Label one container as the manipulated variable and the other as the controlled variables (control).

2. Fill each container with substrate material provided by the mushroom kit, if appropriate for your experimental design.

3. Divide the spores into equal amounts and spread them on the surfaces of the substrate material in your manipulated variable and controlled variables containers (control).

4. Spray each container with water so that the surface is moist.

5. Place the containers in appropriate locations.

6. Record your data in a data table like the one shown below. You will need to record data for two to four weeks depending on the variable you test. For each day, record the number of mushrooms present. Then record the height of each mushroom and the diameter of each cap. You might also include any other observed changes and a sketch of each container.

Day	Container with Controlled Variables (Control)	Container with Manipulated Variable
1	Number: Heights: Diameter of caps:	Number: Heights: Diameter of caps:
2	Number: Heights: Diameter of caps:	Number: Heights: Diameter of caps:

You must decide how to analyze your observations. For example, you could compare:

- The day on which mushrooms first appeared in the two containers.

- The number of mushrooms present in each container.

- The average size (height or diameter) of the mushrooms in each container.

Protists and Fungi • *Chapter Project*   **Scoring Rubric**

Lab zone™ Chapter Project — A Mushroom Farm

In evaluating how well you complete the Chapter Project, your teacher will judge your work in the following categories. In each, a score of 4 is the best rating.

	4	3	2	1
Defining and Controlling Variables and Developing Hypothesis	Student defines the variable being tested and correctly identifies the controlled variables. Hypothesis clearly states a prediction regarding the responding variable.	Student defines the variable being tested and correctly identifies the controlled variables. Hypothesis adequately states a prediction regarding the responding variable.	Student defines the variable being tested, but incorrectly identifies the controlled variables. Hypothesis states a prediction regarding the responding variable.	Student defines the variable being tested, but incorrectly identifies the controlled variables. Student fails to state a hypothesis regarding the responding variable.
Experimental Design and Observations	Experimental design clearly tests the effect of the manipulated variable. Student records detailed observations daily.	Experimental design tests the effect of the manipulated variable. Student records observations on all but one or two days.	Experimental design tests the effect of the manipulated variable. Student records observations on most days.	Experimental design fails to test the effect of the manipulated variable. Student records some observations.
Analysis and Presentation of Results in Poster	Poster thoroughly communicates hypothesis tested, experimental design, one or more graphs of results, and conclusion. Student rejects or accepts hypothesis based on results.	Poster adequately communicates hypothesis tested, experimental design, graph of results, and conclusion. Student rejects or accepts hypothesis based on results.	Poster fails to communicate one of the following: hypothesis tested, experimental design, graph of results, or conclusion. Student fails to reject or accept hypothesis based on results.	Poster fails to communicate two or more of the following: hypothesis tested, experimental design, graph of results, or conclusion. Student fails to reject or accept hypothesis.
Working Cooperatively (optional)	Takes a lead in group planning and in the collection of data.	Participates in all aspects of group planning and in the collection of data.	Participates in most group planning and collection of data.	Participates minimally in group planning and collection of data.

Protists

🕐 *3–4 periods, 1–1 1/2 blocks*

Objectives

A.3.1.1 Describe the characteristics of animal-like protists and give examples.

A.3.1.2 Describe the characteristics of plantlike protists and give examples.

A.3.1.3 Describe the characteristics of fungus-like protists and give examples.

Key Terms

• protist • protozoan • pseudopod
• contractile vacuole • cilia • symbiosis
• mutualism • algae • pigment • spore

ABILITY LEVELS KEY
L1 Basic to Average
L2 For All Students
L3 Average to Advanced

Local Standards

PRETEACH

Build Background Knowledge
Students discuss which characteristics must be considered to determine whether or not "blobs" in a dish are alive.

 **Discover Activity** *What Lives in a Drop of Pond Water?* **L1**

Targeted Resources

❑ **All in One Teaching Resources**
 L2 Reading Strategy Transparency A18: Outlining
❑ ⊙ **PresentationExpress™ CD-ROM**

INSTRUCT

What Is a Protist? Students explore the shared characteristics and tremendous diversity of organisms in the protist kingdom

Animal-Like Protists Students discuss the general traits of animal-like protists and the differences that divide them into four distinct groups.

Plantlike Protists Students identify traits of plantlike protists, called algae, and distinguish the various types, exploring differences in pigments, size, structures, habitats, and functions.

Funguslike Protists Students determine shared characteristics among and differences between three groups of funguslike protists.

Targeted Resources

❑ **All in One Teaching Resources**
 L2 Guided Reading, pp. 165–168
 L2 Transparencies A19, A20, A21, A22
❑ **PHSchool.com** Web Code: cep-1031
❑ ⊙ **Student Edition on Audio CD**

ASSESS

Section Assessment Questions
↻ Have students use their completed Outlining graphic organizers to help answer the questions.

Reteach
Students name features shared by protists and identify the many differences that make the group so diverse.

Targeted Resources

❑ **All in One Teaching Resources**
 Section Summary, p. 164
 L1 Review and Reinforce, p. 169
 L3 Enrich, p. 170

Protists and Fungi

Protists and Fungi ▪ *Section Summary*

Protists

Key Concept

- What are the characteristics of animal-like, plantlike, and funguslike protists?

The protist kingdom is very diverse. All **protists** are eukaryotes that cannot be classified as animals, plants, or fungi. All live in moist surroundings. Most are unicellular, but some are multicellular. Some are heterotrophs, some are autotrophs, and some are both. Protists can be divided into three categories: animal-like, funguslike, and plantlike protists.

Like animals, animal-like protists are heterotrophs, and most are able to move from place to place to obtain food. Animal-like protists are also called **protozoans.** Protozoans can be divided into four types: sarcodines, ciliates, flagellates, and those that are parasites. Sarcodines move and feed by using pseudopods. **Pseudopods** are temporary bulges of the cell. Pseudopods form when cytoplasm flows toward one location and the rest of the organism follows. Protozoans that live in fresh water, such as amoebas, have a **contractile vacuole,** which collects the extra water and expels it from the cell. Ciliates have structures called **cilia,** which are hairlike projections that move with a wavelike motion. Flagellates move using whiplike flagella. Some flagellates live inside the bodies of other organisms in a state of symbiosis. **Symbiosis** is a close relationship between two species in which at least one of the species benefits. Sometimes, flagellates harm their hosts. In other cases, their relationship is one of **mutualism,** in which both partners benefit. Protozoans that are parasites feed on their hosts' cells and body fluids.

Plantlike protists are called **algae. Like plants, algae are autotrophs.** Algae can exist in a variety of colors because they contain many types of **pigments**—chemicals that produce color. Plantlike protists include diatoms, dinoflagellates, euglenoids, red algae, green algae, and brown algae. Diatoms have beautiful, glasslike cell walls. Dinoflagellates are covered by stiff plates and move using two flagella. Euglenoids can be heterotrophs when sunlight is not available. Red algae and brown algae live in the oceans. Green algae live in fresh water, salt water, and moist places on land.

Like fungi, funguslike protists are heterotrophs, have cell walls, and use spores to reproduce. Spores are tiny cells that are able to grow into new organisms. All funguslike protists are able to move at some point in their lives. The three types of funguslike protists are slime molds, water molds, and downy mildews. Slime molds live in moist soil and on decaying plants. Water molds and downy mildews grow as tiny threads in water or moist places.

Protists and Fungi • *Guided Reading and Study*

Protists (pp. 74–83)

This section describes the characteristics of protists.

Use Target Reading Skills

As you read, make an outline about protists that you can use for review. Use the red section headings for the main topics and blue headings for the subtopics.

Protists
I. What is a protist?
II. Animal-like protists
A. Protozoans with pseudopods
B.
C.
D.
III.
A.
B.
C.
D.
E.
F.
IV.
A.
B.
C.

What Is a Protist? (p. 75)

1. Circle the letter of each sentence that is true about protists.

    a. All protists are eukaryotes, organisms that have cells with nuclei.

    b. All protists live in dry surroundings.

    c. All protists are unicellular.

    d. Some protists are heterotrophs, some are autotrophs, and some are both.

Protists and Fungi

Protists (continued)

2. List the three categories into which scientists group protists.

   a. _____

   b. _____

   c. _____

Animal-Like Protists (pp. 75–78)

3. Circle the letter of each characteristic that animal-like protists share with animals.

   a. autotroph   **b.** heterotroph
   c. movement   **d.** unicellular

4. Another name for an animal-like protist is _____.

5. Describe how a sarcodine, such as an amoeba, gets food.

   _____

   _____

   _____

6. Circle the letter of the cell part in an ameoba that removes excess water.

   a. pseudopod   **b.** cilia
   c. contractile vacuole   **d.** cell membrane

7. Is the following sentence true or false? Paramecia have more than one nucleus. _____

Match the animal-like protist with the cell part it uses for movement.

Protist   **Cell Part**

____ **8.** amoeba   **a.** cilia

____ **9.** paramecium   **b.** flagella

____ **10.** flagellate   **c.** pseudopods

11. Is the following sentence true or false? Flagellates living in symbiosis always harm the animal in which they live. _____

Protists and Fungi • *Guided Reading and Study*

12. Protozoans that are _____ feed on the cells and

body fluids of their hosts.

13. Is the following sentence true or false? Protozoans that are parasites never have

more than one host._____

Plantlike Protists (pp. 79–81)

14. Plantlike protists are commonly called _____.

15. Like plants, plantlike protists are _____; most are
able to use the sun's energy to make their own food.

16. Complete this table about the different types of plantlike protists.

Characteristics of Plantlike Protists

Type	Unicellular or Multicellular	Characteristics
Diatoms		
Dinoflagellates		
Euglenoids		
Red Algae		
Green Algae		
Brown Algae		

Protists and Fungi ▪ *Guided Reading and Study*

Protists *(continued)*

Funguslike Protists *(pp. 82–83)*

17. Circle the letter of each sentence that is true about funguslike protists.

    a. Funguslike protists are heterotrophs.

    b. Funguslike protists do not have cell walls.

    c. Funguslike protists use spores to reproduce.

    d. Funguslike protists never move during their lives.

18. List the three types of funguslike protists.

    a. _____

    b. _____

    c. _____

19. Where do most water molds and downy mildews live? _____

_____

20. Circle the letter of each place where slime molds live.

    a. dry soil   **b.** moist soil

    c. decaying plants   **d.** in animals

Protists and Fungi · *Review and Reinforce*

Protists

Understanding Main Ideas

Fill in the blanks in the table below.

Type of Protist	Shared Characteristics	Examples
animal-like	heterotrophs; most move by using pseudopods, cilia, or 1. _____	sarcodines, ciliates, and 2. _____
3. _____	autotrophs	dinoflagellates, euglenoids, red algae, brown algae, 4. _____, and 5. _____
6. _____	heterotrophs, cells walls, reproduce with spores	water molds, downy mildews, and 7. _____

Building Vocabulary

Match each term with its definition by writing the letter of the correct definition in the right column on the line beside the term in the left column.

____ 8. protozoan

____ 9. pseudopod

____ 10. spore

____ 11. contractile vacuole

____ 12. cilia

____ 13. algae

____ 14. symbiosis

____ 15. mutualism

____ 16. pigment

____ 17. protist

a. a form of symbiosis that benefits both species

b. an animal-like protist

c. a tiny cell that is able to grow into a new organism

d. a chemical that produces color

e. a temporary bulge of the cytoplasm used for feeding and movement

f. hairlike projections of ciliates that are used to sweep in food and move

g. plantlike protists

h. structure that collects excess water and expels it from a cell

i. a eukaryote that cannot be classified as an animal, plant, or fungus

j. close relationship between two species in which at least one of the species benefits

Protists and Fungi

Protists and Fungi ▪ *Enrich*

Water Hazards

You learned that freshwater protists must pump excess water from their cells using a contractile vacuole. Protists that live in salt water don't have this problem. Why? The answer involves diffusion.

Small particles dissolved in water constantly move about. This movement, called *diffusion*, causes the particles to spread out evenly in the water. The particles of a substance tend to diffuse from an area of high concentration to an area of low concentration. *Concentration* is the number of particles of a substance per unit volume. Figure 1 illustrates the diffusion of salt particles through a barrier with holes in it. Particles of water also diffuse from an area of high concentration to an area of low concentration. Figure 2 shows what happens if the holes in the barrier allow water but not salt particles to pass through it. Notice that as water diffuses across the barrier, the volume of water on the left side of the barrier increases and the volume on the right side decreases.

A protist cell, like all cells, contains salt particles as well as water particles in its cytoplasm. In addition, its cell membrane acts like the barrier in Figure 2; water particles can pass through it, but not salt particles. In the case of a saltwater protist, there are normally equal concentrations of salt particles and water particles on either side of the cell membrane. The situation for freshwater protists is much different, however. The concentration of salt particles inside the cell is much higher than the concentration of salt particles outside the cell.

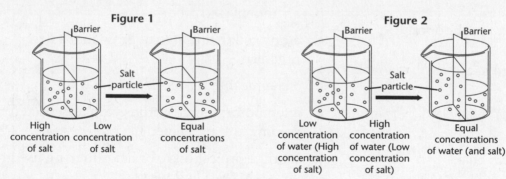

Answer the following questions on a separate sheet of paper.

1. A protist that lives in fresh water faces a situation similar to the one shown in Figure 2. In which direction will diffusion of water particles occur: into the cell, out of the cell, or not at all? Explain.

2. Explain why a protist living in salt water doesn't need a contractile vacuole.

3. Predict what would happen to a protist living in salt water if the number of salt particles in its cytoplasm were increased ten times.

Algal Blooms

 *2–3 periods, 1–1 1/2 blocks*

Objectives

A.3.2.1 Describe the causes and effects of red tides.

A.3.2.2 Describe the causes and effects of eutrophication.

Key Terms
• algal bloom • red tide • eutrophication

PRETEACH

Build Background Knowledge
Students recall that algae live on the surface of water bodies and consider the scenario of algae growing so abundant as to block sunlight from the water.

 Discover Activity *How Can Algal Growth Affect Pond Life?* **L1**

Targeted Resources

❏ **All in One Teaching Resources**
   L2 Reading Strategy Transparency A23: Comparing and Contrasting

❏ ◉ **PresentationExpress™ CD-ROM**

INSTRUCT

Saltwater Blooms Students explore causes and effects of saltwater algal blooms, called red tides.
Freshwater Blooms Students consider the causes and effects of eutrophication, the process by which algae growth increases in a pond or lake over time.

Skills Lab *An Explosion of Life* **L2**

Targeted Resources

❏ **All in One Teaching Resources**
   L2 Guided Reading, pp. 173–174
   L2 Lab: *An Explosion of Life*, pp. 177–178

❏ 📼 **Lab Activity Video/DVD**
   Skills Lab: *An Explosion of Life*

❏ **www.SciLinks.org** Web Code: scn-0132

❏ ◉ **Student Edition on Audio CD**

ASSESS

Section Assessment Questions
↻ Have students use their completed Comparing and Contrasting graphic organizers to answer the questions.

Reteach
Students describe the processes that lead to algal blooms in saltwater and freshwater, then compare the two types of blooms.

Targeted Resources

❏ **All in One Teaching Resources**
   Section Summary, p. 172
   L1 Review and Reinforce, p. 175
   L3 Enrich, p. 176

Protists and Fungi

Name _____ Date _____ Class _____

Protists and Fungi ▪ *Section Summary*

Algal Blooms

Key Concept

■ What are the causes and effects of saltwater and freshwater algal blooms?

Algae are common in saltwater and freshwater environments. The rapid growth of a population of algae is called an **algal bloom. In general, algal blooms occur when nutrients increase in the water.**

Algal blooms in salt water are commonly called **red tides.** Depending on the species of algae causing them, red tides can be brown, green, or colorless, as well as red. When cold ocean water that is rich in nutrients mixes with surface water, algal blooms occur. **Red tides are dangerous when the toxins that the algae produce become concentrated in the bodies of organisms that consume the algae.** Shellfish and fishes feed on the algae and store the algae's toxins in their cells. When large organisms, including people, eat these fishes and shellfish, serious illness or death can result. For this reason, health officials close areas of red tides to swimming, fishing, and shellfish gathering.

Algal blooms can also occur in bodies of fresh water. **Eutrophication** is a natural process in which nutrients such as nitrogen and phosphorus build up in a lake or pond over time, causing an increase in the growth of algae. Natural events and human activities can increase the rate of eutrophication. Nutrients in nearby soils can be washed into lakes and ponds. Sources of nutrients include fertilizers spread onto fields and the leaking wastewater from sewage treatment plants. When these nutrients reach a body of water, they cause a rapid increase in algae growth.

Eutrophication triggers a series of events with serious consequences. First, a thick layer of growing algae prevents sunlight from reaching plants and algae beneath the surface. These organisms die, sink to the bottom, and are broken down by bacteria. The bacteria increase in number and use up the oxygen in the water. Without oxygen, fish and other organisms in the water die.

Protists and Fungi ▪ *Guided Reading and Study*

Algal Blooms (pp. 84–86)

This section describes how the rapid growth of algae affects ocean water and fresh water.

Use Target Reading Skills

As you read, compare and contrast the two types of algal blooms in the table below.

Algal Blooms

Properties	Saltwater Blooms	Freshwater Blooms
Causes	Increase in nutrients or temperature	
Effects		

Saltwater Blooms (p. 85)

1. Circle the letter of each sentence that is true about saltwater algal blooms.

   a. Saltwater algal blooms are commonly called red tides.

   b. The water is red during a red tide because of toxins produced by the algae.

   c. Red tides are never any other color but red.

   d. Dinoflagellates and diatoms are two kinds of algae that often cause red tides.

2. List two conditions that often cause red tides to occur.

   a. _____

   b. _____

Protists and Fungi ▪ *Guided Reading and Study*

Algal Blooms *(continued)*

3. Why are red tides dangerous to people and other organisms?

_____

_____

_____

Freshwater Blooms (p. 86)

4. In a process called _____, nutrients such as nitrogen and phosphorus build up in a lake or pond over time, causing an increase in the growth of algae.

5. Complete the following flowchart to show what occurs when algae grow rapidly in a pond or lake.

Eutrophication

Algae on the water's surface prevent _____

from reaching plants and other algae underwater. These plants

_____ and sink to the bottom.

↓

_____ that break down the remains of the dead

plants increase in number and use up all the _____

in the water.

↓

Fish and other organisms _____ without the

_____ they need to survive.

Protists and Fungi • *Review and Reinforce*

Algal Blooms

Understanding Main Ideas

Listed below are the stages of a red tide. Put these stages in order by writing the letter of the description in the blank next to the number of the stage.

____ **1.** first stage

____ **2.** second stage

____ **3.** third stage

____ **4.** fourth stage

____ **5.** fifth stage

a. The toxins cause sickness and even death in the larger animals.

b. Larger animals eat the fish and shellfish.

c. Cold water rich in nutrients mixes with surface waters of the ocean.

d. The algae population increases. Some algae make toxins.

e. Fish and shellfish eat the algae. They store the toxins in their cells.

Answer the following questions on the lines below.

6. How does a thick layer of algae growing on the surface of a pond affect the lives of other organisms living in the pond?

_____

_____

_____

_____

7. What is a human event that can cause an increase in freshwater algae growth?

_____

_____

Building Vocabulary

Write a definition for each of the following terms on the lines below.

8. algal bloom

_____

9. red tide

_____

10. eutrophication

_____

Protists and Fungi

Name _____ Date _____ Class _____

Protists and Fungi ▪ *Enrich*

Lake Water Mixing and Eutrophication

You learned that eutrophication is the buildup of nutrients in a lake or pond over time. One natural cause of eutrophication is related to the seasonal cycle of lake water mixing. In spring, the sun begins to warm the surface of a lake. The deep layers of the lake remain cold, however. The warm surface layer and the cold deep layer stay separate throughout the summer. Almost no water passes between them. Not until fall, when the surface of the lake cools, do the layers finally mix together.

Oxygen can dissolve in the surface layer of the lake throughout the year. During the spring and summer, however, almost no oxygen moves from the surface into the cold deep layer. Only when the layers mix in the fall, does dissolved oxygen spread throughout the lake.

The organisms in the deep cold layer depend entirely on the oxygen that was mixed in during the previous fall. When there is plenty of oxygen in the cold deep layer, bacteria and other decomposers break down dead organisms that have fallen to the bottom of the lake. This keeps the concentration of nutrients low in the cold deep layer. If the oxygen runs out, however, the decomposers will die and the concentration of nutrients will increase, causing eutrophication.

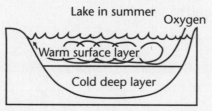 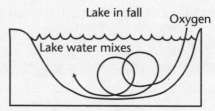

Answer the following questions on a separate sheet of paper.

1. Which of the two lakes shown below is most likely to experience eutrophication? Explain.

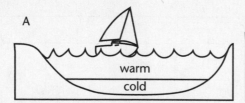 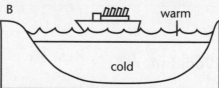

2. During which season of the year do you think a lake is most likely to experience an algal bloom? Why?

3. Streams and rivers wash rocks, mud, and other debris into lakes. This material settles to the bottom, slowly filling up the lake. Knowing this, do you think a lake becomes more or less likely to experience eutrophication as it grows older? Explain.

Name _____ Date _____ Class _____

Protists and Fungi · *Skills Lab*

An Explosion of Life

Problem
How does the amount of fertilizer affect algae growth?

Skills Focus
controlling variables, drawing conclusions, predicting

Materials
4 glass jars with lids   marking pen

aged tap water   aquarium water

graduated cylinder   liquid fertilizer

Procedure

1. Read through the steps in the procedure. Then write a prediction describing what you think will happen in each of the four jars.
2. Be sure to record your data in the data table.
3. Label four jars *A*, *B*, *C*, and *D*. Fill each jar half full with aged tap water.
4. Add aquarium water to each jar until the jar is three-fourths full.
5. Add 3 mL of liquid fertilizer to jar B, 6 mL to jar C, and 12 mL to jar D. Do not add any fertilizer to jar A. Loosely screw the lid on each jar. Place all the jars in a sunny location where they will receive the same amount of direct sunlight.
6. Observe the jars every day for two weeks. Compare the color of the water in the four jars. Record your observations.

Protists and Fungi ▪ *Skills Lab*

An Explosion of Life (continued)

	Data Table			
	Observations			
Date	Jar A (no fertilizer)	Jar B (3 mL fertilizer)	Jar C (6 mL fertilizer)	Jar D (12 mL fertilizer)
Day 1				
Day 2				
Day 3				
Day 4				
Day 5				
Day 6				
Day 7				
Day 8				
Day 9				
Day 10				
Day 11				
Day 12				
Day 13				
Day 14				

Analyze and Conclude

Write your answers on a separate sheet of paper.

1. **Observing** How did the color in the four jars compare at the end of the two-week period? Did your observations match your prediction?

2. **Controlling Variables** What was the purpose of jar A? Explain.

3. **Drawing Conclusions** How can you account for any color differences among the four jars? What process and organisms were responsible for causing that color change?

4. **Predicting** Predict what would have happened if you had placed the four jars in a dark location instead of in sunlight. Explain your prediction.

5. **Communicating** Write a warning label to be placed on a bag of fertilizer. On the label, explain what might happen to fish and other organisms if fertilizer gets into a body of fresh water. Also, outline steps consumers can take to prevent these problems.

Design an Experiment

Some detergents contain phosphates, which are also found in many kinds of fertilizer. Design an experiment to compare how regular detergent and low-phosphate detergent affect the growth of algae. *Obtain your teacher's permission before carrying out your investigation.*

Fungi

🕐 *1–2 periods, 1/2–1 block*

ABILITY LEVELS KEY
L1 Basic to Average
L2 For All Students
L3 Average to Advanced

Objectives

A.3.3.1 Name the characteristics that all fungi share.
A.3.3.2 Describe the ways that fungi reproduce.
A.3.3.3 List the roles fungi play in nature.

Key Terms
• fungi • fruiting body • hyphae • budding
• lichen

Local Standards

PRETEACH

Build Background Knowledge
Students discuss what they know about mushrooms, both those cultivated and those in natural habits, and begin to consider their similarities to plants.

 **Discover Activity** *Do All Molds Look Alike?* **L1**

Targeted Resources

❑ **All in One Teaching Resources**
    L2 Reading Strategy Transparency A24: Asking Questions

❑ ⊙ **PresentationExpress™ CD-ROM**

INSTRUCT

❑

What Are Fungi? Students consider traits shared by fungi and examine their habitats, cell structure, and means of obtaining food.
Reproduction in Fungi Students discuss fungal spores and the fruiting bodies that release them, and determine when and how fungi reproduce either sexually or asexually, and how fungi are characterized this way.
The Role of Fungi in Nature Students explore the many roles of fungi on Earth: decomposers, recyclers, disease agents, disease fighters, and organisms living in symbiosis with other organisms.

 Skills Lab   *What's for Lunch?* **L2**

❑ **All in One Teaching Resources**
❑ **L2** Guided Reading, pp. 181–183
    L2 Transparency A25
    L2 Lab: *What's for Lunch?* pp. 186–188
❑ ▭ **Lab Activity Video/DVD**
    Skills Lab: *What's for Lunch?*
❑ **PHSchool.com** Web Code: ced-1033
❑ **www.SciLinks.org** Web Code: scn-0133
❑ **Discovery SCHOOL** **Video Field Trip**
❑ ⊙ **Student Edition on Audio CD**

ASSESS

Section Assessment Questions
🕐 Have students use their Asking Questions graphic organizers to help answer the questions.

Reteach
Students produce a chart or diagram illustrating basic characteristics of fungi, how they reproduce and obtain food, and the roles they play in nature.

❑ **All in One Teaching Resources**
Section Summary, p. 180
L1 Review and Reinforce, p. 184
L3 Enrich, p. 185

Protists and Fungi

Name _____ Date _____ Class _____

Fungi

Key Concepts

- What characteristics do fungi share?
- How do fungi reproduce?
- What roles do fungi play in nature?

Most **fungi** share several important characteristics: **Fungi are eukaryotes that have cell walls, are heterotrophs that feed by absorbing their food, and use spores to reproduce.** Fungi also need moist, warm places in which to grow. They vary in size from unicellular yeasts to multicellular mushrooms.

Hyphae (singular hypha) are branching, threadlike tubes that make up the bodies of multicellular fungi. What a fungus looks like depends on the arrangement of its hyphae.

Fungi are heterotrophs, but they do not take food into their bodies in the way that animals do. First, the fungus grows hyphae into a food source. Then digestive chemicals ooze from the hyphae into the food. The digestive chemicals break down the food into small substances that can be absorbed by the hyphae. Some fungi feed on the remains of dead organisms. Others are parasites that break down the chemicals in living organisms.

Fungi usually reproduce by making spores. The lightweight spores are surrounded by a protective covering and can be carried easily through the air or water to new sites. Fungi produce spores in reproductive structures called **fruiting bodies.** Unicellular yeasts use a form of asexual reproduction called **budding.** In budding, a small cell grows from the body of a large, well-fed cell. Asexual reproduction results in fungi that are genetically identical to the parent. Fungi may reproduce sexually, especially when conditions become less favorable. This occurs when the hyphae of two fungi grow together and new genetic material is exchanged. In time, a new reproductive structure grows from the joined hyphae and produces spores. These spores develop into fungi genetically different from either parent. Three major groups of fungi include sac fungi, club fungi, and zygote fungi. The groups are named for the appearance of their reproductive structures.

Fungi play important roles as decomposers and recyclers on Earth. Many fungi provide foods for people. Some fungi cause disease while others fight disease. Still other fungi live in symbiosis with other organisms. Fungi break down the chemicals in dead organisms. This returns nutrients to the soil. Yeasts are important in the preparation of foods such as bread. People also eat some types of fungi, such as mushrooms. Many fungi cause disease in crops and in humans. Others, such as *Penicillium,* make useful substances that kill bacteria. The hyphae of some fungi grow among the roots of plants. The hyphae help the plant absorb more water and nutrients from the soil. In return, the fungus feeds on extra food the plant makes. A **lichen** consists of a fungus living in a mutualistic relationship with either algae or autotrophic bacteria.

Protists and Fungi • *Guided Reading and Study*

Fungi (pp. 88–95)

This section explains what fungi are, how they get food, and their role in the environment.

Use Target Reading Skills

Before you read, preview the red headings. In the graphic organizer below, ask a what *or* how *question for each heading. As you read, write answers to your questions.*

Fungi

Question	Answer
What are fungi?	Fungi are . . .

What Are Fungi? (pp. 88–90)

1. Circle the letter before each sentence that is true about fungi.

   a. All fungi are multicellular organisms.

   b. They are eukaryotes.

   c. Most use spores to reproduce.

   d. They are autotrophs.

2. What are three examples of fungi?

   _____

   _____

   _____

Protists and Fungi • *Guided Reading and Study*

Fungi *(continued)*

3. The cells of fungi are arranged in branching, threadlike tubes called
    _____.

4. Is the following sentence true or false? Fuzzy-looking molds that grow on food
    have hyphae that are packed tightly together. _____

5. Identify the structures of the mushroom shown here.

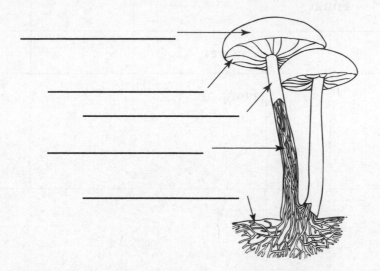

6. Describe the process by which a fungus feeds.

    _____

    _____

    _____

    _____

    _____

7. Is the following sentence true or false? Some fungi are parasites.

    _____

Reproduction in Fungi (pp. 90–91)

8. Most fungi reproduce by making _____.

9. Yeast cells reproduce asexually in a process called _____.

10. Is the following sentence true or false? Fungi reproduce sexually when
    growing conditions become unfavorable. _____

11. What are the three major groups of fungi?

    a. _____ b. _____

    c. _____

Protists and Fungi · *Guided Reading and Study*

The Role of Fungi in Nature (pp. 92–95)

12. Fungi that are _____ break down the chemicals in dead organisms.

13. Is the following sentence true or false? Certain kinds of fungi cause diseases in plants and in humans. _____

14. Some molds produce _____, substances that kill bacteria.

15. How do some fungi help plants grow larger and healthier?

    _____

    _____

    _____

    _____

16. An organism that consists of a fungus and either algae or autotrophic bacteria that live together in a mutualistic relationship is a(n) _____. The fungus provides the algae or autotrophic bacteria with _____. The algae or autotrophic bacteria provide the fungus with _____.

Protists and Fungi • *Review and Reinforce*

Fungi

Understanding the Main Ideas

Figures 1 and 2 show two possible life cycles of fungi. Use these figures to answer questions 1–5. Write the answers on a separate sheet of paper.

Figure 1   **Figure 2**

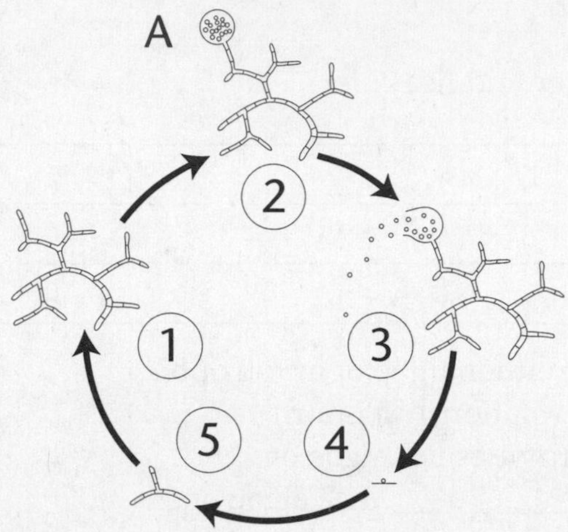

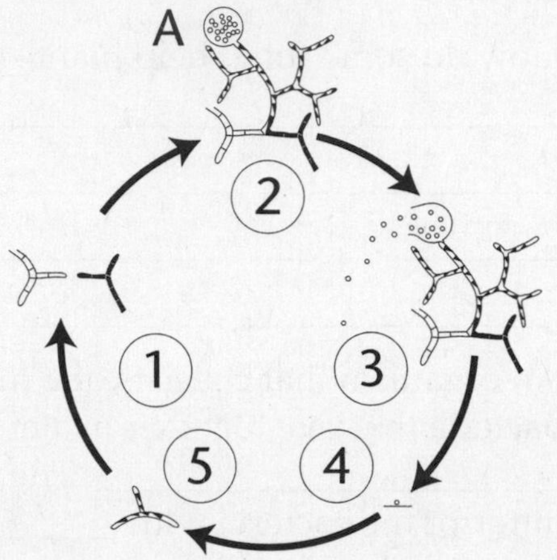

1. What is structure A in Figure 1 called?
2. Step 5 in Figure 1 shows a new fungus. Is it identical to its parent?
3. Step 5 in Figure 2 also shows a new fungus. Is it identical to its parents?
4. What kind of reproduction does Figure 1 show?
5. What kind of reproduction does Figure 2 show?

Answer the following questions on a separate sheet of paper.

6. Does a fungus get its food the same way you do? Explain.
7. Describe what would happen if fungi did not exist.

Building Vocabulary

Fill in the space to complete each sentence.

8. A(n) _____ consists of the mutualistic relationship of a fungus and either algae or autotrophic bacteria.

9. A(n) _____ is one of the branching, threadlike tubes that make up the bodies of multicellular fungi.

10. _____ is a form of asexual reproduction in yeast that does not require the production of spores.

11. A(n) _____ is a structure that produces the spores of a fungus.

12. _____ are eukaryotes that have cell walls and are heterotrophs.

Name _____ Date _____ Class _____

A Really Big Fungus

Because many fungi live in the soil, we normally aren't aware of them. However, their underground networks of hyphae can become enormous.

In 1982, scientists discovered a specimen of the fungus *Armillaria bulbosa* living beneath about 150,000 square meters of soil in Michigan. Of course, scientists couldn't see the entire fungus directly. Instead, they compared the DNA of fungus samples taken at different locations. DNA is the substance that determines an organism's inherited characteristics. Each individual's DNA is slightly different from that of others of its species. Scientists saw that DNA from fungus samples taken from neighboring locations were identical. Because of this, they knew they were looking at samples of one very large fungus.

Scientists have taken samples of the fungus *Armillaria bulbosa* at the numbered locations on the map below. Seven DNA types were identified from the samples. Assume that each DNA type identifies an individual fungus.

DNA Type	Location	DNA Type	Location
Type 1	1, 2, 7	Type 5	12, 19, 26, 27
Type 2	8, 14, 15, 22	Type 6	6, 13, 20
Type 3	3, 9, 10, 16, 17, 23, 24, 25	Type 7	21, 28, 29
Type 4	4, 5, 11, 18		

Answer the following questions on a separate sheet of paper. Show your work.

1. Find the locations of each DNA type on the map. Draw lines on the map dividing the DNA types from one another.

50 meters

2. Assume that each sample location corresponds to an area of 1,600 m². How many square meters do the largest and smallest individual fungi on the map cover?

3. Assume that there is 0.75 kg of fungus per square meter of fungus. What is the weight of the largest and smallest fungi on the map?

4. If the hyphae in each square meter of fungus were lined up end to end, they would stretch about 90 m. What is the length in kilometers of the hyphae in the largest fungus on the map?

Name _____ Date _____ Class _____

Protists and Fungi ▪ *Skills Lab*

What's for Lunch?

Problem

How does the presence of sugar or salt affect the activity of yeast?

Skills Focus

measuring, inferring, drawing conclusions

Materials

5 small plastic narrow-necked bottles

5 round balloons

5 plastic straws

dry powdered yeast

sugar

salt

warm water (40–45°C)

marking pen

beaker

graduated cylinder

metric ruler

string

Procedure

1. Read over the entire procedure to see how you will test yeast activity in bottles A through E. Write a prediction about what will happen in each bottle.

2. Gently stretch each of the balloons so that they will inflate easily.

3. Using the marking pen, label the bottles *A*, *B*, *C*, *D*, and *E*.

4. Use a beaker to fill each bottle with the same amount of warm water. **CAUTION:** *Glass is fragile. Handle the beaker gently to avoid breakage. Do not touch broken glass.*

5. Put 25 mL of salt into bottle B.

Protists and Fungi • *Skills Lab*

6. Put 25 mL of sugar into bottles C and E.

7. Put 50 mL of sugar into bottle D.

8. Put 6 mL of powdered yeast into bottle A, and stir the mixture with a clean straw. Remove the straw and discard it.

9. Immediately place a balloon over the opening of bottle A. Make sure that the balloon opening fits very tightly around the neck of the bottle.

10. Repeat Steps 8 and 9 for bottle B, bottle C, and bottle D.

11. Place a balloon over bottle E without adding yeast to the bottle.

12. Place the five bottles in a warm spot away from drafts. Every ten minutes for 40 minutes, measure the circumference of each balloon by placing a string around the balloon at its widest part. Include your measurements in the data table.

Protists and Fungi ▪ *Skills Lab*

What's for Lunch? *(continued)*

Data Table						
Bottle	**Prediction**	**Observations**	**Circumference**			
			10 min	**20 min**	**30 min**	**40 min**
A (Yeast alone)						
B (Yeast and 25 mL of salt)						
C (Yeast and 25 mL of sugar)						
D (Yeast and 50 mL of sugar)						
E (No yeast and 25 mL of sugar)						

Analyze and Conclude

Write your answers on a separate sheet of paper.

1. **Measuring** Which balloons changed in size during this lab? How did they change?

2. **Inferring** Explain why the balloon changed size in some bottles and not in others. What caused that change in size?

3. **Interpreting Data** What did the results from bottle C show, compared with the results from bottle D? Why was it important to include bottle E in this investigation?

4. **Drawing Conclusions** Do yeast use salt or sugar as a food source? How do you know?

5. **Communicating** In a paragraph, summarize what you learned about yeast from this investigation. Be sure to support each of your conclusions with the evidence you gathered.

Design an Experiment

Develop a hypothesis about whether temperature affects the activity of yeast cells. Then design an experiment to test your hypothesis. *Obtain your teacher's permission before carrying out your investigation.*

Key Terms

Match each definition on the left with the correct term on the right. Then write the number of each term in the appropriate box below. When you have filled in all the boxes, add up the numbers in each column, row, and two diagonals. The sums should be the same. Some terms may not be used.

A. Asexual reproduction in yeast

B. A temporary bulge of the cytoplasm used for feeding and movement

C. An interaction between two species in which at least one of the species benefits

D. Nutrients build up in a lake over time, causing an increase in algal growth

E. Reproductive hyphae that grow out of a fungus

F. Chemical that produces color

G. An interaction between two species in which both partners benefit

H. Hairlike projections from cells that move with a wavelike pattern

I. The rapid growth of a population of algae

1. pseudopod
2. mutualism
3. pigment
4. algal bloom
5. fruiting bodies
6. budding
7. eutrophication
8. symbiosis
9. cilia
10. spore
11. contractile vacuole
12. lichen

A	B	C	= _____
_____	_____	_____	= _____
D	E	F	
_____	_____	_____	= _____
G	H	I	
_____	_____	_____	= _____
=	=	=	= _____
_____	_____	_____	

Connecting Concepts

Develop a concept map that uses the Key Concepts and Key Terms from this chapter. Keep in mind the big idea of this chapter. The concept map shown is one way to organize how the information in this chapter is related. You may use an extra sheet of paper.

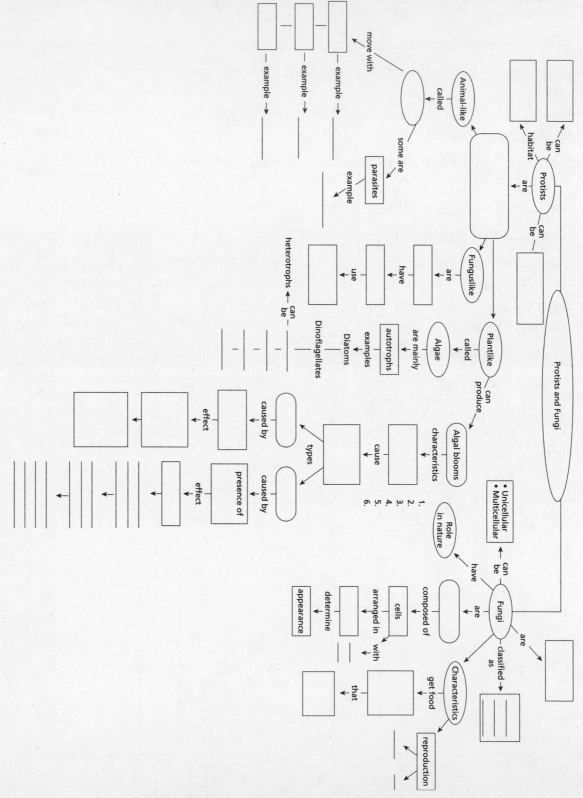

Comparing Protists

Key Concept

Protists are a diverse group of eukaryotic organisms that live in moist environments.

Skills Focus

observing, inferring, classifying, communicating

Time

40 minutes

Materials *(per group)*

- 3 plastic droppers
- amoeba culture
- microscope slide
- 3 coverslips
- paper towel
- microscope
- piece of cotton
- euglena culture
- paramecium culture
- Alternate materials: Other protists may be used. Use prepared slides if live protists are not available.

Advance Preparation

Cultures of organisms are available from biological supply companies.

Teaching Tips

- Keep separate cultures for each protist. Make sure students use separate droppers for each culture.

- Review how to make a wet-mount slide before students make theirs.

- You may want to provide reference photos of protists for identification purposes.

- Consider adding a drop of dilute methyl cellulose solution to slides to slow down protists' movements before students make sketches.

- (More to Explore) Objects such as cotton strands or toothbrush bristles could be added as obstacles to the paramecia. Alternatively, add boiled, crushed wheat seeds to a culture of paramecia and let the culture sit for several days. The seeds serve as obstacles. Students could then make a wet mount with a drop of the culture. They could search for a paramecium near a seed particle under low power. The paramecium will back up when it encounters an object, and then move forward in a new direction. To do this, the cilia briefly reverse the direction of their beating. The body of the paramecium may turn on its long axis, or it may bend.

Protists and Fungi • *Laboratory Investigation*

Comparing Protists

Pre-Lab Discussion

Protists are organisms that have nuclei and live in wet environments, such as ponds, oceans, and the bodies of larger organisms. Other than that, protists don't have much in common. For example, some live independently as separate cells; others form colonies of many unattached cells. Plantlike protists are autotrophs—organisms that can make their own food. Animal-like protists and funguslike protists are heterotrophs—organisms that cannot make their own food.

In this investigation, you will observe and compare three common protists: amoebas, euglenas, and paramecia.

1. Protists are eukaryotes. What does that mean?

   _____

2. Name three different protist structures that aid in movement.

   _____

   _____

Problem

How are protists similar? How are they different?

Materials *(per group)*

3 plastic droppers   microscope

amoeba culture   piece of cotton

microscope slide   euglena culture

3 coverslips   paramecium culture

paper towel

Safety 🧤🔬 *Review the safety guidelines in Appendix A of your textbook.*

Do not use the same droppers for different cultures. Always use both hands to pick up or carry a microscope. Hold the microscope base with one hand and hold the microscope arm with your other hand. Handle glass slides carefully. Don't handle broken glass. Wash your hands thoroughly after the lab.

Procedure

1. With a plastic dropper, place a drop of the amoeba culture on the slide.
2. Make a wet-mount slide by gently laying the coverslip over the drop of amoeba culture.

Name _____ Date _____ Class _____

Protists and Fungi · *Laboratory Investigation*

3. Touch a piece of paper towel to the edge of the coverslip to blot up any excess liquid. See Figure 1.

4. Place the slide on the stage of the microscope. Use the low-power objective to bring an amoeba into focus. Have the teacher check to see that you have an amoeba in focus.

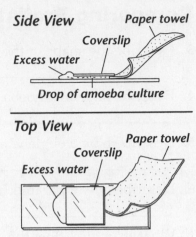

5. Switch to the high-power objective. **CAUTION:** *When turning to the high-power objective, always look at the objective from the side of your microscope. Don't let the objective hit the slide.*

6. Use the fine-adjustment knob to bring the organism into sharper focus. **CAUTION:** *Never focus the high-power objective with the coarse-adjustment knob. The objective could break the slide.*

7. Observe an amoeba and draw what you see in Plate 1 in Observations. Label the nucleus, cell membrane, cytoplasm, food vacuole, and pseudopods. Record the microscope magnification that you used below your sketch.

8. Carefully clean and dry the slide with a paper towel.

9. Separate a few strands of cotton and place them on the slide. The cotton strands will help slow down the euglena. Using a clean dropper, add a drop of the euglena culture to the strands of cotton.

10. Repeat steps 2–6 with the drop of euglena culture.

11. Observe a euglena and draw what you see in Plate 2 in Observations. Label the nucleus, cell membrane, cytoplasm, eyespot, flagellum, and chloroplasts. Record the microscope magnification you used below your sketch.

12. Carefully clean and dry the slide.

13. Separate a few strands of cotton and place them on the slide. Using a clean dropper, add a drop of the paramecium culture to the strands of cotton.

14. Repeat steps 2–6 with the drop of paramecium culture.

15. Observe a paramecium and draw what you see in Plate 3 in Observations. Label the cytoplasm, cell membrane, cilia, nucleus, contractile vacuole, food vacuoles, oral groove, and gullet. Record the microscope magnification you used below your sketch.

16. Clean and dry the slide once again. Return all the materials to the teacher. Wash your hands when you're finished with the lab.

Observations

1. Describe the shape of the amoeba.

   _____

2. Describe the shape of the euglena.

   _____

Protists and Fungi ▪ *Laboratory Investigation*

Comparing Protists *(continued)*

3. Describe the shape of the paramecium.

   _____

4. Describe how an amoeba moves.

   _____

5. Describe how a euglena moves.

   _____

6. Describe how a paramecium moves.

   _____

7. What structures does the euglena have that the amoeba and paramecium do not have?

   _____

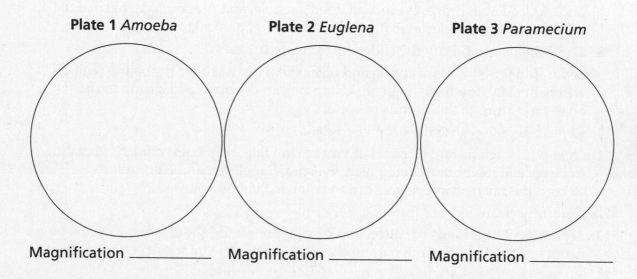

| **Plate 1** *Amoeba* | **Plate 2** *Euglena* | **Plate 3** *Paramecium* |

Magnification _____   Magnification _____   Magnification _____

Analyze and Conclude

1. What structures do all the protists have?

   _____

2. Which protist has structures that are characteristic of both autotrophs and heterotrophs?

   _____

3. Classify the three protists that you observed as animal-like, funguslike, or plantlike protists. Give a reason for your answers.

   _____

   _____

   _____

Protists and Fungi ▪ *Laboratory Investigation*

4. Which is the slowest moving of the three protists?

_____

5. Why are some protists able to move faster than others?

_____

_____

Critical Thinking and Applications

1. Why is the eyespot an important structure in the euglena?

_____

_____

2. The paramecium has two types of cilia. One type covers its entire surface. The other is at the entrance to the gullet. How does the paramecium use each type?

_____

_____

_____

3. Certain cells in your body, such as white blood cells, move by amoeboid motion. What does this mean?

_____

_____

More to Explore

A paramecium has thousands of cilia that project through the pellicle—the covering that gives the paramecium its shape. These cilia beat with a wavelike pattern that keeps a paramecium moving smoothly in one direction. Write a hypothesis for how a paramecium will respond when it runs into objects that are in its path. Write a procedure you would follow to test your hypothesis. Have the teacher approve your procedure before you carry out the investigation. Describe how the paramecium responds. Did your results support your hypothesis?

Protists and Fungi

Modeling Protists

Students are presented with the problem of creating a model of an animal-like protist, a funguslike protist, and a plantlike protist using the materials provided. Students are challenged to model as many characteristics of these organisms as they can. To solve this problem, students must apply what they have learned about protists.

Expected Outcome

Students should choose particular types of protists to model. For example, a student might choose an amoeba, a water mold, and brown algae. Not only will students' choice of protists vary, but so will the materials they use to make their models and the characteristics they choose to model. Some examples of possible models follow. A student could make a model of an amoeba with clay. Circles in a different color of clay could be used to represent the cell nucleus and contractile vacuoles. The student could show clay amoebas in the process of surrounding a smaller clay organism. A student could model a water mold with cotton. The cotton could be attached to a clay model of a fish to show that the water mold is heterotrophic. A student could model brown algae with brown construction paper and clay. The clay could be used to make a holdfast and a stalk. The construction paper could be cut into bladelike shapes and stuck into the clay. Students could show the watery environment of their protists by mounting their models on cardboard they have colored blue. The final product in this case would be models mounted on cardboard, with names and characteristics carefully labeled.

Content Assessment

This Performance Assessment tests students' understanding of the characteristics of protists in general and of particular types of protists.

Skills Adressed

making models, applying concepts

Materials

- Provide students with materials for making models, such as modeling clay in different colors, toothpicks, cotton balls, markers or colored pencils, glue, string, paper clips, construction paper, and scissors. You may want to place the materials at two or three central areas rather than distributing each type of material to each student.

- Provide students with cardboard on which to mount their models.

Advance Preparation

- You may want to have books about protists or pictures of protists available for students to look at as they make their models.

Time

40 minutes

Monitoring the Task

- Provide a place for students to dispose of leftover materials such as scraps of construction paper or extra clay.

- After students have completed the Performance Assessment, consider having them present their models to the class.

Protists and Fungi ▪ *Performance Assessment*   **Scoring Rubric**

Modeling Protists

In assessing students' performance, use the following rubric.

	4	3	2	1
Making Models	Student models a protozoan, an alga, and a funguslike protist. Each model shows at least three characteristics of the protist it represents. Each protist and all of its characteristics are clearly labeled.	Student models a protozoan, an alga, and a funguslike protist. Two models show three characteristics of the protist it represents. Each protist and most of its characteristics are labeled.	Student models a protozoan, an alga, and a funguslike protist. Most models show less than three characteristics of the protist it represents. Each protist is labeled. Only a few characteristics are labeled.	Student models only two of the following: a protozoan, an alga, and a funguslike protist. Both models show less than three characteristics of the protists they represent. Protists and their characteristics are largely unlabeled.
Concept Understanding	Student demonstrates a mastery of the characteristics of protists in general and of particular types of protists.	Student demonstrates an adequate understanding of the characteristics of protists in general and of particular types of protists.	Student demonstrates a partial understanding of the characteristics of protists in general and of particular types of protists.	Student demonstrates a minimal understanding of the characteristics of protists in general and of particular types of protists.

Protists and Fungi

Protists and Fungi ▪ *Performance Assessment*

Modeling Protists

Problem

How can you make a model of an animal-like protist, a plantlike protist, and a funguslike protist?

Suggested Materials

- modeling clay in different colors
- cotton balls
- glue
- string
- construction paper
- toothpicks
- markers or colored pencils
- cardboard
- paper clips
- scissors

Devise a Plan

1. Choose a type of animal-like protist, such as a ciliate, that you would like to model. Also choose a type of plantlike protist and a type of funguslike protist.

2. Make a list of the characteristics of each of the protists you chose. Study the materials provided and think of a way that you could model each protist. Try to show as many characteristics of the protists as you can. For full credit, include at least three characteristics for each.

3. Make your models and mount them on cardboard. Label the protists and the characteristics of each that you modeled.

Analyze and Conclude

After you have finished your models, answer the following questions on a separate sheet of paper.

1. How are your models similar to real protists? How are they different?

2. What characteristics of your protists weren't you able to show in your models?

3. How is your animal-like protist similar to animals? How is it different?

4. What characteristics does your funguslike protist share with your other two protists?

5. How is the way your plantlike protist gets food different from the way your other two protists get food?

Protists and Fungi · *Chapter Test*

Protists and Fungi

Multiple Choice

Write the letter of the correct answer on the line at the left.

_____ 1. Which of the following is a characteristic of all protists?

    a. unicellular   **b.** heterotroph

    c. eukaryote   **d.** multicellular

_____ 2. Which of the following is NOT a characteristic of fungi?

    a. heterotroph   **b.** makes its own food

    c. reproduce with spores   **d.** eukaryotes

_____ 3. Protozoans are

    a. animal-like autotrophs.   **b.** plantlike fungi.

    c. efungusliike protists.   **d.** animal-like protists.

_____ 4. Saltwater blooms are dangerous when

    a. the algae use up oxygen, causing fish and other organisms to suffocate.

    b. algal toxins become concentrated in the bodies of animals that eat them.

    c. some algae feed on the tissues of fishes and shellfish.

    d. the algae prevent sunlight from reaching plants beneath the surface.

_____ 5. Funguslike protists are able to

    a. make their own food.   **b.** move at some point in

    c. capture food with pseudopods.   their lives.

                                       d. live in dry environments.

_____ 6. Which group of animal-like protists captures food using pseudopods?

    a. sarcodines   **b.** ciliates

    c. flagellates   **d.** parasites

_____ 7. In a freshwater algal bloom, pond animals may die because of

    a. lack of oxygen.   **b.** algal toxins.

    c. lack of nutrients.   **d.** a decrease in bacteria.

_____ 8. Unlike other algae, euglenoids

    a. can be heterotrophs under   **b.** can make their own food.

        certain circumstances.   **d.** do not have pigments .

    c. can move from place to place.

_____ 9. Budding is

    a. the growth of a fruiting body.   **b.** the formation of a pseudopod.

    c. a form of asexual   **d.** a decrease in bacteria.

        reproduction.

Protists and Fungi

Protists and Fungi ▪ *Chapter Test*

_____ **10.** A type of unicellular plantlike protist with glasslike cell walls is a
  a. water mold.   **b.** ciliate.
  c. green algae.   **d.** diatom.

Completion

Fill in the line to complete each statement.

11. Fungi produce spores in structures called _____.

12. A freshwater protozoan uses its _____ to pump excess water out of its body.

13. _____ is a close relationship between two species in which both species benefit.

14. _____ are funguslike protists that sometimes creep together to form a multicellular mass.

15. In the process of _____, nutrients build up in ponds and lakes, causing an increase in the growth of algae.

True or False

If the statement is true, write true. *If it is false, change the underlined word or words to make the statement true.*

_____ **16.** <u>Flagella</u> are hairlike projections from cells that move with a wavelike pattern.

_____ **17.** Giant kelps that form large "forests" off the Pacific coast are examples of <u>brown algae</u> .

_____ **18.** <u>Spores</u> are chemicals that produce the many colors in algae.

_____ **19.** <u>Yeasts</u> are the branching, threadlike tubes that make up the bodies of multicellular fungi.

_____ **20.** Plantlike protists are also known as <u>algae</u>.

Name _____ Date _____ Class _____

Protists and Fungi ▪ *Chapter Test*

Using Science Skills

Use the diagram below to answer the following questions.

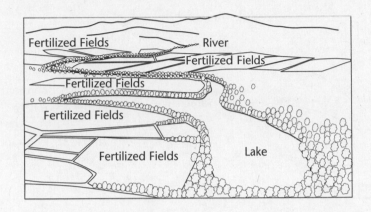

21. **Observing** What do you see in this illustration that could affect the level of nutrients in the lake?

   _____

   _____

22. **Drawing Conclusions** What may happen to the lake as a result?

   _____

Essay

Write an answer for each of the following on a separate sheet of paper.

23. Describe what takes place during a red tide. Explain why red tides are dangerous.
24. Give an example of symbiosis in protists or fungi. Explain how each partner benefits from the relationship.
25. Describe how a fungus feeds.

Name _____ Date _____ Class _____

Protists and Fungi ▪ *Chapter Test*

Using Science Skills

Use the diagram below to answer the following questions.

The Effect of Light on Three Samples of Protists

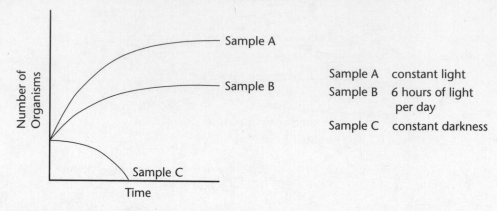

Sample A   constant light
Sample B   6 hours of light
              per day
Sample C   constant darkness

26. Interpreting a Diagram What happened to the protist in Sample C?

_____

_____

27. Interpreting a Diagram What can you conclude about the effect of light on the protist in Sample C?

_____

_____

28. Inferring Each sample contains only one species of protist. Is the protist in Sample C most likely classified as animal-like, plantlike, or funguslike? Explain.

_____

_____

_____

Essay

Write an answer for each of the following on a separate sheet of paper.

29. Describe asexual and sexual reproduction in fungi.

30. Name at least three ways that fungi are beneficial to other organisms.

Chapter Project Worksheet 1

1. Answers will vary. Sample: availability of nutrients

2. Answers will vary. Sample: I predict that mushrooms will grow better in a substrate with nutrients than in a substrate without nutrients.

3. Answers will vary. Sample: In the treatment with a manipulated variable, the spores will be spread on vermiculite, which does not contain nutrients. In the treatment with the controlled variables, the spores will be spread on peat moss, which contains nutrients.

4. Answers will vary. Sample: Both containers will be kept in the dark. Both will be kept under the same constant heat source. Both will be watered the same amount by spraying each container the same number of times.

5. Answers will vary. Sample: My hypothesis would be supported if mushrooms first appeared in the container with peat moss or if more mushrooms grew in this container. It would also be supported if the mushrooms in the peat moss container were taller or had larger caps.

6. Answers will vary. Sample: My hypothesis would be shown to be incorrect if mushrooms first appeared in the container with vermiculite or if more mushrooms grew in this container. It would also be shown to be incorrect if the mushrooms in the vermiculite container were taller or had larger caps.

Chapter Project Worksheet 2

Check that daily measurements are made. Students' data and graphs will vary. Graphs should be line graphs. Plotted along the x-axis should be time or day. Plotted along the y-axis should be be number of mushrooms, average height of mushrooms, and/or average diameter of mushroom caps.

Protists
Guided Reading and Study

Use Target Reading Skills
Protists
I.   What Is a Protist?
II. Animal-Like Protists
   A. Protozoans With Pseudopods
   B. Protozoans With Cilia
   C. Protozoans With Flagella
   D. Protozoans That Are Parasites
III. Plantlike Protists
   A. Diatoms
   B. Dinoflagellates
   C. Euglenoids
   D. Red Algae
   E. Green Algae
   F. Brown Algae

IV. Funguslike Protists
   A. Slime Molds
   B. Water Molds
   C. Downy Mildews

1. a, d

2. **a.** animal-like protists, **b.** plantlike protists, **c.** funguslike protists

3. b, c

4. protozoan

5. The amoeba extends a pseudopod on each side of the food particle. The two pseudopods join together, trapping the particle inside.

6. c

7. true

8. c

9. a

10. b

11. false

12. parasites

13. false

14. algae

15. autotrophs

16. Diatoms—Unicellular; Glasslike cell walls; move by gliding in slime oozed from slits in their cell walls
Dinoflagellates—Unicellular; Surrounded by stiff plates, variety of colors, two flagella
Euglenoids—Unicellular; Green; can be heterotrophs; have flagella
Red Algae—Multicellular; Red pigment; found at deep ocean depths
Green Algae—Both; colonies; Green; live in fresh or salt water or moist areas on land
Brown Algae—Multicellular; Green, yellow, orange, and brown pigments; plantlike structures; live in cool, rocky water

17. a, c

18. **a.** slime molds, **b.** downy mildews, **c.** water molds

19. Most live in water or moist places.

20. b, c

Protists
Review and Reinforce

1. flagella
2. flagellates
3. plantlike
4. green algae or diatoms
5. green algae or diatoms
6. funguslike
7. slime molds
8. b
9. e
10. c
11. h
12. f
13. g
14. j

15. a
16. d
17. i

Protists
Enrich

1. The concentration of water outside the cell is greater than the concentration of water inside the cell. As a result, water particles will diffuse into the cell.
2. Water is distributed evenly inside and outside the cell. Therefore, excess water will not build up in the cell and there is no need for a contractile vacuole.
3. Water would diffuse into the cell to balance the extra number of salt particles.

Algal Blooms
Guided Reading and Study

Use Target Reading Skills
Saltwater blooms—Effects: toxins concentrated in fish and shellfish that eat algae can cause illness to people and other large organisms when they consume the fish or shellfish. Freshwater blooms—Causes: Nutrients build up, causing a rapid increase in algae growth; Effect: Fish and other organisms in the water die.
1. a, d
2. **a.** An increase of nutrients in the water; **b.** An increase in ocean temperature
3. The algae produces toxins that become concentrated in the fish and shellfish that eat the algae. When people or other organisms eat the fish and shellfish, they can become seriously ill or even die.
4. eutrophication
5. sunlight, die, Bacteria, oxygen, die, oxygen

Algal Blooms
Review and Reinforce

1. c
2. d
3. e
4. b
5. a
6. The layer of algae on a pond's surface prevents sunlight from reaching plants and other algae beneath the surface. These organisms die and sink to the bottom of the pond. Then, the bacteria involved in breaking down the bodies of these dead organisms increase in number. These bacteria use up the oxygen in the water. The other organisms in the water that need oxygen to survive die.

7. Answers may vary. Sample: When farmers spread fertilizer on fields, some of these chemical nutrients can run off into nearby lakes and ponds. Sewage treatment plants can leak their contents into the soil. These nutrients make their way from the soil into the water that leads into lakes and ponds.
8. An algal bloom is the rapid growth of a population of algae.
9. A red tide is a saltwater algal bloom. Red tides are dangerous when the toxins that the algae produce become concentrated in the bodies of organisms that consume the algae.
10. Eutrophication is a natural process in which nutrients such as nitrogen and phosphorus build up in a lake or pond over time and cause an increase in the growth of algae.

Algal Blooms
Enrich

1. Lake A is more likely to experience eutrophication because its cold deep layer is more shallow. Therefore, it is more likely to run out of oxygen before the end of the summer. As a result, bacteria and other decomposers will die and nutrients will build up.
2. An algal bloom is most likely in the fall, when the mixing of lake water would bring any nutrients from the deep water to the surface, where they could nourish algae.
3. As debris slowly fills in the lake bottom, the lake' cold layer has less and less volume. This makes it more likely to experience eutrophication.

An Explosion of Life
Skills Lab

For answers, see the Teacher's Edition.

Fungi
Guided Reading and Study

Use Target Reading Skills
Possible questions and answers are:
What are fungi? (*Fungi are eukaryotes that have cell walls, are heterotrophs that feed by absorbing their food, and use spores to reproduce.*)
How do fungi reproduce? (*Fungi usually reproduce by making spores.*)
What is the role of fungi in nature? (*Fungi are important decomposers and recyclers.*)
1. b, c
2. Examples include cricket-killing fungus, bread mold, mushrooms, yeast, and bracket fungi.

3. hyphae
4. false
5.

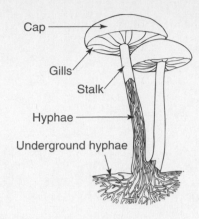

Cap
Gills
Stalk
Hyphae
Underground hyphae

6. Hyphae from the fungus grow into a food source. Digestive chemicals ooze from the hyphae into the food. The digestive chemicals break down the food so the hyphae can absorb it.
7. true
8. spores
9. budding
10. true
11. **a.** sac fungi, **b.** club fungi, **c.** zygote fungi
12. decomposers
13. true
14. antibiotics
15. The fungi's hyphae grow among the plant's roots and absorb water and nutrients from the soil for the plant.
16. lichen; shelter, water, and minerals; food

Fungi
Review and Reinforce

1. a fruiting body
2. yes
3. no
4. asexual reproduction
5. sexual reproduction
6. Answers may vary. Sample: No, a fungus digests its food outside of its body. Its hyphae ooze digestive chemicals into the food. The chemicals break down the food, and then the hyphae absorb it.
7. Answers may vary. Sample: If fungi did not exist, dead organisms would not be decomposed as fast and their nutrients would not be recycled as fast. We would not have foods such as mushrooms and some cheeses and breads. Some diseases, such as athlete's foot, would not exist, but neither would some antibiotics. Many plants would not survive without the fungi that

grow among their roots.
8. lichen
9. hypha
10. Budding
11. fruiting body
12. Fungi

Fungi
Enrich

1. Position of lines may vary slightly as long as all locations with the same DNA type are in the

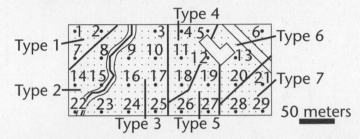

Type 4
Type 1
Type 6
Type 2
Type 7
Type 3   Type 5
50 meters

same area. Sample:
2. The area of the largest fungus is 12,800 m^2, and the area of the smallest fungus is 4,800 m^2.
3. The mass of the largest fungus is 9,600 kg (0.75 kg/m^2 × 12,800 m^2), and the mass of the smallest is 3,600 kg (0.75 kg/m^2 × 4,800).
4. 1,152 km ((90 m/m^2 × 12,800 m^2)/ 1,000 m/km)

What's for Lunch?
Skills Lab

For answers, see the Teacher's Edition.

Key Terms

    A. 6
    B. 1
    C. 8
    D. 7
    E. 5
    F. 3
    G. 2
    H. 9
    I. 4
All column, row, and diagonal sums = 15.

Protists and Fungi

Connecting Concepts

This concept map is only one way to represent the main ideas and relationships in this chapter. Accept other logical answers from students.

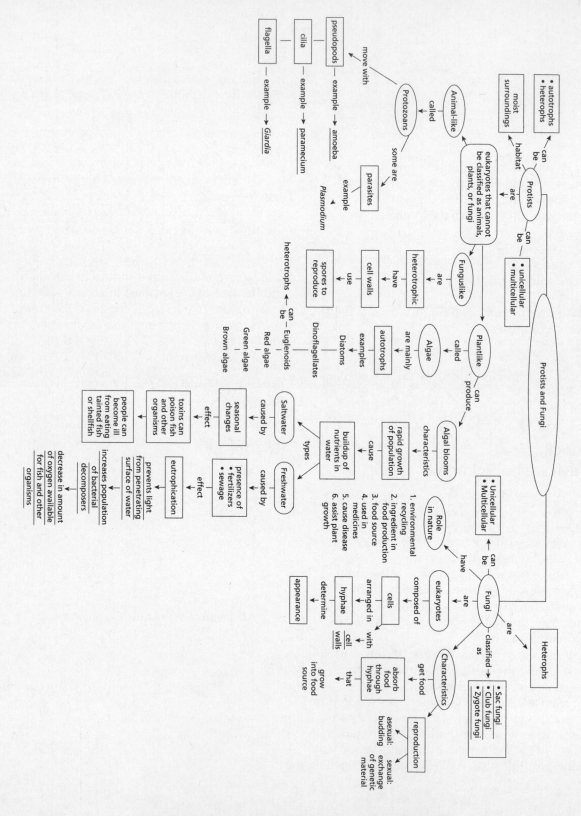

Laboratory Investigation

Comparing Protists

1. It means that protists all have cells with nuclei.

2. The three structures that protists use in moving are pseudopods, cilia, and flagella.

Observations

1. no definite shape

2. oval, with one pointed end and one round end

3. slipper shape

4. It moves by forming pseudopods.

5. whiplike motion of flagellum

6. beating of cilia

7. eyespot, flagellum, and chloroplasts

Analyze and Conclude

1. nucleus, cytoplasm, cell membrane, vacuoles

2. euglena

3. The amoeba and paramecium are animal-like protists. Animal-like protists are heterotrophs and move using pseudopods, cilia, or flagella to obtain food. The euglena is a plantlike protist. Plantlike protists are autotrophs.

4. amoeba

5. The amoeba moves by extending pseudopods. The euglena and paramecium have specialized structures for movement that allow them to move faster.

Critical Thinking and Applications

1. Autotrophs need light to make their own food. The eyespot of the euglena helps it move towards light.

2. The paramecium uses the cilia covering its body to move and sense its environment. It uses the other cilia to sweep food into its oral groove.

3. These cells can move slowly and surround smaller objects like parasites.

Chapter Performance Assessment

Analyze and Conclude

1. Answers will vary depending on protists and characteristics modeled. Samples: My model of a ciliate shows its cilia, its nucleus, its contractile vacuole, and that it lives in water. My model of a water mold shows that it is a heterotroph that lives in water and looks like tiny threads. My model of a brown alga shows its holdfast, blades, and stalk. I also showed its brown pigment. None of my models is alive or made from cells. My model of a ciliate is much larger than a real ciliate. The blades of my brown alga are much flatter than real blades.

2. Answers will vary. Sample: I wasn't able to show that my ciliate is a heterotroph. I wasn't able to show the nuclei of my water mold, its cell walls, or that it reproduces with spores. I wasn't able to show the nuclei and chloroplasts of my brown alga or that it is an autotroph.

3. Both animals and animal-like protists are heterotrophs and eukaryotes. Animal-like protists are unicellular, but animals are multicellular. All protists live in moist surroundings, but not all animals do.

4. All protists are eukaryotes and live in moist environments.

5. Plantlike protists are autotrophs. Funguslike and animal-like protists are heterotrophs.

Chapter Test

1. c

2. b

3. d

4. b

5. b

6. a

7. a

8. a

9. c

10. d

11. fruiting bodies

12. contractile vacuole

13. Mutualism
14. Slime molds
15. eutrophication
16. Cilia
17. true
18. Pigments
19. Hyphae
20. true
21. Fertilizer from the fields will most likely run off into the lake. This will increase the level of nutrients in the lake.
22. An algal bloom could occur that would eventually kill almost all other life in the pond.
23. During red tides, a population of algae increases rapidly. Many of these algae produce toxins. When fishes and shellfish eat the algae during a red tide, the toxins become concentrated in their bodies. When humans and other large animals eat these fishes and shellfish, serious illness or death can result.
24. Answers may vary. Sample: Some fungi have a symbiotic relationship with plants. The fungi grow among the plant's roots. Their hyphae help the plant to collect water and nutrients from the soil. The fungi benefit by feeding on extra food made by the plant.
25. The fungus grows hyphae into a food source. Then digestive chemicals ooze from the hyphae into the food. The digestive chemicals break down the food into small substances that can be absorbed by the hyphae.
26. The protist in Sample C died out over time.
27. This protist needs light in order to survive.

28. This protist is most likely a plantlike protist. Because the organism must have light to survive, it is probably an autotroph. The only protists that are autotrophs are the plantlike protists.
29. Most fungi reproduce both asexually and sexually. When there is adequate moisture and food, fungi reproduce asexually and make thousands of spores. Fungi that develop from spores produced by asexual reproduction are genetically identical to the parent. When growing conditions become unfavorable, fungi may reproduce sexually. The hyphae of two fungi grow together. A spore-producing structure grows from the joined hyphae. These spores can develop into fungi that differ from either parent.
30. Answers may vary. Samples: Fungi decompose dead organisms. Humans use fungi to make foods such as bread and wine. We also eat some types of fungi. Some fungi produce substances that kill disease-causing bacteria. Some fungi live in symbiotic relationships with plants, algae, or autotrophic bacteria.

Introduction to Plants

Lab zone Chapter Project Design and Build an Interactive Exhibit

The following steps will walk you through the Chapter Project. Use the hints and detailed directions as you guide your students through the design, construction, presentation, and evaluation of their exhibits.

Chapter Project Overview

In this project, students will design and build an interactive exhibit to teach young children how plants can produce useful products. The purpose of this activity is for students to investigate the process through which a plant or plant part is transformed into products for human use. Students will construct an interactive museum exhibit that showcases the process and product they have studied. (If an interactive exhibit is not a realistic option for your classroom, you may assign students to prepare computer-generated visual presentations as an alternative.) Because their exhibits should be designed for young children, students will need to test their exhibit design on students in the target age group. They will use their feedback to redesign their exhibit.

After students have read the project description in the textbook, distribute the Chapter Project Overview, which lists the expected steps and outcomes for the project. The Overview also includes a table, which summarizes products derived from plants. Review the rules for the project. Encourage students to ask questions. You may also want to hand out the Chapter Project Scoring Rubric, so students will understand what is expected of them.

Set a deadline for the completion of the interactive exhibit and some interim dates, such as at the end of Sections 1, 2, and 4, for checking students' progress. Have students copy the dates in their Project Timeline.

To launch the project, organize the class into small groups. Groups of three to four students should be given the initial task of deciding which plant product they would like to investigate. Make sure students understand what is expected of each member of a group. Later in the project, each member will also be responsible for suggesting changes to improve the exhibit, even though the final interactive exhibit will be a collaborative effort.

Students will need time to ensure that sufficient information is available for the plant products they are considering. Be aware of the fact that some students may select plants or plant products that are rare and/or obscure. To reduce student frustration, monitor their research efforts and encourage them to choose topics that are well supported by information in available resources.

Once they have completed their research, lead a brainstorming session to get the students thinking about the characteristics of a successful interactive exhibit. Treat the brainstorming sessions as guided creativity. Interject ideas only when necessary. Ask students questions about how the exhibit will present information about each plant and the product(s) derived from it. Encourage students to remember the interests and limitations of their target audience (for example, students must remain aware of a young child's reading level).

Students must then build a prototype of their exhibit to test with young children in a "market study." To conduct this market study, students must present their exhibit to small groups of younger students. Help students develop criteria by which to gauge the success of the exhibit. When the test is completed, students should work to redesign their exhibit to satisfy the suggestions of the test audience. Construction of the actual exhibit can begin once the group and the teacher have agreed upon a final design.

Materials and Preparation

You may wish to give students a list of plants to choose from. Suitable plants include food plants such as grains (wheat, rice, corn), root crops (potatoes, yams, carrots, sweet potatoes, cassava, radishes, turnips, beets), legumes (beans, peas), and fruits. Students might also want to choose from among those tree species that are harvested for their wood and/or wood pulp (pine, maple, oak, mahogany, cherry, ash), or plants that are grown as a source of fibers (cotton, flax, sisal) or medicines (yew, periwinkle).

An alternative approach would be to select one plant (or one plant family) that is a source of many commercial products. This could be especially relevant to students if the plant is locally grown and plays a significant role in the regional economy.

Although the groups will decide for themselves what materials to use, you will need to provide basic materials and tools as needed.

Begin collecting materials such as shoe boxes, paper towel rolls, cardboard, oak tag, colored paper, plastic wrap, and sheets of colored foam core before the project begins. Simple materials should be used to construct the prototypes. For the final interactive exhibit, a larger range of material options is possible. Steer student teams toward materials such as foam core and sturdier paper products, which are less expensive and easier to work with than materials such as wood or plastic acrylic. However, lightweight, easy-to-use wood products, such as craft sticks, balsa wood, and dowels should be on hand. Teams will also need tape, staples, and craft glue.

To represent plants and plant parts, students should consider using polystyrene foam or silk flowers rather than real plant materials. Samples of wood, plastic, or rubber can sometimes be ordered directly from companies, often free of charge. Students can contact companies directly and gain valuable practice in dealing with members of the technical community.

Keep Students on Track— Section 1

While students consider which plant or plant product to research, guide them to begin by selecting at least two plants or plant products for initial consideration. If information is scarce for one of their choices, help them to be open to choosing a different plant or process. As a planning device, ask groups to mutually develop a list of four learning objectives (exhibit goals) that their completed exhibit will meet.

Distribute Chapter Project Worksheet 1. Make sure students understand they will need to use this worksheet as they plan their exhibits.

Keep Students on Track— Section 2

As students design their exhibits, have them begin by first planning the educational content. Help students decide what kinds of information should (and should not) be included in the exhibit. Have students list the kinds of items that will be labeled in their exhibit. Suggest that labels be parallel (like subheads in a textbook) so that viewers can easily move through the information and visualize the relationships among the items in the exhibit. At the end of Section 2, ask each group to submit Worksheet 1.

Encourage students to be imaginative in developing their exhibit designs and to find ways to make the information appealing and easy to remember. Make sure that students are planning to present content at a level that is appropriate for their young audience. Distribute Chapter Project Worksheet 2.

Keep Students on Track— Section 4

After students present their exhibit to young children, discuss with students which aspects of the exhibit seemed to meet the requirements in the most effective and/or creative way. At the end of Section 4, ask each group to submit Worksheet 2.

Chapter Project Wrap Up

As you review each group's final exhibit, ask the members to "talk you through" the various portions of the exhibit. Ask students to explain the parts of the exhibit and supply a rationale explaining the structure of the exhibit. When appropriate, encourage the more reticent students to play a greater role in presenting the exhibit. Encourage other students in the class to ask questions about the exhibit and its features.

Ask students to evaluate how well they accomplished the assignment, including how well the final exhibit matched the final design the group had agreed upon. Invite students to make suggestions about what they think would have made the project better.

Extension

This project can be extended for an entire class or on an individual basis. If time allows, students might want to show their exhibits to other classes or take a field trip to a nearby elementary school for additional showings. If possible, bring in a guest speaker from industry to view the completed exhibits and provide an example of their product.

You may wish to assign writing exercises as a way to provide a more in-depth study of the subject matter. Students will benefit from a writing piece summarizing the preliminary "market study" and the subsequent improvements in the exhibit. A slightly more in-depth writing exercise could explore ways to improve the plant product that the student studied. This will be challenging, but might offer an opportunity for certain students to think critically about the research they have just conducted.

Name _____ Date _____ Class _____

Design and Build an Interactive Exhibit

In this project, you will work as a group to design and create an interactive exhibit that will teach young students how plants can be transformed into useful products. After choosing a plant, you will think about how to design your exhibit. Your group needs to consider the most effective ways to present information to a young audience.

After your teacher reviews your exhibit design, you will develop a prototype. You will then test the prototype on your target audience. After you have tested your prototype, you will use the feedback to alter your exhibit as needed. Your group will begin by researching one or more plant species. Plants serve as sources for many kinds of products. Here are some examples:

Plant Source	Examples of Products
Familiar fruits and vegetables	Food items, including grains (wheat, rice, corn), root crops (potatoes, yams, carrots), and legumes (beans and peas)
Corn	Livestock feed; Sweet corn, popcorn; Corn syrup (sweetening agent); Corn meal (corn bread, tamales, tortillas); Cornstarch (powders, cooking); Industrial products such as ceramics, explosives, construction materials, paints, ethanol
Soybeans	Tofu, soy sauce, high-protein meat substitute; Industrial products such as paint, adhesives, fertilizers
Trees	Paper products; Lumber; Cork
Cotton, flax, papyrus, sisal	Fibers used for cloth, paper, or rope
Various plant species	Medicines such as codeine, cortisone, ephedrine, taxol, vincristine

Project Rules

■ After you have chosen a plant, you will need to learn how the plant is grown, how it is harvested, and what kinds of products are made from the plant. You'll also need to find out how the product is manufactured and what parts of the plant are used.

■ Once you have completed the research, your group will need to create a list of four learning objectives (exhibit goals). These learning objectives will summarize what your exhibit must do in order to be successful. Writing these objectives will help your group decide what is most important for your audience to learn when they visit your exhibit.

■ Your group will brainstorm designs for an interactive exhibit. Remember that a successful design must meet the learning objectives that your group created. Keep any sketches you make in a Project Folder.

■ Within your group, review one another's ideas and sketches. Come to a consensus (agreement) on a design for the exhibit you want to build as a group. Submit your design and your materials list to your teacher in Worksheet 1 at the end of Section 2.

■ Build a prototype of your exhibit. The prototype is a real-life version of your design.

■ Before you test your prototype, develop a brief questionnaire for the test audience to complete after viewing the exhibit. The questionnaire will help your group determine how well the exhibit achieved your objectives.

Introduction to Plants • *Chapter Project*   **Overview**

- Test your prototype with a small group of young students. Then have the students complete the questionnaire. Using the feedback from the questionnaire, meet with your group to brainstorm ideas for changes that could make your exhibit more effective. Discuss any design modifications with your teacher at the end of Section 4.
- Build the final exhibit.

Suggested Materials

- Your teacher will provide you with materials such as paper, cardboard, tape, staples, and craft glue to construct the prototypes.
- For the final exhibit, you may consider a wider range of materials. Possibilities include shoe boxes, paper towel rolls, oak tag, colored paper, plastic wrap, or sheets of colored foam core. If available, you may also wish to use lightweight, easy-to-use wood products, such as craft sticks, pre-cut pine shapes, balsa wood, and dowels.
- To represent plants and plant parts, use polystyrene foam or silk flowers.
- Manufacturers of some plant products may provide free samples upon request. Your teacher may require that you contact companies to request samples of your product.

Project Hints

- Read reference materials to find information about your plant species and plant product. If the plant is commercially grown, you will need to learn how it is grown and harvested. You will also need to discover the geographic regions in which the plant is found, its growing conditions, and its growing season. You will need to find out which parts of the plant are used to produce the product and how it is made.
- As soon as possible, begin to collect materials that you will use to build the exhibit. Your teacher may provide materials, but be prepared to bring some things from home.
- Think about the most effective ways to organize your exhibit and label its components. For example, you will want to present the information on plant structure separately from the part of the exhibit that describes the product and how it is made. If your exhibit includes sequential information (such as events that occur during manufacturing), you may wish to use numbered steps.
- Make sure that the information in your exhibit is presented at a level that your young audience can understand. Use simple language and short sentences.

Project Timeline

Tasks	Date Due
1. Complete your research.	_____
2. Write learning objectives (exhibit goals).	_____
3. Finish design, materials list, and sketches for Worksheet 1.	_____
4. Construct prototype.	_____
5. Write questions for market test.	_____
6. Conduct market test of prototype.	_____
7. Summarize feedback and refine exhibit design for Worksheet 2.	_____
8. Prepare final exhibit.	_____

Introduction to Plants

Design Your Exhibit

This worksheet will help you get started in selecting a topic and making a design for your exhibit.

What Materials Come From Plants?

1. List three plant products that you have used today.

   _____

2. Think about your most recent meal. What plant products were included in the meal?

   _____

Planning the Exhibit

3. What plant will your exhibit show?

   _____

4. What plant product will your exhibit describe? Explain how your exhibit will show how this product is made.

   _____

   _____

   _____

5. List the parts of the plant that your exhibit will label.

   _____

   _____

6. What materials will you need to build this exhibit?

   _____

   _____

   _____

7. List the four objectives (exhibit goals) that your group has agreed upon for this exhibit.

   _____

   _____

   _____

   _____

8. How will your group choose the best design?

   _____

   _____

   _____

9. On a separate sheet of paper, sketch an exhibit your group could build. Keep the sketch in your Project Folder. Take this worksheet and your sketch to your group meeting. Discuss your ideas with group members.

Introduction to Plants · *Chapter Project*   **Worksheet 2**

Testing the Prototype

Now that you have designed a prototype, it is time to test it by showing it to
a group of young students. This worksheet will help you organize feedback
from the test and list changes that will occur as a result.

1. What part of the exhibit do the students like the most?
   _____

2. What part of the exhibit do the students like the least? What don't they
   like about it?
   _____

   _____

3. Do the students understand the process being displayed?
   _____

4. Do the students know what the product is used for?
   _____

5. Are the students interested in the exhibit?
   _____

6. What is one thing about this exhibit that the students will remember?
   _____

   _____

7. List the objectives that are met inadequately or not at all by the design.
   _____

   _____

   _____

8. What modifications should be made to the design?
   _____

   _____

   _____

9. On a separate sheet of paper, sketch the revised exhibit your group can
   build. Keep the sketch in your Project Folder. Take this worksheet and
   your sketch to your group meeting. Discuss your ideas with group
   members. Then construct the final exhibit.

Introduction to Plants

Design and Build an Interactive Exhibit

Lab zone Chapter Project

In evaluating how well you complete the Chapter Project, your teacher will judge your work in four categories. In each, a score of 4 is the best rating.

	4	3	2	1
Designing the Exhibit	Student designs show originality and a thorough understanding of plant structures and how the plant product is made. Exhibit design is completely engaging and appropriate for target audience.	Student designs show some originality and a good understanding of plant structures and how the plant product is made. Exhibit design is generally engaging and appropriate for target audience.	Student designs show some understanding of plant structures and how the plant product is made. Exhibit design is somewhat appropriate for target audience.	Student designs show an incomplete and/or inaccurate understanding of plant structures and how the plant product is made. Exhibit design is inappropriate for target audience.
Building the Prototype	Prototype is well constructed and meets all objectives. All plant structures are neatly and correctly labeled. Depiction of how plant product is made is detailed, thorough, and accurate.	Prototype is adequately constructed and meets 3 of the 4 objectives. Most plant structures are neatly and correctly labeled. Depiction of how plant product is made is generally thorough and accurate.	Prototype is somewhat sloppy and meets 2 of the 4 objectives. Some plant structures are neatly and correctly labeled. Depiction of how plant product is made includes some inaccuracies and/or is only partially complete.	Prototype is poorly constructed and meets 1 or none of the 4 objectives. Few plant structures are neatly and correctly labeled. Depiction of how plant product is made is inaccurate and incomplete.
Testing the Prototype and Building the Final Exhibit	Student effectively collects and organizes feedback from testing. Applies findings strategically to significantly improve the final exhibit.	Student satisfactorily collects and organizes feedback from testing. Applies findings appropriately to improve the final exhibit.	Student collects and organizes partial feedback from testing. Applies some of the findings to improve the final exhibit.	Student collects little feedback from testing. Organization is poor. Applies few of the findings to improve the final exhibit.
Working Cooperatively	Student takes a lead in planning and constructing the exhibit.	Student participates in all aspects of planning and constructing the exhibit.	Student participates in most aspects of planning and constructing the exhibit.	Student plays a minor role in planning and constructing the exhibit.

The Plant Kingdom

🕐 *2–3 periods, 1–1 1/2 blocks*

ABILITY LEVELS KEY
- **L1** Basic to Average
- **L2** For All Students
- **L3** Average to Advanced

Objectives

A.4.1.1 Identify characteristics that all plants share.

A.4.1.2 Name all the things that a plant needs to live successfully on land.

A.4.1.3 Compare vascular and nonvascular plants.

A.4.1.4 Describe the plant life cycle.

Key Terms

- photosynthesis • tissue • chloroplast
- vacuole • cuticle • vascular tissue
- fertilization • zygote • nonvascular plant
- vascular plant • chlorophyll • sporophyte
- gametophyte

Local Standards

PRETEACH

Build Background Knowledge
Ask students to explain how plants and animals are different.

 **Discover Activity** *What Do Leaves Reveal About Plants?* **L1**

Targeted Resources

- ☐ **All in One Teaching Resources**
  L2 Reading Strategy: Building Vocabulary
- ☐ 💿 **PresentationExpress™ CD-ROM**

INSTRUCT

What Is a Plant? Use discussion to emphasize that nearly all plants are autotrophs, that is, they produce their own food, and that all plants are eukaryotes that contain many cells.

Adaptations for Living on Land Help students understand that, to live on land, all plants need a way to get water and nutrients from their surroundings, transport water and nutrients within their bodies, support their bodies, and reproduce.

Classification of Plants Assist students in discerning two major categories of plants: plants with true vascular tissue and plants without.

Complex Life Cycles Help students recognize that a plant's life cycle consists of two stages: the sporophyte stage and the gametophyte stage.

Targeted Resources

- ☐ **All in One Teaching Resources**
  L2 Guided Reading, pp. 219–222
  L2 Transparencies A27, A28
- ☐ **PHSchool.com** Web Code: cep-1041
- ☐ **Discovery SCHOOL Video Field Trip**
- ☐ **PHSchool.com** Web Code: ceh-1040
- ☐ 💿 **Student Edition on Audio CD**

ASSESS

Section Assessment Questions
🔄 Have students use their own definitions to help them answer questions.

Reteach
Direct students to make a chart listing the adaptations plants need to live on land and identify the adaptations as belonging to vascular plants.

Targeted Resources

- ☐ **All in One Teaching Resources**
  Section Summary, p. 218
  L1 Review and Reinforce, p. 223
  L3 Enrich, p. 224

Introduction to Plants • *Section Summary*

The Plant Kingdom

Key Concepts

■ What characteristics do all plants share?

■ What do plants need to live successfully on land?

■ How do nonvascular plants and vascular plants differ?

■ What are the different stages of a plant's life cycle?

Nearly all plants are autotrophs, organisms that produce their own food. All plants are eukaryotes that contain many cells. In addition, all plants cells are surrounded by cell walls.

The process by which plants make food is called **photosynthesis.** During photosynthesis, a plant uses carbon dioxide gas and water to make food and oxygen.

Plant cells are organized into **tissues,** groups of similar cells that perform a specific function. Plant cells are enclosed by a cell wall, a boundary that surrounds the cell membrane and separates the cell from the environment. Plant cell walls are made mostly of cellulose, a material that makes the walls rigid. Plant cells contain **chloroplasts,** structures in which food is made. Plant cells also contain vacuoles. A **vacuole** is a large storage sac that can expand and shink. The vacuole stores many substances, including water, wastes, and food.

Most plants live on land. **For plants to survive on land, they must have ways to obtain water and other nutrients from their surroundings, retain water, transport materials within their bodies, support their bodies, and reproduce.** Most plants have a waxy, waterproof layer covering their leaves called a **cuticle.** The cuticle helps keep water inside a plant cell rather than let it evaporate into the air. Some plants have **vascular tissue,** a system of tubelike structures inside the plant through which food, minerals, and water move. All plants undergo sexual reproduction that involves fertilization. **Fertilization** occurs when a sperm cell unites with an egg cell. The fertilized egg is called a **zygote.**

Scientists informally group plants into two major groups—nonvascular and vascular plants. Nonvascular plants do not have a well-developed system of tubes for transporting water and other materials. They grow low to the ground. **Vascular plants** have well-developed vascular tissue to transport and move materials quickly and efficiently throughout the plant's body. Vascular tissue also provides strength, stability, and support to a plant. Thus, vascular plants are able to grow quite tall.

Biologists studied a green pigment called **chlorophyll,** which is found in the chloroplasts of plants, algae, and some bacteria, to find the ancestors of today's plants. Biologists found that land plants and green algae contain the same forms of chlorophyll, leading biologists to infer that ancient green algae were the ancestors of today's land plants.

Plants have complex life cycles that include two different stages, the sporophyte stage and the gametophyte stage. In the **sporophyte** stage, the plant produces spores, tiny cells that can grow into new organisms. A spore develops into the plant's other stage, called the **gametophyte** stage. In the gametophyte stage, the plant produces two kinds of sex cells: sperm cells and egg cells.

Introduction to Plants ▪ *Guided Reading and Study*

The Plant Kingdom (pp. 104–111)

This section explains the features that plants share. It also describes what plants need to survive and how they reproduce.

Use Target Reading Skills

The first column in the chart lists Key Terms in this section. In the second column, write what you know about the Key Term. As you read the section, write a definition of the Key Term in your own words in the third column. Some examples are done for you.

Key Term	What You Know	Definition
Photosynthesis		
Tissue		
Chloroplast	*chloro* means "green"	
Vacuole		
Cuticle		Waxy, waterproof layer of a plant that reduces water loss.
Vascular tissue		
Fertilization		
Zygote		
Nonvascular plant	*non* means "no"	
Vascular plant		
Chlorophyll	*chloro* means "green"	
Sporophyte		
Gametophyte		

Introduction to Plants

Name _____ Date _____ Class _____

The Plant Kingdom *(continued)*
What Is a Plant? (pp. 104–105)

1. Circle the letter of each characteristic that plants share.

   a. heterotroph
   b. autotroph
   c. prokaryote
   d. eukaryote

2. Is the following sentence true or false? Plants make their own food in the process of photosynthesis. _____

3. Plant cells have a(n) _____, a boundary that surrounds the cell membrane and separates the cell from the environment.

4. Cell walls are made mostly of _____, a chemical that makes the walls rigid.

5. Label the diagram of the plant cell below.

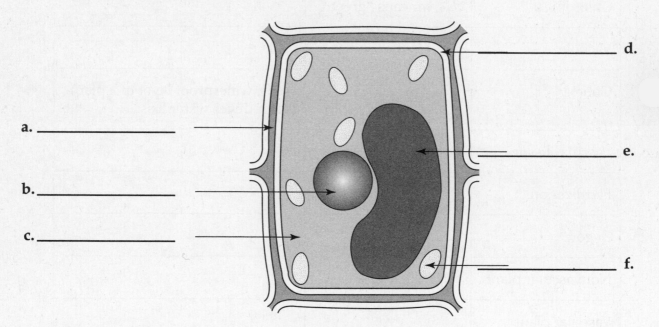

a. _____

b. _____

c. _____

d. _____

e. _____

f. _____

6. Is the following sentence true or false? Only some plants are multicellular. _____

7. A group of similar cells that perform a specific function in an organism is a(n) _____.

Introduction to Plants ▪ *Guided Reading and Study*

Adaptations for Living on Land (pp. 106–107)

8. List five things that plants must do to survive on land.

    a. _____

    b. _____

    c. _____

    d. _____

    e. _____

9. Plants living on land get water and nutrients from the
    _____.

10. Why can a plant on land lose water and dry out?

    _____

    _____

    _____

    _____

11. Circle the letter of one adaptation that land plants have to keep from
    drying out.

    a. chlorophyll   b. cell wall

    c. cuticle   d. cell membrane

12. Some plants move water, minerals, and food with a system of tubelike
    structures called _____.

13. Is the following sentence true or false? Some land plants are supported
    by vascular tissue. _____

Introduction to Plants ▪ *Guided Reading and Study*

The Plant Kingdom (continued)

14. What occurs during fertilization?

_____

_____

15. Circle the letter of the name of a fertilized egg.
   a. sporophyte
   b. gamete
   c. gametophyte
   d. zygote

Classification of Plants (pp. 108–110)

16. How do biologists learn which organisms were the ancestors of today's plants?

_____

17. A green pigment found in the chloroplasts of plants is called _____.

18. Why do biologists think that ancient green algae were the ancestors of today's plants?

_____

_____

Complex Life Cycles (pp. 110–111)

19. Plants produce spores during the _____ stage and

produce sex cells during the _____ stage.

20. Is the following sentence true or false? The sporophyte of a plant looks

the same as the gametophyte. _____

21. What are two kinds of sex cells that a gametophyte produces?
   a. _____   **b.** _____

Introduction to Plants • *Review and Reinforce*

The Plant Kingdom

Understanding Main Ideas
Answer the following on a separate sheet of paper.

1. What characteristics do all plants share?
2. What do plants need to live successfully on land?

Building Vocabulary
From the list below, choose the term that best completes each sentence and write it in the blank.

photosynthesis	tissue	gametophyte
chloroplast	zygote	vascular plant
vascular tissue	chlorophyll	nonvascular plant
vacuole	cuticle	sporophyte
fertilization		

3. A group of similar cells that perform a similar function is called a(n) _____.

4. The internal transporting system through which water, minerals, and food move inside the plant is called _____.

5. In the _____ stage, the plant produces two kinds of sex cells.

6. The _____ is a structure inside a plant's cell in which food is made.

7. The process by which plants make food is called _____.

8. A plant that does not have a well-developed system of tubes for transporting water and other materials is called a _____.

9. When a sperm cell unites with an egg cell, _____ occurs.

10. A(n) _____ is a waxy, waterproof layer that covers the leaves and stems of most plants.

11. A storage area in a plant cell is called a(n) _____.

12. The green pigment called _____ reflects most of the green light in the visible spectrum.

13. In the _____ stage, the plant produces spores.

14. A plant with true vascular tissue is called a _____.

15. A fertilized egg is called a(n) _____.

Name _____ Date _____ Class _____

Introduction to Plants • *Enrich*

Desert Survival

You learned that all plants must have adaptations for obtaining and retaining water. This is especially true of plants that live in the desert. To obtain water, some desert plants have very deep root systems that can absorb moisture far underground. Others have shallow, horizontal root systems that can quickly absorb a large amount of water when it rains.

The aboveground surfaces of many desert plants are covered with spines. These spines help to shade the plant from the sun and keep it from getting too hot. They also help to reduce water loss from the plant by shielding it from dry winds. Some plants in the desert have thick, fleshy stems that can store water for long periods of time.

Many plants, such as the one shown below, survive dry periods by becoming *dormant* or inactive. When a plant is dormant, it needs very little water.

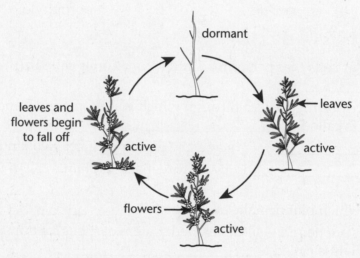

Answer the following questions on a separate sheet of paper.

1. What do you think causes the plant in the figure above to come out of dormancy and become active?

2. Why do you think the plant loses its leaves and flowers when it becomes dormant?

3. Do you think the plant shown above is more likely to have deep roots or shallow horizontal roots? Explain.

4. A desert plant called the creosote bush has a double root system: It has both shallow horizontal roots and deep vertical roots. Why would this type of root system be an advantage to a desert plant?

5. Do you think a desert plant is more likely to have a thin cuticle or a thick cuticle? Explain.

Photosynthesis and Light

🕐 *2–3 periods, 1–1 1/2 blocks*

Objectives

A.4.2.1 Explain what happens when light strikes a green leaf.
A.4.2.2 Describe the overall process of photosynthesis.

Key Terms

• transmission • reflection • absorption
• accessory pigment

Local Standards

PRETEACH

Build Background Knowledge
Prompt students to describe how colored light affects the way we see colored objects.

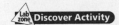 **Discover Activity** *What Colors Make Up Sunlight?* **L1**

Targeted Resources

❏ **All in One Teaching Resources**
   L2 Reading Strategy Transparency A29: Previewing Visuals

❏ 💿 **PresentationExpress™ CD-ROM**

INSTRUCT

The Nature of Light Lead students through this subsection which discusses visible light, what happens when light strikes an object, plants and light, and the relationship between light and plant pigments.
The Photosynthesis Process Explain the equation for photosynthesis and discuss light's participation in the process.

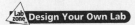 **Design Your Own Lab** *Eye on Photosynthesis* **L2**

Targeted Resources

❏ **All in One Teaching Resources**
   L2 Guided Reading, pp. 227–229
   L2 Transparencies A30, A31
   L3 Lab: *Eye on Photosynthesis*, pp. 232–234

❏ 📼 **Lab Activity Video/DVD**
   Design Your Own Lab: *Eye on Photosynthesis*

❏ **PHSchool.com** Web Code: cep-1042

❏ 💿 **Student Edition on Audio CD**

ASSESS

Section Assessment Questions
🔄 Have students use their Previewing Visuals graphic organizers to answer the questions.

Reteach
Provide an illustration showing photosynthesis and direct students to label the components of the process: carbon dioxide, water, light energy, sugar, and water.

Targeted Resources

❏ **All in One Teaching Resources**
   Section Summary, p. 226
   L1 Review and Reinforce, p. 230
   L3 Enrich, p. 231

Introduction to Plants ▪ *Section Summary*

Photosynthesis and Light

Key Concepts

■ What happens when light strikes a green leaf?

■ How do scientists summarize the process of photosynthesis?

The light that you see is called white light. White light is made up of the colors of the rainbow—red, orange, yellow, green, blue, and violet. These colors are called the visible spectrum. Some objects reflect some colors of the visible spectrum and absorb others. When light strikes a red shirt, the shirt absorbs most colors and reflects red. The shirt looks red because your eyes see the reflected color.

Some objects such as glass and other transparent materials allow light to pass through them. This process is called **transmission.** When light hits a shiny surface such as mirror, the light bounces back. This process is called **reflection.** When dark objects, such as street pavements, take in light, it is called **absorption.**

Like most other objects, plants absorb some colors and reflect others. **When light strikes the green leaves of a plant, most of the green part of the spectrum is reflected. Most of the other colors of light are absorbed.** Chlorophyll absorbs most of the blue and red light. **Accessory pigments,** which include orange and yellow pigments, are also found in leaves and absorb different colors of light than chlorophyll. Most accessory pigments are not visible in plants because they are masked by chlorophyll.

Plants use energy from light to power the process of photosynthesis. Carbon dioxide gas from the air and water from the soil are the raw materials for photosynthesis. Sugar and oxygen are the products. **The many chemical reactions of photosynthesis can be summarized by this equation:**

$$\text{carbon dioxide} + \text{water} \xrightarrow{\text{light energy}} \text{sugar} + \text{oxygen}$$
$$(CO_2) \qquad (H_2O) \qquad (C_6H_{12}O_6) \qquad (O_2)$$

This equation reads, "carbon dioxide and water combine in the presence of light to produce sugar and oxygen." Photosynthesis takes place in the parts of a plant that contain chlorophyll.

Introduction to Plants · *Guided Reading and Study*

Photosynthesis and Light (pp. 114–119)

This section explains how plants get energy from sunlight and describes what occurs during photosynthesis.

Use Target Reading Skills

Preview the figure "The Photosynthesis Process" in the textbook. Then write two questions that you have about the diagram below. As you read, answer your questions.

The Photosynthesis Process

Q. How is sunlight involved in photosynthesis?
A.
Q.
A.

The Nature of Light (pp. 115–116)

1. Circle the letter of each sentence that is true about light.

    a. The sun is the source of energy on Earth.

    b. The light you can see is called a prism.

    c. White light is made up of red, orange, yellow, green, blue, and violet light.

    d. Shiny surfaces absorb light and dark surfaces reflect light.

2. The colors of light that make up white light are referred to as the

    _____.

3. A shirt looks red because it _____ red light.

Introduction to Plants ▪ *Guided Reading and Study*

Photosynthesis and Light *(continued)*

4. Circle the color of light that is reflected by plant leaves.

   a. green
   b. blue
   c. yellow
   d. red

5. Light is absorbed by _____ found in the chloroplasts of plant cells.

6. Circle the letter of each color of light that is absorbed by chlorophyll.

   a. green
   b. blue
   c. yellow
   d. red

7. Circle the letter of each sentence that is true about plant pigments.

   a. Accessory pigments absorb the same colors of light that chlorophyll does.
   b. Accessory pigments are always visible in plants.
   c. Accessory pigments absorb different colors of light than chlorophyll.
   d. Most accessory pigments are not visible in plants because they are masked by chlorophyll.

The Photosynthesis Process (pp. 117–119)

8. How is the light energy absorbed by plants important to photosynthesis?

   _____

   _____

   _____

9. In addition to light, what do plants need for photosynthesis?

   _____

   _____

Name _____ Date _____ Class _____

Introduction to Plants ▪ *Guided Reading and Study*

10. In the diagram below, draw arrows to show which materials the plant is taking up and which materials the plant is giving off or using.

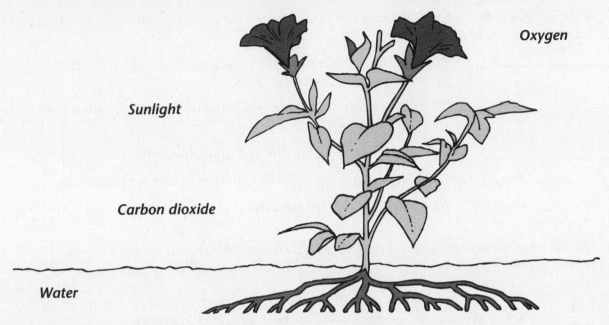

Oxygen

Sunlight

Carbon dioxide

Water

11. Write the chemical equation for the process of photosynthesis.

_____

12. What happens to excess food made by plants?

_____

_____

Introduction to Plants • *Review and Reinforce*

Photosynthesis and Light

Understanding Main Ideas

If the statement is true, write true. *If it is false, change the underlined word or words to make the statement true.*

_____ 1. White light is made of all the colors of the rainbow, referred to as the <u>visible spectrum</u>.

_____ 2. When light strikes a green leaf, most of the green part of the spectrum is <u>reflected</u>.

_____ 3. Chlorophyll absorbs mostly <u>red and blue</u> light.

_____ 4. <u>Accessory pigments</u> include yellow and orange pigments.

_____ 5. A red object looks red because it <u>absorbs</u> red light.

Use the equation below to answer the following questions. Write your answers on the line provided.

$$carbon\ dioxide\ +\ water\ \xrightarrow{\ light\ energy\ }\ sugar\ +\ oxygen$$

6. What process is illustrated by the equation shown above?

_____

_____

7. What provides the energy to power this process?

_____

_____

8. What are the products of the process illustrated above?

_____

_____

Introduction to Plants ▪ *Enrich*

Absorption and Action

The solid line on the graph below shows the absorption of light by chlorophyll at various colors of the spectrum. This type of graph is called an *absorption spectrum*. Scientists obtain an absorption spectrum by shining light of a particular color at a sample of chlorophyll suspended in water. The amount of light shone at the sample is compared with the amount that shines through the sample. This allows scientists to determine how much light the chlorophyll absorbed. The process is continued with different colors of light until data have been gathered on the entire visible spectrum.

   The dashed line on the graph shows the rate of photosynthesis at various colors of light. This type of graph is called an *action spectrum*. Scientists obtain an action spectrum by shining light of a particular color on a plant and measuring and recording the rate at which the plant gives off oxygen. This process is also continued for the entire visible spectrum of light.

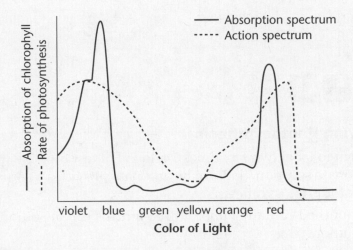

Answer the following questions on a separate sheet of paper.

1. What do the peaks of the absorption spectrum indicate? What do the low portions indicate?

2. What do the peaks and low points of the action spectrum indicate?

3. Does the rate of photosynthesis appear to be related to the absorption of light by chlorophyll? Explain.

4. Predict what would happen to a plant grown in green light. Explain your reasoning.

5. Predict the rate of photosynthesis of a plant grown in white light. Will it be high or low? Explain.

Introduction to Plants

Name _____ Date _____ Class _____

Introduction to Plants · *Design Your Own Lab*

Eye on Photosynthesis

Problem

What raw materials and conditions are involved in photosynthesis?

Skills Focus

observing, controlling variables, designing experiments

Materials

Elodea plants

water (boiled, then cooled)

wide-mouthed container

sodium bicarbonate solution

2 test tubes

wax pencil

lamp (optional)

Procedure

PART 1 Observing Photosynthesis

1. Use a wax pencil to label two test tubes *1* and *2*. Fill test tube 1 with sodium bicarbonate solution. Sodium bicarbonate provides a source of carbon dioxide for photosynthesis.

2. Fill the wide-mouthed container about three-fourths full of sodium bicarbonate solution.

3. Hold your thumb over the mouth of test tube 1. Turn the test tube over, and lower it to the bottom of the container. Do not let in any air. If necessary, repeat this step so that test tube 1 contains no air pockets. **CAUTION:** *Glass test tubes are fragile. Handle the test tubes carefully. Do not touch broken glass.*

4. Fill test tube 2 with sodium bicarbonate solution. Place an *Elodea* plant in the tube with the cut stem at the bottom. Put your thumb over the mouth of the test tube, and lower it into the container without letting in any air. Wash your hands.

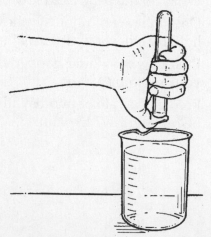

5. Place the container with the two test tubes in bright light. After a few minutes, examine both test tubes for bubbles.

Introduction to Plants • *Design Your Own Lab*

6. If bubbles form in test tube 2, observe the *Elodea* stem to see if it is producing the bubbles. The bubbles are oxygen bubbles. The production of oxygen signals that photosynthesis is taking place.

7. Leave the set-up in bright light for 30 minutes. Observe what happens to any bubbles that form. Record your observations.

PART 2 Is Carbon Dioxide Needed for Photosynthesis?

8. Your teacher will provide a supply of water that has been boiled and then cooled. Boiling drives off gases that are dissolved in the water, including carbon dioxide.

9. Based on what you learned in Part 1, design an experiment to show whether or not carbon dioxide is needed for photosynthesis. Obtain your teacher's approval before carrying out your experiment. Record all your observations.

PART 3 What Other Conditions Are Needed for Photosynthesis?

10. Make a list of other conditions that may affect photosynthesis. For example, think about factors such as light, the size of the plant, and the number of leaves.

11. Choose one factor from your list. Then design an experiment to show how the factor affects photosynthesis. Obtain your teacher's approval before carrying out your experiment. Record all your observations.

Introduction to Plants

Introduction to Plants ▪ *Design Your Own Lab*

Eye on Photosynthesis (continued)

Analyze and Conclude

Write your answers on a separate sheet of paper.

1. **Observing** What process produced the bubbles you observed in Part 1?

2. **Controlling Variables** In Part 1, what was the purpose of test tube 1?

3. **Designing Experiments** For the experiments you carried out in Parts 2 and 3, identify the manipulated variable and the responding variable. Explain whether or not your experiments were controlled experiments.

4. **Drawing Conclusions** Based on your results in Part 2, is carbon dioxide necessary for photosynthesis?

5. **Posing Questions** What question about photosynthesis did you explore in Part 3? What did you learn?

6. **Communicating** In a paragraph, summarize what you learned about photosynthesis from this investigation. Be sure to support each of your conclusions with evidence from your experiments.

More to Explore

A small animal in a closed container will die, even if it has enough water and food. A small animal in a closed container with a plant, water, and food will not die. Use what you have learned in this experiment to explain these facts.

Mosses, Liverworts, and Hornworts

ABILITY LEVELS KEY
L1 Basic to Average
L2 For All Students
L3 Average to Advanced

⏱ *2–3 periods, 1–1 1/2 blocks*

Objectives

A.4.3.1 Name some nonvascular plants and list the characteristics they all share.
A.4.3.2 Describe the structure of a moss plant.

Key Terms

• rhizoid • bog • peat

Local Standards

PRETEACH

Build Background Knowledge
Invite students to describe any mosses with which they are familiar.

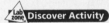 **Discover Activity** *Will Mosses Absorb Water?* **L1**

Targeted Resources

❑ **All in One Teaching Resources**
  L2 Reading Strategy Transparency A32: Identifying Main Ideas

❑ 💿 **PresentationExpress™ CD-ROM**

INSTRUCT

Mosses Help students recognize the simple plant parts of a moss plant—their stemlike, leaflike, and rootlike structures—as well as their importance.

Liverworts and Hornworts Assist students as they learn how to distinguish two remaining groups of nonvascular plants—liverworts and hornworts.

 Skills Lab *Masses of Mosses* **L2**

Targeted Resources

❑ **All in One Teaching Resources**
  L2 Guided Reading, pp. 237–239
  L2 Transparency A33
  L2 Lab: *Masses of Mosses* pp. 242–243

❑ 📼 **Lab Activity Video/DVD**
  Skills Lab: *Masses of Mosses*

❑ **www.SciLinks.org** Web Code: scn-0143

❑ 💿 **Student Edition on Audio CD**

ASSESS

Section Assessment Questions
🔄 Have students use their Identifying Main Ideas graphic organizers as they answer the questions.

Reteach
Ask students to describe the life cycle of moss, describing how the sporophyte is formed and its function.

Targeted Resources

❑ **All in One Teaching Resources**
  Section Summary, p. 236
  L1 Review and Reinforce, p. 240
  L3 Enrich, p. 241

Introduction to Plants

Introduction to Plants • *Section Summary*

Mosses, Liverworts, and Hornworts

Key Concept

■ What characteristics do the three groups of nonvascular plants share?

The three major groups of nonvascular plants are mosses, liverworts, and hornworts. These low-growing plants live in moist environments where they can absorb water and other nutrients directly from their environment. The watery surroundings also enable sperm cells to swim to egg cells during reproduction.

The familiar green, fuzzy part of the moss is the gametophyte generation of the plant. Structures that look like tiny leaves grow off a small, stemlike structure. Thin, rootlike structures called **rhizoids** anchor the moss and absorb water and nutrients. The sporophyte generation grows out of the gametophyte. The sporophyte includes a long, slender stalk with a capsule at the end. The capsule contains spores.

Sphagnum moss is a type of moss that grows in a wetland called a **bog.** The still water in a bog is so acidic that decomposers cannot live in the water. Thus, when the plants die, they do not decay. Instead, the dead plants accumulate at the bottom of the bog. Over time, the mosses become compressed into layers and form a blackish-brown material called **peat.** Peat can be used as a fuel to heat homes and to cook food.

Two other kinds of nonvascular plants are liverworts and hornworts. The body of a liverwort looks somewhat like a human liver. Liverworts are often found growing as a thick crust on moist rocks or soil along the sides of a stream. Hornworts grow hornlike structures that are the sporophytes. Hornworts usually live in moist soil, often mixed in with grass plants.

Introduction to Plants • *Guided Reading and Study*

Mosses, Liverworts, and Hornworts (pp. 122–124)

This section describes the characteristics of nonvascular plants.

Use Target Reading Skills

As you read the section, write the main idea—the biggest or most important idea—in the graphic organizer below. Then write three supporting details that give examples of the main idea.

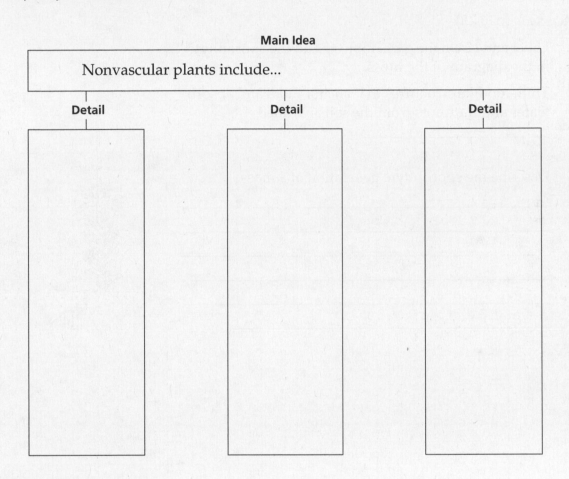

Main Idea

Nonvascular plants include...

Detail   **Detail**   **Detail**

Introduction (p. 122)

1. List two characteristics of nonvascular plants.

   a. _____

   b. _____

2. Is the following sentence true or false? Nonvascular plants can become very large and tall because of their support system. _____

Introduction to Plants

Introduction to Plants ▪ *Guided Reading and Study*

Mosses, Liverworts, and Hornworts (continued)

3. How do nonvascular plants get water?

    _____

    _____

4. Is the following true or false? Nonvascular plants must have water to let the sperm cells swim to the egg cells. _____

Mosses (p. 123)

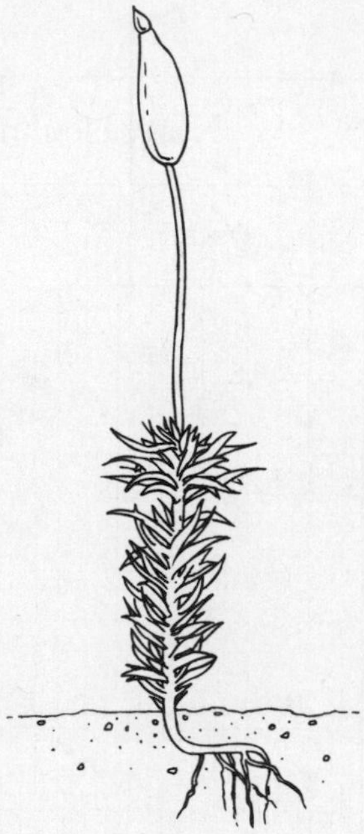

5. Label and circle the gametophyte and the sporophyte in the diagram of the moss.

6. Thin, rootlike structures that anchor moss and absorb water and nutrients from the soil are called

    _____.

7. Describe the sporophyte generation of a moss.

    _____

    _____

    _____

    _____

    _____

    _____

Introduction to Plants • *Guided Reading and Study*

8. Circle the letter of each way people use peat moss.
    a. as food
    b. in gardening
    c. as a fuel
    d. as cloth

9. Is the following sentence true or false? Peat moss forms in bogs where dead plants do not decay, but are pressed into layers as they fall to the bottom of the bog. _____

Liverworts and Hornworts (p. 124)

10. Where are liverworts often found growing?
    _____
    _____

11. Is the following sentence true or false? There are more species of hornworts than there are liverworts. _____

Introduction to Plants ▪ *Review and Reinforce*

Mosses, Liverworts, and Hornworts

Understanding Main Ideas

Replace each number in the table with the correct word or phrase.

Characteristic	Mosses	1.	Hornworts
contain vascular tissue	no	2.	no
height	3.	low-growing	low-growing
size	small	small	4.
moisture needs	5.	places high in moisture	places high in moisture
where they grow	tree trunks or wet rocks	moist rocks or moist soil	6.

Building Vocabulary

Write the letter of the correct answer on the line at the left.

_____ 7. Peat is made of

    a. clay.
    b. layers of dead moss.
    c. sandy soil.
    d. fossilizing plant matter.

_____ 8. A bog is a type of wetland with

    a. stagnant water.
    b. only dead plants.
    c. warm, slow-moving water.
    d. still, acidic water.

_____ 9. The structures that anchor a moss and absorb water and nutrients from the soil are called

    a. stems.
    b. rhizoids.
    c. sporophytes.
    d. gametophytes.

Name _____ Date _____ Class _____

Sphagnum Bogs

Bogs are marshy areas often found in cool regions such as Canada, northern Europe, and Russia. The plant life of bogs consists mostly of sphagnum mosses. Sphagnum bogs sometimes form over a small lake or pond. The layers of such a bog are shown below. Eventually, the entire lake or pond will be filled with dead moss.

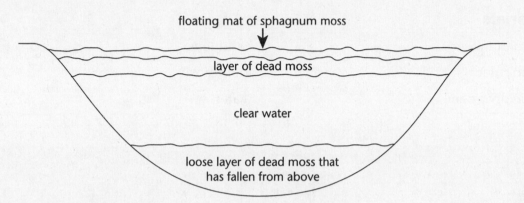

Answer the following questions on a separate sheet of paper.

1. A sphagnum bog is said to have a "false" bottom and a "true" bottom. Explain this statement.

2. If you were an archeologist searching for ancient tools, in which layer of the bog would you look?

3. What characteristics of mosses let them form floating mats over small lakes and ponds?

4. Bogs of the type shown above do not form on larger lakes or rivers. Why do you think this is true?

Name _____ Date _____ Class _____

Masses of Mosses

Problem

How is a moss plant adapted to carry out its life activities?

Skills Focus

observing, measuring

Materials

clump of moss   hand lens

metric ruler   toothpicks

plastic dropper   water

Procedure

1. Your teacher will give you a clump of moss. Examine the clump from all sides. Draw a diagram of what you see. Measure the size of the overall clump and the main parts of the clump. Record your observations.

2. Using toothpicks, gently separate five individual moss plants from the clump. Be sure to pull them totally apart so that you can observe each plant separately. If the moss plants appear to dry up as you are working, moisten them with a few drops of water.

Introduction to Plants ▪ *Skills Lab*

3. Measure the length of the leaflike, stemlike, and rootlike structures on each plant. If brown stalks and capsules are present, measure them. Find the average length of each structure.

4. Make a drawing of a single moss plant. Label the parts, give their sizes, and record the color of each part. When you are finished observing the moss, return it to your teacher. Wash your hands thoroughly.

5. Obtain class averages for the sizes of the structures you measured in Step 3. Also, if the moss that you observed had brown stalks and capsules, share your observations about those structures.

Analyze and Conclude

Write your answers on a separate sheet of paper.

1. **Observing** Describe the overall appearance of the moss clump, including its color, size, and texture.

2. **Measuring** What was the typical size of the leaflike portion of the moss plants, the typical height of the stemlike portion, and the typical length of the rootlike portion?

3. **Inferring** In which part(s) of the moss does photosynthesis occur? How do you know?

4. **Communicating** Write a paragraph explaining what you learned about mosses from this investigation. Include explanations of why mosses cannot grow tall and why they live in moist environments.

More to Explore

Select a moss plant with stalks and capsules. Use toothpicks to release some of the spores, which can be as small as dust particles. Examine the spores under a microscope. Create a labeled drawing of what you see.

Ferns, Club Mosses, and Horsetails

2–3 periods, 1–1 1/2 blocks

ABILITY LEVELS KEY
L1 Basic to Average
L2 For All Students
L3 Average to Advanced

Objectives
A.4.4.1 Name some seedless vascular plants and list the characteristics they all share.
A.4.4.2 Describe the structure of a fern and how it reproduces.

Key Term
• frond

Local Standards

PRETEACH

Build Background Knowledge
Have students draw what they think a fern looks like and then describe its characteristics.

 **Discover Activity** *How Quickly Can Water Move Upward?* **L1**

Targeted Resources
❏ **All in One** Teaching Resources
  L2 Reading Strategy Transparency A34: Asking Questions
❏ ⊙ **PresentationExpress™ CD-ROM**

INSTRUCT

Characteristics of Seedless Vascular Plants
Stress that plants with vascular tissue can grow taller than nonvascular plants but that, without seeds, the plants must still live in moist areas to complete reproduction.
Ferns Have students study the structure of ferns and their reproduction through spores.
Club Mosses and Horsetails Have students read about the characteristics of club mosses and horsetails.

Targeted Resources
❏ **All in One** Teaching Resources
  L2 Guided Reading, pp. 246–248
  L2 Transparency A35
❏ ⊙ **Student Edition on Audio CD**

ASSESS

Section Assessment Questions
⊙ Have students use their Asking Questions graphic organizers to answer the questions.
Reteach
Have students write brief paragraphs to describe the life cycle of ferns.

Targeted Resources
❏ **All in One** Teaching Resources
  Section Summary, p. 245
  L1 Review and Reinforce, p. 249
  L3 Enrich, p. 250

Introduction to Plants ▪ *Section Summary*

Ferns, Club Mosses, and Horsetails

Key Concept

■ What are the main characteristics of seedless vascular plants?

Ferns, club mosses, and horsetails are seedless vascular plants. **Ferns, club mosses, and horsetails share two characteristics. They have true vascular tissue and they do not produce seeds. Instead of seeds, these plants reproduce by releasing spores.**

Vascular plants can grow quite tall because their vascular tissue provides an effective way of transporting materials throughout the plant. The strong tubelike structures in vascular plants give the plants strength and stability.

Ferns, club mosses, and horsetails need to grow in moist surroundings because they produce spores. These spores grow into gametophytes. When the gametophytes produce egg cells and sperm cells, there must be enough water available for the sperm to swim toward the eggs.

Like other vascular plants, ferns have true stems, roots, and leaves. The stems of most ferns are underground. Leaves grow upward from the top side of the stems, while roots grow downward from the bottom of the stems. The roots anchor the fern to the ground and absorb water and nutrients from the soil. The leaves of ferns are called **fronds.** The upper surface of each frond is coated with a cuticle that helps the plant retain water.

The familiar fern, with its visible fronds, is the sporophyte stage of the plant. Spores develop in tiny spore cases on the underside of the mature fronds. When the spores are released, wind and water carry them great distances. If a spore lands in moist, shaded soil, it develops into a tiny gametophyte.

Two other groups of seedless vascular plants are the club mosses and horsetails. Like ferns, club mosses and horsetails have true leaves, stems, and roots. They also have a similar life cycle. There are relatively few species of club mosses and horsetails alive today.

Club mosses, sometimes called ground pine or princess pine, look like the small branch of a pine tree. Club mosses usually grow in moist woodlands and near streams. Horsetails have long, coarse, needlelike branches that grow in a circle around each joint. Small leaves grow flat against the stem just above each joint. The stems contain silica, a gritty substance also found in sand.

Introduction to Plants

Introduction to Plants · *Guided Reading and Study*

Ferns, Club Mosses, and Horsetails (pp. 126–129)

This section describes the characteristics of plants that have vascular tissue, but do not produce seeds.

Use Target Reading Skills

Before you read, preview the red headings. In the graphic organizer below, ask a what, how, *or* where *question for each heading. As you read, write the answers to your questions.*

Ferns, Club Mosses, and Horsetails

Question	Answer
What are the characteristics of seedless vascular plants?	Seedless vascular plants have...

Characteristics of Seedless Vascular Plants (p. 127)

1. List two characteristics that ferns, club mosses, and horsetails share.

   a. _____

   b. _____

2. Circle the letter before each sentence that is true about vascular tissue.

   a. Plants can grow tall without vascular tissue.

   b. Nonvascular plants are better suited to life on land.

   c. Vascular tissue transports water and food throughout a plant's body.

   d. Vascular tissue gives a plant strength and stability.

Introduction to Plants ▪ *Guided Reading and Study*

3. Why must ferns, club mosses, and horsetails grow in moist surroundings?

_____

_____

_____

Ferns (p. 128)

4. Is the following sentence true or false? Ferns are small plants that can only grow low to the ground. _____

5. The stems of most ferns are located _____. Leaves grow _____ from the top side of the stems, and roots grow _____ from the bottom of the stems.

6. Why are the developing leaves in many ferns called fiddleheads?

_____

_____

7. Circle the letter of each sentence that is true about the function of a fern's roots.
    a. Roots anchor the fern to the ground.
    b. Roots keep the fern from losing water.
    c. Roots produce spores.
    d. Roots absorb water and nutrients from the soil.

Introduction to Plants ▪ *Guided Reading and Study*

Ferns, Club Mosses, and Horsetails *(continued)*

8. Fern leaves are called _____.

9. What is the function of the cuticle on the upper surface of fern leaves?

   _____

10. Circle the letter of each sentence that is true about reproduction in ferns.

    a. The familiar fern plant with its large fronds is the gametophyte stage.

    b. Spores develop in spore cases on the underside of mature fronds.

    c. Wind and water carry released spores great distances.

    d. Spores will grow into gametophytes in dry, sunny soil.

Club Mosses and Horsetails (p. 129)

11. How are club mosses and horsetails similar to ferns?

    _____

    _____

    _____

12. Circle the letter before each sentence that is true about club mosses and horsetails.

    a. There are thousands of different species of club mosses and horsetails.

    b. Club mosses usually grow in moist woodlands and near streams.

    c. Club mosses have jointed stems with long, needlelike branches that grow in a circle around each joint.

    d. Horsetail stems contain silica, a gritty substance also found in sand.

Introduction to Plants • *Review and Reinforce*

Ferns, Club Mosses, and Horsetails

Understanding Main Ideas

Choose the correct word to label the parts in the diagram below.

frond   stem   root   spore cases

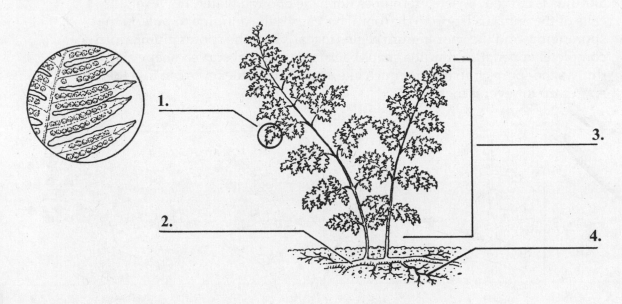

Use the diagram to fill in the blanks with the correct term.

5. The entire organism represented above is the _____
   stage of the plant.

6. When a spore falls into moist, shaded soil, it develops into the
   _____ stage.

Answer the following questions on the lines provided.

7. In addition to ferns, what two other groups of plants are also seedless
   vascular plants?

   _____

8. What are plants that have vascular tissue called?

   _____

9. How do seedless vascular plants reproduce?

   _____

Name _____ Date _____ Class _____

Spore Toss

The tiny spore cases that grow on the undersides of fern fronds are called *sporangia* (singular *sporangium*). Some kinds of ferns can actually throw their spores using their sporangia. The sporangia of these ferns consist of a single layer of thin-walled cells plus an annulus. An *annulus* (plural *annuli*) is a row of thickened cells that encircles the sporangium. In moist conditions, an annulus is curved. When a fern does not have enough water, however, the cells of the annulus begin to dry out. This causes the annulus to pull on the sporangium and the sporangium begins to tear. Once the sporangium is torn completely open, the annulus snaps back to its original curved shape and throws the spores into the air, much like a catapult. Some ferns can toss their spores up to several meters.

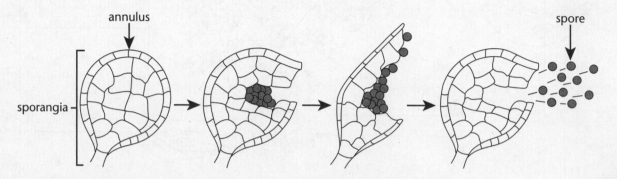

Answer the following questions on a separate sheet of paper.

1. Write a caption for each of the illustrations shown above, using what you have learned about how some ferns release their spores.
2. Why is it advantageous to ferns to have their spores carried long distances by wind or water?
3. Some ferns do not throw their spores. Instead, their spores are carried away from their sporangia by the wind. What is one advantage that spore-throwing ferns have over these ferns?
4. What type of weather precedes the release of spores? Explain.

Name _____ Date _____ Class _____

Key Terms

Use the clues to fill in the blanks with Key Terms from the chapter. Then put the numbered letters in the correct spaces to find the hidden message.

Clues	Key Terms

Stage in which plant produces spores

__ __ __ __ __ __ __ __ __ __
1   2 3   4 5

Fern leaf

__ __ __ __ __
6 7   8 9

Group of cells that has a specific job

__ __ __ __ __
10 11 12   13

Rootlike structure that anchors moss

__ __ __ __ __ __
14   15   16

Type of wetleand

__ __ __
17

Saclike storage area in a plant cell

__ __ __ __ __ __
18 19 20 21 22

Stage in which plant produces sex cells

__ __ __ __ __ __ __ __
   23   24 25   26 27

Layer of dead mosses compressed at the bottom of a bog

__ __ __ __
28 29 30

Mosses and liverworts are _____ plants

__ __ __ __ __ __ __ __
31   32   33 34 35 36 37 38

Green pigment

__ __ __ __ __ __
 39   40   41

Hidden Message

__ __ __ __ __ __ __ __   __ __ __ __ __ __   __ __ __
18 23 12 35 13 21 37 14 3 39 33 8 25 34 29 38 5

__ __ __ __ __ __   __ __ __ __ __ __   __ __   __ __ __ __
17 22 4 26 24 7 1 20 15 10 28 9 30 40 41 11 6 27

__ __   __ __ __ __ .
2 32 36 19 31 16

Connecting Concepts

Develop a concept map that uses the Key Concepts and Key Terms from this chapter. Keep in mind the big idea of this chapter. The concept map shown is one way to organize how the information in this chapter is related. You may use an extra sheet of paper.

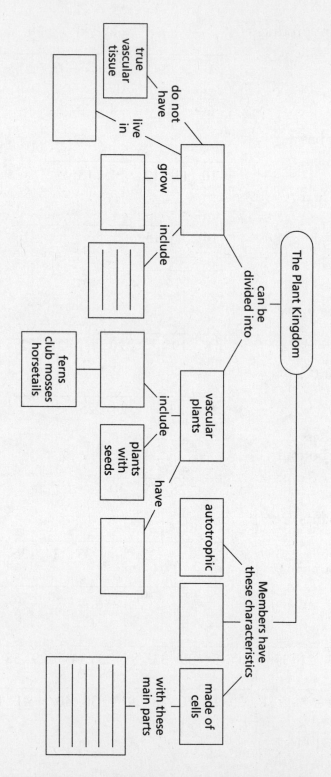

Investigating Stomata

Key Concept

Stomata in leaves are in the best places for gas exchange.

Skills Focus

observing, inferring, predicting

Time

60 minutes

Materials *(per group)*

leaf from a land plant

leaf from a floating water plant

scissors

microscope

2 slides

dropper

2 coverslips

Alternate Materials: Students could use prepared slides instead of fresh plants.

Advance Preparation

Have students bring in plants to examine. The land plants could be houseplants, garden, or outdoor plants near the school. Good plants to use include geraniums, *Coleus*, *Tradescantia*, fresh spinach, and lettuce. Water plants such as water lilies can be obtained from florists, or they can be ordered from a biological supply company. Check local ordinances before obtaining plants from the environment.

Teaching Tips

- Be sure students understand that the epidermis is the outermost layer of cells on the leaf—the leaf's "skin." Students may have a hard time removing the epidermis. You might want to provide some prepared epidermis or prepared slides.

- You may want to compile a class data table on the board.

- (More to Explore) Students could make two wet-mount slides of the epidermis of a leaf, one with plain water and the other with a few drops of salt solution. Students compare the two slides by counting how many stomata are open and how many are closed.

Name _____ Date _____ Class _____

Investigating Stomata

Pre-Lab Discussion

For an organism to live and grow naturally in any place, it must be adapted to the conditions of that place. A land plant, for example, must have adaptations that prevent it from drying out. A thick, waxy layer of tissue, called the cuticle, is one adaptation that prevents water loss. However, the cuticle also prevents exchange of oxygen and carbon dioxide with the environment. Photosynthesis cannot take place without this exchange of gases. Small openings, called stomata (singular *stoma*), allow gases to move into and out of the plant. Each stoma is surrounded by two guard cells that control the size of the opening. When these guard cells absorb water, the stoma opens; when the guard cells lose water, the stoma closes.

In this investigation, you will observe stomata in a land plant and in a floating water plant.

1. Why is photosynthesis important for plants?

_____

_____

_____

2. What adaptations make it possible for plants to live on land?

_____

_____

_____

Problem

How do the number and position of stomata differ in plants from different environments?

Materials (*per group*)

leaf from a land plant

leaf from a floating water plant

scissors

microscope

2 slides

dropper

2 coverslips

Name _____ Date _____ Class _____

Introduction to Plants · *Laboratory Investigation*

Safety   *Review the safety guidelines in Appendix A of your textbook.*

Use caution in handling sharp scissors. Handle glass slides carefully. Do not let the microscope lens touch the slide.

Procedure

1. Predict where stomata are on the leaf of a land plant. Give a reason for your prediction.

   _____

   _____

2. Select a land plant. With the lower epidermis (underside of the leaf) facing upward, bend and then tear the leaf at an angle as illustrated below. This will reveal part of the thin, colorless, lower epidermis.

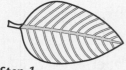

Step 1

Step 2

Step 3

3. With the scissors, cut off a strip of the colorless tissue and make a wet-mount slide. Place the slide on the microscope stage and focus under low power. Locate the stomata. Switch to high power. Draw the stomata, the guard cells, and a few of the lower epidermis cells in Observations. Count the stomata seen in the field of vision under high power. Record your data in the Data Table. (Identify and record the name of your lab group in the first column of the Data Table. Record data only in the row for your group.)

4. Repeat Step 3, using the upper epidermis of the same leaf. Draw your observations. Count the stomata seen in the field of vision under high power and record your data.

5. Predict where stomata are on the leaf of a floating water plant. Give a reason for your prediction.

   _____

   _____

6. Repeat Step 3, using the lower epidermis of a leaf from a water plant. Draw what you see in Observations. Count the stomata in the field of vision and record this number in the Data Table.

7. Repeat Step 3, using the upper epidermis of a leaf from the water plant. Draw your observations and record your data.

8. Exchange and record data from other groups to complete your Data Table.

Name _____ Date _____ Class _____

Investigating Stomata *(continued)*

Observations

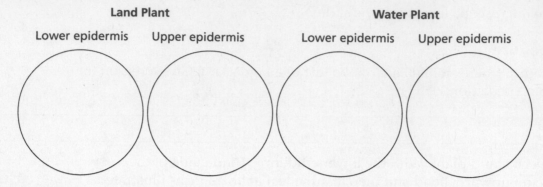

Data Table

| Group | Land Plant: _____ | | Floating Water Plant: _____ | |
	Lower Epidermis	Upper Epidermis	Lower Epidermis	Upper Epidermis

Analyze and Conclude

1. Is the class information more reliable than the information gathered by one group? Give a reason for your answer.

   _____

2. Using data from the entire class, compare the number of stomata in the upper and lower epidermis of land plants.

   _____

3. Using data from the entire class, compare the number of stomata in the upper and lower epidermis of water plants.

   _____

Introduction to Plants · *Laboratory Investigation*

Critical Thinking and Applications

1. What advantage could the number of stomata and their location provide for land plants?

   _____

   _____

   _____

2. What advantage could the number of stomata and their location provide for floating water plants?

   _____

   _____

3. When do you think stomata are usually open—during the day or at night? Give a reason for your answer.

   _____

   _____

4. How could you change the procedure you followed to improve the accuracy of the data?

   _____

   _____

More to Explore

New Problem Are stomata affected by a salt solution?

Possible Materials Consider which materials you can use from the previous part of the lab. What other materials might you need?

Procedure Develop a procedure to solve the problem. Keep in mind that in osmosis, water moves from an area where it is concentrated to an area where it is less concentrated. Write your procedure on a separate sheet of paper. Have the teacher approve your procedure before you carry out the investigation.

Observations Keep records of your observations on a separate sheet of paper.

Analyze and Conclude Were more stomata open or closed in the salt solution? What might explain your results?

_____

_____

_____

Sporophyte Versus Gametophyte

Students are presented with the problem of making a model of the gametophyte of a moss and the sporophyte of a fern using the available materials. To solve this problem, students must apply the concepts they have learned about the structures of mosses and ferns.

Expected Outcome

Students' models of the gametophyte of a moss should show its stemlike structure, leaflike structures, and rhizoids. One way in which this could be modeled is by attaching "leaves" made of crepe paper or construction paper to a pipe cleaner or straw. A student could make a small hole in a piece of cardboard to mount the model upright and to indicate the soil surface. Then pieces of string could be attached to the bottom of the cardboard to represent rhizoids. Students' models of the sporophyte of a fern should show its fronds, underground stems, and roots. For example, a student might model the fronds with pipe cleaners and construction paper cut into a frondlike pattern. The underground stems of a fern could be modeled by sticking the stalks of the fronds through holes in a piece of cardboard and then into small slits cut into a straw. Pieces of string could be attached to the straw to indicate roots. Creative students might use tiny balls of clay attached to the bottom of the fronds to represent spores or a coiled pipe cleaner to represent a fiddlehead.

Content Assessed

The Performance Assessment tests students' understanding of the two-generation life cycle of plants and the structures of mosses and ferns.

Skills Assessed

making models, applying concepts

Materials

- Provide students with a variety of materials for constructing models, such as string, modeling clay, straws, colored pens and pencils, crepe paper, construction paper, scissors, glue, pipe cleaners, and pieces of cardboard.

Advance Preparation

- You may want to have pictures of ferns and mosses for students to look at.

- Consider placing the materials at two or three central locations where all students will have access to them rather than distributing each material to each student.

- Students may have made detailed drawings of a moss and a fern in earlier activities in this chapter. If so, consider allowing students to reference their drawings when making their models.

Time

40 minutes

Monitoring the Task

- Remind students to label each of the structures that they model.

- You may want to have students present their models to the class.

Sporophyte Versus Gametophyte

In assessing students' performance, use the following rubric.

	4	3	2	1
Making Models	Student's model of the gametophyte of a moss clearly shows its stemlike structure, leaflike structures, and rhizoids. Student's model of the sporophyte of a fern clearly shows its fronds, underground stems, and roots. Student shows extra creativity by modeling spores or a fiddlehead of the fern. Each plant and all of its structures are labeled.	Student's model of the gametophyte of a moss shows its stemlike structure, leaflike structures, and rhizoids. Student's model of the sporophyte of a fern shows its fronds, underground stems, and roots. Each plant and most of its structures are labeled.	Student's model of the gametophyte of a moss shows only some structures. Student's model of the sporophyte of a fern shows only its fronds and roots. Each plant and some of its structures are labeled.	Student's model of the gametophyte of a moss shows only some structures. Student's model of the sporophyte of a fern shows only its fronds. Neither plant nor their structures are properly labeled.
Concept Understanding	Student demonstrates a mastery of the structures of ferns and mosses.	Student demonstrates an adequate understanding of the structures of ferns and mosses.	Student demonstrates a partial understanding of the structures of ferns and mosses.	Student demonstrates a minimal understanding of the structures of ferns and mosses.

Introduction to Plants

Introduction to Plants · *Performance Assessment*

Sporophyte Versus Gametophyte

Problem

How can you model the sporophyte of a fern and the gametophyte of moss?

Suggested Materials

string

modeling clay

straws

colored pens and pencils

crepe paper

construction paper

scissors

glue

pipe cleaners

cardboard

Devise a Plan

1. Think about the different structures that make up a fern and a moss. Study the materials and think of a way you could use them to model the sporophyte of a fern and the gametophyte of a moss.

2. Use the materials to make your models. Try to show as many structures of these plants as you can, including the underground structures.

3. On each of your models, neatly label the type of plant and its structures.

Analyze and Conclude

After you have finished your models, answer the following questions on a separate sheet of paper.

1. How did you model the sporophyte of a fern? The gametophyte of a moss?

2. Compare and contrast your model of a fern with your model of a moss.

3. What characteristics of ferns and mosses were you not able to show in your models?

4. Do mosses have sporophytes? Do ferns have gametophytes? Explain.

Name _____ Date _____ Class _____

Introduction to Plants

Multiple Choice
Write the letter of the correct answer on the line at the left.

_____ 1. For plants to survive on land, they need all of the following EXCEPT
    a. ways to retain water.   **b.** ways to live in a moist environment.
    c. ways to transport food.   **d.** ways to support their bodies.

_____ 2. A zygote is
    a. a fertilized egg.   **b.** a sperm cell.
    c. a gamete.   **d.** a sporophyte.

_____ 3. Accessory pigments reflect colors that chlorophyll does not, such as
    a. black.   **b.** green.
    c. white.   **d.** yellow.

_____ 4. One of the products of photosynthesis is
    a. carbon dioxide.   **b.** water.
    c. oxygen.   **d.** light energy.

_____ 5. The function of a rhizoid is to
    a. store food, water, and waste.   **b.** absorb water and nutrients from the soil.
    c. fertilize the egg.   **d.** absorb light energy.

_____ 6. Which of the following is a vascular plant?
    a. liverwort   **b.** hornwort
    c. fern   **d.** sphagnum moss

_____ 7. Hornworts live on
    a. moist soil.   **b.** the bark of trees.
    c. moist rocks.   **d.** the root systems of grass plants.

_____ 8. Ferns can be classified as _____ plants.
    a. seedless vascular   **b.** seedless nonvascular
    c. rhizoid nonvascular   **d.** rhizoid vacuole

_____ 9. The coiled, developing leaves of a fern are called
    a. coils.   **b.** fronds.
    c. spores.   **d.** fiddleheads.

_____ 10. In the sporophyte stage, plants produce
    a. sperm cells.   **b.** spores.
    c. energy.   **d.** food.

Name _____ Date _____ Class _____

Introduction to Plants · *Chapter Test*

Completion

Fill in the line to complete each statement.

11. A waxy, waterproof layer called a(n) _____ covers the leaves of most plants.

12. Some plants have an internal system of tubelike structures through which water and food move. This tissue is called _____.

13. Plants use light energy to make food in a process called _____.

14. Sphagnum moss grows in a wetland with still, acidic water called a(n) _____.

15. The leaves of a fern are called _____.

True or False

If the statement is true, write true. *If it is false, change the underlined word or words to make the statement true.*

_____ 16. A fern is an <u>autotroph</u>.

_____ 17. White light is made up of the colors red, orange, yellow, green, blue, and <u>black</u>.

_____ 18. Plant leaves appear green because chlorophyll <u>absorbs</u> green light.

_____ 19. <u>Vascular plants</u> do not have roots for absorbing water from the ground.

_____ 20. Ferns need to release their spores into <u>dry</u> environments in order for reproduction to occur.

Name _____ Date _____ Class _____

Introduction to Plants ▪ *Chapter Test*

Using Science Skills

Use the diagram below to answer the following questions in the spaces provided.

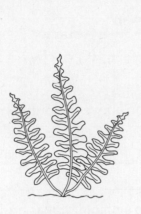

Figure 1   **Figure 2**

21. **Classifying** Is the plant in Figure 1 vascular or nonvascular? How can you tell?

    _____

    _____

22. **Applying Concepts** The plant in Figure 2 lives in a moist environment. Why is this type of environment important to the reproduction of this plant?

    _____

    _____

23. **Comparing and Contrasting** How are the plants in the illustrations above alike? How are they different?

    _____

    _____

Essay

Answer each of the following questions in the spaces provided.

24. Describe the two different stages of a plant's life cycle.

    _____

    _____

25. Explain what plants need to make and store food.

    _____

    _____

    _____

    _____

Introduction to Plants ▪ *Chapter Test*

Using Science Skills

Use the equation below to answer the following questions in the spaces provided.

$$\text{carbon dioxide} + \text{water} \xrightarrow{\text{light energy}} \text{sugar} + \text{oxygen}$$
$$(CO_2) \quad\quad + (H_2O) \quad\quad\quad\quad\quad (C_6H_{12}O_6) + \quad (O_2)$$

26. Interpreting Diagrams Express the equation above in your own words.

_____

_____

_____

27. Applying Concepts What would happen to a plant if it was moved into an environment where carbon dioxide was not present? Into an environment where water was not present? Explain.

_____

_____

_____

Essay

Answer the following question in the space provided.

28. On the lower surface of mature fronds, many ferns have structures that contain spores. What advantage for the fern might there be for the structures to be located there?

_____

_____

Chapter Project Worksheet 1

1.–9. Answers will vary

Chapter Project Worksheet 2

1.–9. Answers will vary

The Plant Kingdom
Guided Reading and Study

Use Target Reading Skills
Students' definitions will vary. Check to see that definitions are appropriate or call on volunteers to share their definitions.

1. b, d
2. true
3. cell wall
4. cellulose
5. **a.** cell wall, **b.** nucleus, **c.** cytoplasm, **d.** cell membrane, **e.** vacuole, **f.** chloroplast
6. false
7. tissue
8. **a.** Have ways to obtain water and other nutrients, **b.** Retain water, **c.** Transport materials within their bodies, **d.** Support their bodies, **e.** Reproduce
9. soil
10. Because there is more water in plant cells than in the air, water from the plant evaporates into the air, causing the plant to dry out.
11. c
12. vascular tissue
13. true
14. A sperm cell unites with an egg cell.
15. d
16. They study fossils and compare the chemicals in modern plants to those in other organisms.
17. chlorophyll
18. Plants and green algae have the same form of chlorophyll.
19. sporophyte, gametophyte
20. false
21. **a.** sperm cells, **b.** egg cells

The Plant Kingdom
Review and Reinforce

1. Nearly all plants produce their own food; all are made up of many cells.
2. They need to get water and other materials from their surroundings, retain water, transport materials within their bodies, support their bodies, and reproduce.
3. tissue
4. vascular tissue

5. gametophyte
6. chloroplast
7. photosynthesis
8. nonvascular plant
9. fertilization
10. cuticle
11. vacuole
12. chlorophyll
13. sporophyte
14. vascular plants
15. zygote

The Plant Kingdom
Enrich

1. The plant comes out of dormancy after a rain shower.
2. It loses its leaves and flowers to help conserve water.
3. Because the plant grows leaves and flowers after a rain shower, it probably absorbs a large amount of rainwater. This suggests that the plant has shallow horizontal roots.
4. It could absorb large amounts of water after a rain with its roots near the surface and could get water from deep in the earth during dry periods with its vertical roots.
5. Because desert plants must survive with very little water, they need to reduce water loss as much as possible and they are more likely to have thick cuticles.

Photosynthesis and Light
Guided Reading and Study

Use Target Reading Skills
Possible questions and answers include: **How is sunlight involved in photosynthesis?** (*The energy in sunlight is used to make sugar.*)
Why does a plant need sugar? (*The plant uses energy from the sugar to carry out life functions.*)
How does the plant use the water its roots take in? (*Water molecules combine with carbon dioxide to form sugar and oxygen during photosynthesis.*)

1. a, c
2. visible spectrum
3. reflects
4. a
5. pigments
6. b, d
7. c, d
8. The light energy that is absorbed by plants powers the process of photosynthesis.
9. Plants need carbon dioxide gas and water.

10.

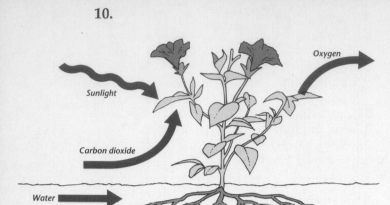

Sunlight

Oxygen

Carbon dioxide

Water

11. carbon dioxide (CO_2) + water (H_2O) →
sugar ($C_6H_{12}O_6$) + oxygen (O_2)
12. It is stored in the roots, stems, leaves, or
fruits.

Photosynthesis and Light
Review and Reinforce

1. true
2. true
3. true
4. true
5. reflects
6. photosynthesis
7. light energy
8. sugar and oxygen

Photosynthesis and Light
Enrich

1. The peaks of the absorption spectrum indicate the colors of light that are most absorbed by
chlorophyll. The low portions indicate the colors that are the least absorbed, or reflected, by
chlorophyll.
2. The peaks represent the colors of light that
result in the greatest rates of photosynthesis.
The low points represent the colors of light that
result in the lowest rates of photosynthesis.
3. Yes, the rate of photosynthesis appears to be
related to the absorption of light by chlorophyll.
This can be inferred by comparing the absorption spectrum of chlorophyll with the action
spectrum of photosynthesis, which have similar
peaks and low points.
4. It would grow very slowly because it would
have a low rate of photosynthesis.
5. White light contains both red and blue light
so the rate of photosynthesis will be high,
probably higher than either red light or blue
light alone.

Eye on Photosynthesis
Design Your Own Lab

For answers, see the Teacher's Edition.

Mosses, Liverworts, and Hornworts
Guided Reading and Study

Use Target Reading Skills
Details include: Mosses, liverworts, and
hornworts
1. a. Low-growing, b. Live in moist environments
2. false
3. They get water directly from their
surroundings.
4. true
5. Sporophyte and Gametophyte should be
labeled and circled.
6. rhizoids
7. The sporophyte generation grows out of the
gametophyte. It has a slender stalk with a capsule at the end. The capsule contains spores.
8. b, c
9. true
10. Liverworts are often found growing as a
thick crust on moist rocks or soil along the sides
of streams.
11. false

Mosses, Liverworts, and Hornworts
Review and Reinforce

1. Liverworts
2. no
3. low-growing
4. small
5. places high in moisture
6. moist soil
7. b
8. d
9. b

Mosses, Liverworts, and Hornworts
Enrich

1. The false bottom is at the bottom of the layer
of clear water. The layer of dead moss below it is
not firm. If something dense is dropped into the
bog, it will fall through the false bottom to the
true bottom of the bog.
2. In the dead layer of moss at the bottom of the
bog
3. Their small size and low density compared
to water lets them form floating mats on the surface of the water.

4. The water needs to be still. Larger lakes have waves, and rivers have currents, that would break apart the floating mats of moss.

Masses of Mosses
Skills Lab

For answers, see the Teacher's Edition.

Ferns, Club Mosses, and Horsetails
Guided Reading and Study

Use Target Reading Skills
Possible questions and answers: **What are the characteristics of seedless vascular plants?** *(Seedless vascular plants have vascular tissue; they do not produce seeds; they reproduce by releasing spores.)*
How do ferns reproduce? *(Ferns reproduce by spores that form on the underside of their fronds.)*
How do club mosses differ from true mosses? *(Club mosses have vascular tissue.)*
1. a. Have true vascular tissue, **b.** Use spores to reproduce
2. c, d
3. When the gametophytes produce egg cells and sperm cells, there must be enough water available for the sperm to swim to the eggs.
4. false
5. underground, upward, downward
6. The developing leaves are coiled at first and resemble the top of a violin.
7. a, d
8. fronds
9. The cuticle helps the plant retain water.
10. b, c
11. They are seedless, vascular plants that have true leaves, stems, and roots. They also have a similar life cycle.
12. b, d

Ferns, Club Mosses, and Horsetails
Review and Reinforce

1. spore cases
2. stem
3. frond
4. roots
5. sporophyte
6. gametophyte
7. club mosses and horesetails
8. vascular plants
9. They reproduce by making spores.

Ferns, Club Mosses, and Horsetails
Enrich

1. (1) A sporangia under normal conditions (2) As the cells of the annulus dry out, they begin to pull on the sporangium and the sporangium begins to tear. (3) The sporangium is torn completely open. (4) The annulus snaps back to its original position, throwing the spores.
2. It gives the spores a chance to land in a more favorable environment than their parent fern.
3. Answers may vary. Samples: Spores that are thrown do not have to rely on the wind to travel away from their parent plant. Spores that are thrown have a better chance of being caught by the wind.
4. The spores aren't released until the annulus dries out. Therefore, dry weather precedes the release of spores.

Key Terms

sporophyte
frond
tissue
rhizoid
bog
vacuole
gametophyte
peat
nonvascular
chlorophyll
Hidden Message: Vascular plants are better suited to life on land.

Connecting Concepts

This concept map is only one way to represent the main ideas and relationships in this chapter. Accept other logical answers from students.

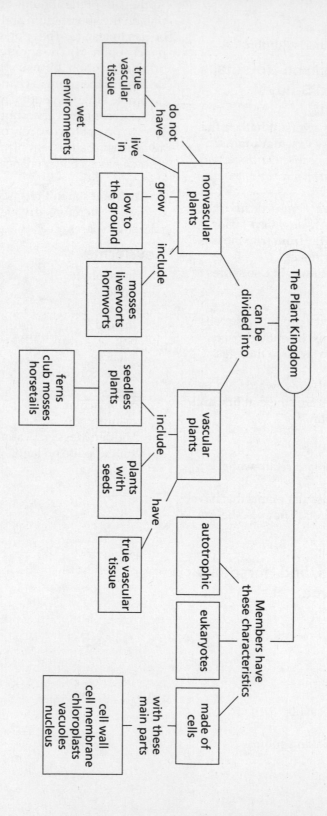

Laboratory Investigation

Investigating Stomata

1. Plants use photosynthesis to make their own food.

2. Plants have to absorb water and other materials from the soil, retain water, transport materials throughout the plant, support their bodies, and reproduce without water for fertilization.

Procedure

1. Predictions will vary. Most of the stomata are usually located on the underside of the leaves to prevent the plant from drying out when the stomata are open. Many plants have stomata on both the upper and lower surfaces of the leaves.

5. Predictions will vary. In floating water plants, stomata are usually located only on the upper side of the leaves because oxygen and carbon dioxide are more accessible there.

Observations

Data Table

Land Plant

Lower Epidermis: Numbers will vary; several stomata should be seen.

Upper Epidermis: Numbers will vary; usually there are few stomata on the upper eidermis.

Floating Water Plant

Lower Epidermis: Numbers will vary; very few, if any, stomata are on the lower surface.

Upper Epidermis: Numbers will vary; several stomata should be visible.

Analyze and Conclude

1. Yes, because more plants were studied.

2. The lower epidermis has more stomata.

3. The upper epidermis has more stomata.

Critical Thinking and Applications

1. The number and location of stomata prevent the plant from drying out in the sun when the stomata are open. The location prevents dirt that settles on the leaf from clogging up stomata.

2. The upper surface has better access to air; on the upper surface, stomata ensure adequate gas exchange.

3. Stomata are open during the day, when photosynthesis takes place in sunlight. At night, they close so that the plants do not lose too much water.

4. The actual area of the microscope field could be calculated to provide the number of stomata for a specific area. Students could also take more data samples.

More to Explore

Analyze and Conclude

More stomata should be closed in the salt solution. The salt solution makes water leave the plant through osmosis. The decrease in water pressure closes the stomata.

Chapter Performance Assessment

Analyze and Conclude

1. Answers will vary. Sample: I modeled the sporophyte of a fern with pipe cleaners and construction paper cut into leaf shapes (fronds). I modeled its spores with tiny balls of clay attached to bottoms of the leaves. I used straws as underground stems and string as roots. I modeled the gametophyte of a moss with a pipe cleaner (stemlike structure) and pieces of construction paper cut into leafy shapes (leaflike structures). I modeled the rhizoids with pieces of string.

2. Answers may vary. Sample: Both have stems or stemlike structures, and both have leaves or leaflike structures. The leaves of the fern are much bigger than the leaflike structures of the moss. The stems of the fern are underground and the stemlike structure of the moss is above ground. The moss has rhizoids and the fern has roots. In making the models, some students may recognize the sporophyte fern produces spores and the gametophyte moss has no spore producing structures.

3. Answers may vary. Sample: Both ferns and mosses are autotrophs that make their own food by the process of photosynthesis. Both are multicellular eukaryotes. The cells of both have cell walls made of cellulose. Mosses do not have true vascular tissue, but ferns do.

4. Answers may vary. Sample: All plants have sporophytes and gametophytes. Usually, we are familiar with only one of the two generations of a particular plant. The sporophyte of a moss is stalklike and remains attached to the gametophyte. The gametophytes of ferns are tiny plants that grow low to the ground.

Chapter Test

1. b
2. a
3. d
4. c
5. b
6. c
7. a
8. a
9. d
10. b
11. cuticle
12. vascular tissue
13. photosynthesis
14. bog
15. fronds
16. true
17. violet
18. reflects
19. Nonvascular plants
20. moist
21. The plant in Figure 1—a fern—is vascular because in order to be able to transport water and minerals from their environment to all parts of a plant that size, it must have an internal transportation system.
22. Figure 2 shows a moss plant, a nonvascular plant. The sperm cells of nonvascular plants need water through which to swim to egg cells for reproduction.
23. The plants are alike in their needs for survival on land. They are also both autotrophs and eukaryotes. However, the moss in Figure 2 is a nonvascular plant, without an internal transportation system to help support it or transport water and minerals throughout the plant. The fern in Figure 1 is a vascular plant that does possess an internal transportation system.
24. In the sporophyte stage, the plant produces spores that can grow into new plants. A spore develops into the plant's other stage, called the gametophyte. In the gametophyte stage, the plant produces the gametes, which are sperm cells and egg cells. They join to form a zygote that develops into a sporophyte. Then the cycle begins again.
25. Plants need light energy, carbon dioxide, and water to make food. To store food, they need a way to transport the food, such as vascular tissue, and a place to store the food, such as stems and roots.
26. Carbon dioxide and water combine in the presence of sunlight to produce sugar and oxygen.
27. The plant would not be able to produce food and eventually would die. Both carbon dioxide and water are necessary for photosynthesis to occur.
28. Answers will vary. Samples: Having the spore-producing structures on a leaf's lower surface leaves the upper surface free to gather light energy. The spores can more easily fall to the ground. The frond might protect the spore-producing structures from rain or other things that might fall on them.

Seed Plants

 **Cycle of a Lifetime**

The following steps will walk you through the Chapter Project. Use the hints as you guide your students through planning, observing the plants, and poster design.

Chapter Project Overview

Before introducing the project, bring a plant into the classroom to show to students. Talk about how the plant developed from a seed. Also, discuss how it makes new seeds to produce new plants.

Have students read the Chapter Project Overview. Review the project's rules and hand out the Chapter Scoring Rubric that you will use for scoring students' work. Discuss with students what is expected of them.

Set a deadline for the project presentation and interim dates for the Keep Students on Track activities at the end of Section 1, Section 3, and Section 5. Encourage students to copy the dates in the Project Timeline.

Distribute copies of Chapter Project Worksheet 1. This worksheet will help students set up their data tables for the project.

Chapter Project Worksheet 2 will help students design their life cycle diagrams. Distribute this worksheet once they have completed seed collection. Also refer students to the cycle diagrams in their textbooks.

Remind students to refer to the hints in the Chapter Project Overview as they plan and carry out the project.

Materials and Preparation

If space and resources are limited, consider organizing the class into groups to do the project. If time is short, you may want to plant the seeds several days prior to the project start date. This way, the seeds will have germinated by the time students are ready to begin the project.

Students will need basic gardening supplies for this project: seeds from fast-growing plants from biological suppliers or from tomatoes, peas, etc., potting trays, potting soil, water, and cotton swabs for transferring pollen. Choose plants that will complete their life cycle in approximately one month.

Provide students with instructions on how to plant their seeds. Students should plant more than one seed and care for more than one plant in this experiment. This will help ensure the success of this project. Make sure students save a few seeds to compare with the seeds they harvest from their plants.

Pollination of the flowers can be achieved in many ways. Commercial kits are available for this purpose. These kits use real bee parts for pollination. If you do not use a kit, pollen can be collected by tapping the flower over a piece of paper. This pollen can then be placed on the stigma with a cotton swab. Cotton swabs can also be used to transfer pollen directly from one flower to another.

Keep Students on Track— Section 1

Check students' plants for germination. If some seeds have not germinated, have students plant new seeds.

Give students time in class each day to care for their plants, and record their observations. Stress that students should use the terms and concepts presented in the chapter when describing their observations and labeling their illustrations.

Review students' data tables. They should have left room for recording such observations as the height of the stems and the number and size of leaves and flowers. They should also make the data table long enough to record their observations each day they are in school for approximately a month.

Make sure that as students measure the growth of their plants, they are also making labeled diagrams, drawings, or photographs that illustrate the different phases of the plant's life cycle.

Keep Students on Track— Section 3

Check students' observation records on a regular basis. Be sure students include details about changes in the appearance, health, and growth of their plants.

Periodically check the health of the plants. Some students may not notice the declining health of their plants. If you think a plant is in poor condition, immediately discuss the situation with the student, and help the student come up with a plan to deal with the situation.

Assist students in pollination. Some students may need more help than others. Make sure students continue to observe the flowers after pollination, recording all changes.

Keep Students on Track—Section 5

Make sure students are still caring for the plants, making labeled illustrations, and recording observations in their data tables.

Check students' data tables for completeness. Also, review their illustrations, making sure they are labeled appropriately.

Assist students in seed collection. Have them compare these seeds to the originals. These comparisons should also be documented by illustrations and observations entered in their data tables. If time permits, students can plant these seeds so that they can observe a second life cycle.

Chapter Project Wrap Up

Assist students in their poster design, making sure they include both pictures and written descriptions of the plant's life cycle.

Discuss the success of the project with students. Encourage students who may have had difficulties growing their plants to discuss their experiences, explaining why they think that their plants did not grow.

Discuss the life cycle of seed plants. Make sure students understand that the cycle will repeat with the new generation of seeds.

Extension

If space and resources are limited, have students work in groups of two or three. If time is limited, or to ensure that all students have a plant to work with, plant the seeds prior to the project start date, so they will have germinated by the time students start the project. Alternatively, provide round-the-clock artificial lighting to speed plant growth.

At the end of the project, take your students to a nature center or greenhouse to learn more about seed plants.

You might relate this project to today's genetic engineering or to basic genetic concepts by leading a discussion about Mendel and his pea plant experiments.

Seed Plants ▪ *Chapter Project*   **Overview**

🔺 Lab zone Chapter **Project** ▶ Cycle of a Lifetime

This project is designed to give you a better understanding of the life cycle of plants that produce seeds. These plants need help with pollination. Wind and insects are two common pollination methods plants use in nature, but in this project you will be the plant's assistant.

   In this project, you will grow a type of plant that goes through its entire life cycle in a short period of time (approximately one month). During this period, you will be studying the plant's growth and recording all observations in a data table. When the flowers have formed and opened, you will need to transfer the pollen from the anther to the stigma. You will then collect the seeds that form. If you have time, your teacher may have you plant some of the seeds you gathered. This will give you the opportunity to observe the life cycle as it starts all over again.

Project Rules

- Care for your plants on a daily basis. Observe and record the daily growth of your plants in a data table.

- Diagram (sketch) the different developments in the plant's life as they happen. Make sure you label all of your drawings, using the terms you have learned in the text.

- You will be responsible for pollinating your plants and also for gathering the seeds that the pollinated plants produce. Make sure you thoroughly understand how to do these steps before attempting them.

- Always treat your plants well. If any plant appears unhealthy, consult with your teacher as soon as you can. You are responsible for the well-being of your plants and should care for them in the best possible way.

- At the end of the project, you will be creating a poster that illustrates what you have observed. This poster must include both diagrams and written descriptions of the plant's life cycle.

Suggested Materials

- You will need basic gardening supplies for this project: potting trays, potting soil, water, seeds, and cotton swabs for transferring pollen.

Seed Plants · *Chapter Project*   **Overview**

Project Hints

- Protect your plant from extreme conditions (heat, cold, too much water, too little water, etc.). Make sure that it receives adequate light.

- If possible, measure your plants at the same time each day. Also, make your measurements on the same part of the plant (for example, measure the same leaf).

- Make your observations and drawings as new developments occur; do not trust your memory. Refer to the text when labeling your drawings.

Project Timeline

Tasks   **Date Due**

1. Plant the seeds.   _____

2. Set up the data tables.   _____

3. Collect the new seeds.   _____

4. Plant the new seeds. (optional)   _____

5. Complete your observations.   _____

6. Present your exhibit to the class.   _____

Name _____ Date _____ Class _____

Making Observations

Answer the following questions on a separate sheet of paper as you begin your project.

1. What type of plant will you be growing? Write a few sentences describing your expectations for the life cycle of this plant.

2. Draw a sketch of the outside of the seeds that your teacher has given to you. Select one seed. Carefully remove its seed covering, and separate it into two halves. Examine the inside of the seed and draw what you see.

3. Plant your seeds according to your teacher's directions. Place your pot(s) in a safe location where your plants will receive ample sunlight and not be disturbed. Once your seeds have germinated, you will be making daily observations of your plants' growth. You will need to set up a data table in which you can record these observations. Use a data table like the one below. Make sure to leave enough space to include descriptions of the plants, how healthy they appear, number and size of leaves, number and size of flowers, and anything else you think is important. Make sure your data table is long enough to include your daily observations for approximately one month.

Date	Time	Observation

Seed Plants · *Chapter Project*   **Worksheet 2**

Cycle Diagrams

By now you should have collected new seeds from your plant and compared them with the seeds you planted at the beginning of this project. The life of the seed plant exists in a cycle. To illustrate a sequence of events that takes place as a cycle, cycle diagrams are used. These diagrams are similar to flowcharts in that they help you to understand the order of events. They differ by showing that a series of events is repeated.

You will be creating a cycle diagram on a separate piece of paper to illustrate the life cycle of your plant. Begin by writing a brief description of your seeds in a box at the top center of the page. Then, moving in a clockwise direction around the piece of paper, write descriptions of plant growth, leaf development, flower development, pollination, and seed production. Form a continuous circle by drawing arrows to connect each event to the one that comes next. The example below should help you think about how to organize a cycle diagram.

Changing Seasons in the Northern Hemisphere

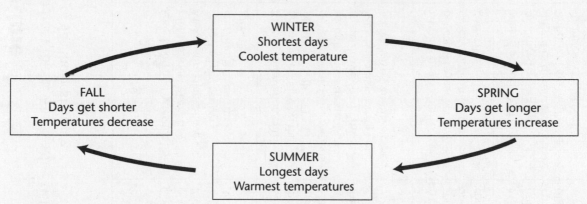

Analyzing and Presenting

Complete the following tasks on a separate sheet of paper. When they have been completed, you are ready to put together your poster.

1. Write several sentences summarizing your research. Did your plants grow and produce seeds as you expected? Give some reasons to explain why or why not.

2. Write several sentences summarizing your observations from the data table.

3. You will need to create a poster that communicates what you have learned to your classmates. Your poster must contain both diagrams and written descriptions of your plant at each stage in its life cycle. You might consider using the life cycle diagram you created. Write a few sentences describing the layout you will use for your poster.

Seed Plants ▪ *Chapter Project*   **Scoring Rubric**

Lab zone Chapter Project

Cycle of a Lifetime

In evaluating how well you complete the Chapter Project, your teacher will judge your work in four categories. In each, a score of 4 is the best rating.

	4	3	2	1
Caring for the Plants	Checks on and cares for the plants daily. Makes sure plants have all the proper conditions to encourage growth.	Checks on and cares for the plants almost every day. Makes sure plants have almost all the proper conditions to encourage growth.	Checks on and cares for the plants on most days. Provides some of the proper conditions to encourage growth.	Occasionally checks on or cares for the plants. Provides few of the proper conditions to encourage growth.
Observing the Plants	Makes complete, daily observation entries on the plants' growth and development. Observations include complete measurements of stems, leaves, and flowers. Makes labeled sketches of seeds, leaves, and flowers.	Makes observation entries almost every day on the plants' growth and development. Observations include measurements of stems, leaves, and flowers. Makes labeled sketches of seeds, leaves, and flowers.	Makes observation entries on most days. Some entries are unorganized or incomplete. Makes incomplete sketches of seeds, leaves, and flowers that are not fully labeled.	Makes only a few observation entries. Most entries are unorganized or incomplete. Makes incomplete sketches of seeds, leaves, and flowers that are not labeled.
Applying Chapter Concepts	Correctly applies many of the chapter concepts to his/her observations.	Applies many chapter concepts to his/her observations, most of them correctly.	Applies some chapter concepts to his/her observations, most of them correctly.	Applies few chapter concepts to his/her observations, most incorrectly.
Presenting the Exhibit	Makes a thorough, well-organized poster that presents a complete description of the plant's life cycle. Poster includes both labeled diagrams and written descriptions.	Makes a good, well-organized poster that describes the life cycle's most important events. Poster includes both labeled diagrams and written descriptions.	Makes a poster that describes only a few life cycle events and includes few labeled diagrams. The poster is not well organized.	Makes an inadequate poster that is unorganized, contains only brief written descriptions of the plant's life cycle, and does not include any labeled diagrams.

The Characteristics of Seed Plants

🕐 *2–3 periods, 1–1 1/2 blocks*

ABILITY LEVELS KEY
L1 Basic to Average
L2 For All Students
L3 Average to Advanced

Objectives

A.5.1.1 Identify the two characteristics that seed plants share.

A.5.1.2 Explain how seeds become new plants.

A.5.1.3 Describe the functions of roots, stems, and leaves.

Local Standards

Key Terms
• phloem • xylem • pollen • seed • embryo
• cotyledon • germination • root cap
• cambium • stomata • transpiration

PRETEACH

Build Background Knowledge
Ask students to generate a list of plants they see often and identify which have seeds and which do not.

 **Discover Activity** *Which Plant Part Is It?* **L1**

Targeted Resources

☐ **All in One Teaching Resources**
L2 Reading Strategy Transparency A37: Outlining

☐ ◉ **PresentationExpress™ CD-ROM**

INSTRUCT

What Is a Seed Plant? Discuss that all seed plants have vascular tissue and produce pollen and seeds.
How Seeds Become New Plants Ask questions and use an illustration to discuss the structure of seeds and how they germinate.
Roots Identify the functions, types, and structures of roots.
Stems Use illustrations to describe the functions of stems.
Leaves Use a cross-section of a leaf to examine its functions.

Targeted Resources

☐ **All in One Teaching Resources**
L2 Guided Reading, pp. 281–285
L2 Transparencies A38, A39, A40, A41, A42

☐ **PHSchool.com** Web Code: ced-1051

☐ **Discovery SCHOOL Video Field Trip**

☐ ◉ **Student Edition on Audio CD**

ASSESS

Section Assessment Questions
🔄 Have students use their outlines to help them answer the questions.
Reteach
Use the section figures to summarize the functions of roots, stems, and leaves.

Targeted Resources

☐ **All in One Teaching Resources**
Section Summary, p. 280
L1 Review and Reinforce, p. 286
L3 Enrich, p. 287

Seed Plants • *Section Summary*

The Characteristics of Seed Plants

Key Concepts

- What characteristics do seed plants share?
- How do seeds become new plants?
- What are the main functions of roots, stems, and leaves?

Seed plants share two important characteristics. They have vascular tissue, and they use pollen and seeds to reproduce. They all have body plans that include leaves, stems, and roots.

Water, food, and minerals are transported throughout plants in vascular tissue. There are two types of vascular tissue. **Phloem** is the vascular tissue through which food moves. When food is made in the plant's leaves, it enters the phloem and travels to other parts of the plant. Water and minerals travel in the vascular tissue called **xylem.** The plant's roots absorb water and minerals from the soil. These materials enter the root's xylem and move upward into the stems and leaves.

Seed plants can live in a variety of environments. They produce **pollen,** tiny structures that contain the cells that later become sperm cells. Pollen delivers sperm cells directly near the eggs, therefore seed plants do not need water for fertilization to occur. **Seeds** are structures that contain a young plant inside a protective covering. **Inside a seed is a partially developed plant. If a seed lands in an area where conditions are favorable, it sprouts out of the seed and begins to grow.** A seed has three main parts—an embryo, stored food, and a seed coat.

The young plant that develops from the zygote, or fertilized egg, is called the **embryo** and has the beginnings of roots, stems, and leaves. The embryo also has one or two seed leaves, or **cotyledons.** In some seeds, the cotyledons store food. The outer covering of a seed is called the seed coat. A seed may remain inactive for awhile. **Germination** occurs when the embryo begins to grow again and pushes out of the seed.

Roots anchor a plant in the ground, absorb water and minerals from the soil, and sometimes store food. The tip of the root is covered by a **root cap**. The root cap protects the root from injury from rocks as the root grows through the soil.

The stem carries substances between the plant's roots and leaves. The stem also provides support for the plant and holds up the leaves so they are exposed to the sun. Stems can be herbaceous or woody. In woody stems, a layer of cells called the **cambium** divide to produce new phloem and xylem.

Leaves capture the sun's energy and carry out the food-making process of photosynthesis. The surfaces of the leaf have small openings, or pores, called **stomata.** These open and close to control when gases enter and leave the leaf. The process by which water evaporates from the stomata in a plant's leaves is called **transpiration.**

The Characteristics of Seed Plants (pp. 136–145)

This section tells about the characteristics of seed plants. It also describes the parts of a seed and the functions of leaves, stems, and roots.

Seed Plants

Use Target Reading Skills

As you read, make an outline about seed plants that you can use for review. Use the red headings for the main topics and blue headings for the supporting ideas.

The Characteristics of Seed Plants
I. What is a Seed Plant?
A. Vascular Tissue
B.
II. How Seeds Become New Plants
A.
B.
C.

What Is a Seed Plant? (pp. 136–137)

1. Circle the letter of each sentence that is true about seed plants.

   a. Seedless plants outnumber seed plants.
   b. Seed plants do not have vascular tissue.
   c. Seed plants use seeds to reproduce.
   d. All seed plants have roots, leaves, and stems.

2. In seed plants, the plants that you see are in the _____ stage of the life cycle. The _____ stage is microscopic.

3. In what two ways does vascular tissue help seed plants to live on land?

   a. _____

   b. _____

4. Circle the letter of the vascular tissue through which food moves.

   a. xylem
   b. phloem
   c. roots
   d. stems

Seed Plants · *Guided Reading and Study*

The Characteristics of Seed Plants *(continued)*

5. Circle the letter of the vascular tissue through which water moves.

   a. xylem
   b. phloem
   c. roots
   d. stems

6. Food made in the plant's _____ travels to the roots and stems.

7. Water and nutrients absorbed by the plant's _____ travel to the stems and leaves.

8. What is a seed?

   _____

   _____

9. Is the following sentence true or false? Pollen delivers sperm cells directly near the eggs. _____

How Seeds Become New Plants (pp. 138–140)

Match the part of the seed with its function.

Seed Part	Function
____ **10.** embryo	**a.** Keeps the seed from drying out
____ **11.** cotyledon	**b.** Young plant that develops from the fertilized egg
____ **12.** seed coat	**c.** A seed leaf that sometimes stores food

13. What do seeds need to develop into a new plant?

   _____

   _____

14. Is the following sentence true or false? Seeds can begin to grow in any place they land. _____

Name _____ Date _____ Class _____

Seed Plants • *Guided Reading and Study*

15. Complete the concept map to show ways that seeds are dispersed.

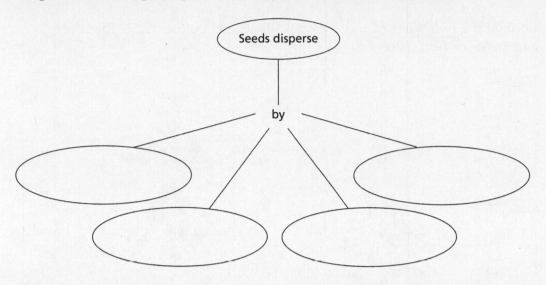

16. What is germination?

_____

_____

17. Circle the letter before each sentence that is true about germination.

    a. All seeds germinate immediately after they are dispersed.

    b. The embryo uses its stored food to begin to grow.

    c. First, the embryo's leaves and stem grow upward.

    d. Seeds that are dispersed far away from the parent have a better chance of survival.

Roots (pp. 140–142)

18. List three functions of roots.

    a. _____

    b. _____

    c. _____

Seed Plants • *Guided Reading and Study*

The Characteristics of Seed Plants *(continued)*

19. Look at the two types of root systems illustrated below. Label the roots as taproot or fibrous roots.

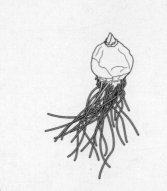 

a. _____   b. _____

Match the root structure with its function.

Root Structure	Function
____ **20.** root cap	**a.** Moves food to the roots and other parts of plant
____ **21.** root hairs	**b.** Protects the root from injury during growth
____ **22.** phloem	**c.** Moves water and minerals to the stems and leaves
____ **23.** xylem	**d.** Increase the amount of water and minerals absorbed by the root

24. Circle the letter of the cell layer that produces new phloem and xylem.
    a. heartwood
    b. sapwood
    c. bark
    d. cambium

Stems (pp. 142–143)

25. List three functions of stems.

    a. _____

    b. _____

    c. _____

Seed Plants · *Guided Reading and Study*

26. Is the following sentence true or false? Herbaceous stems are hard and rigid and have an outer layer called bark. _____

27. What is heartwood?

_____

_____

28. Circle the letter before the tissue that makes up a tree's annual rings.

    a. xylem   **b.** phloem

    c. cambium   **d.** bark

29. Is the following sentence true or false? One year's growth of a tree is represented by one pair of light and dark rings in the tree's stem. _____

Leaves (pp. 144–145)

30. What role do leaves play in a plant?

_____

_____

_____

Match the leaf part with its function.

Leaf Part		Function
____ **31.** cuticle	**a.**	Widely spaced cells allow carbon dioxide and oxygen to pass in and out of the leaf.
____ **32.** xylem		
____ **33.** phloem	**b.**	Carries water from the roots to the leaves
____ **34.** stomata	**c.**	Waxy, waterproof coating that covers a leaf's surface
____ **35.** lower leaf cells	**d.**	Contain the most chloroplasts
____ **36.** upper leaf cells	**e.**	Carries food made in the leaves to the rest of the plant
	f.	Tiny pores that open and close to let carbon dioxide in and water vapor and oxygen out

37. Is the following sentence true or false? The tightly packed cells of the upper leaf enable the leaf to trap the energy in sunlight. _____

38. The process by which water evaporates from a plant's leaves is called

_____.

39. Is the following sentence true or false? Stomata close to keep the plant from losing water. _____

Seed Plants • *Review and Reinforce*

The Characteristics of Seed Plants

Understanding Main Ideas

Answer the following questions in the space provided.

1. What characteristics do seed plants share?

_____

_____

_____

_____

2. What are three main parts of a seed?

_____

_____

_____

Building Vocabulary

Fill in the spaces in the table below.

Part of Plant	Function
leaf	**3.** _____
cambium	**4.** _____
5. _____	anchors plants and absorbs water and minerals
seed	**6.** _____
7. _____	the vascular tissue through which water and minerals travel
8. _____	the vascular tissue through which food moves
root cap	**9.** _____
10. _____	small openings or pores on the surface of leaves
stem	**11.** _____
cotyledon	**12.** _____

Seed Plants · *Enrich*

Bubbling Leaves

Carbon dioxide enters leaves through stomata. Oxygen, produced during photosynthesis, passes out of leaves through stomata. April designed an experiment to find out more about these tiny pores on a leaf. She picked a few fresh leaves from the trees near her house. Then, while pinching the stalk of one of the leaves, she dipped the leaf in a glass of hot water. After observing what happened, she did the same thing with the rest of the leaves, one at a time. The diagram below shows what April saw when she dipped two different leaves into the glass of hot water.

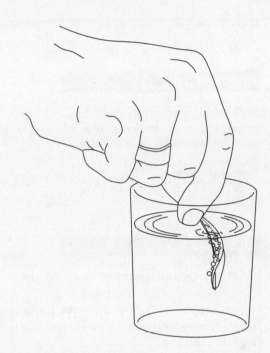

Answer the following questions on a separate sheet of paper.

1. What did April observe coming out of the stomata of each leaf?

2. In the figure, bubbles are coming out of both sides of one leaf, while bubbles are coming out of only one side of the other leaf. What does this tell you about the location of the stomata on these two leaves?

3. What do you think would happen if April did not pinch the stalk of the leaf before dipping it into the hot water?

4. In most plants, most of the stomata are located on the lower surface of the leaves. Explain how this adaptation helps control water loss.

5. Would you expect to find the stomata on a lily pad on the top or on the bottom? Explain your answer.

Gymnosperms

🕐 *2–3 periods, 1 1/2–2 blocks*

Objectives

A.5.2.1 Identify the characteristics of gymnosperms.
A.5.2.2 Describe how gymosperms reproduce.
A.5.2.3 Describe important products from gymnosperms.

Local Standards

Key Terms

• gymnosperm • cone • ovule • pollination

PRETEACH

Build Background Knowledge
Prompt students to name trees that stay green all year and describe their features.

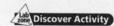 **Discover Activity** *Are All Leaves Alike?* **L1**

Targeted Resources

❑ **All in One Teaching Resources**
L2 Reading Strategy Transparency A43: Previewing Visuals

❑ 💿 **PresentationExpress™ CD-ROM**

INSTRUCT

What Are Gymnosperms? Analyze the characteristics of gymnosperms.
Reproduction in Gymnosperms Use a cycle diagram to identify the steps in reproduction of gymnosperms.
Gymnosperms in Everyday Life Identify useful products that come from conifers.

Targeted Resources

❑ **All in One Teaching Resources**
L2 Guided Reading, pp. 290–292
L2 Transparency A44

❑ **PHSchool.com** Web Code: scn-0152

❑ 💿 **Student Edition on Audio CD**

ASSESS

Section Assessment Questions
🔄 Have students use their preview questions and answers to help them answer the questions.
Reteach
Have students fill in blanked out labels of the diagram showing reproduction of gymnosperms, then discuss as a class.

Targeted Resources

❑ **All in One Teaching Resources**
Section Summary, p. 289
L1 Review and Reinforce, p. 293
L3 Enrich, p. 294

Seed Plants · *Section Summary*

Gymnosperms

Key Concepts

- What are the characteristics of gymnosperms?
- How do gymnosperms reproduce?
- What important products come from gymnosperms?

A **gymnosperm** is a seed plant that produces naked seeds—seeds that are not enclosed by a protective fruit. **Every gymnosperm produces naked seeds. In addition, many gymnosperms have needle-like or scalelike leaves and deep-growing root systems.** Most gymnosperms are trees, although a few are shrubs and vines. Gymnosperms are classified into four groups—the cycads, the conifers, the ginkgoes, and the gnetophytes. The conifers are the largest group of gymnosperms on Earth today.

Most gymnosperms have reproductive structures called **cones**. Most gymnosperms produce two types of cones: male cones and female cones. Male cones produce pollen. Female cones contain at least one ovule at the base of each scale. An **ovule** is a structure that contains an egg cell. After being fertilized, the ovule develops into a seed.

To reproduce, **first, pollen falls from a male cone onto a female cone. In time, a sperm cell and an egg cell join together in an ovule on the female cone.** The transfer of pollen from a male reproductive structure to a female reproductive structure is called **pollination.**

Many useful products come from conifers. **Paper and other products, such as the lumber used to build homes, come from conifers.** Conifers are also used to make the rayon fibers in clothes, cellophane food wrappers, and turpentine.

Conifers are grown in large, managed forests. When adult trees in managed forests are cut down, young trees are planted to replace them. This practice helps ensure a steady supply of these important trees.

Seed Plants • *Guided Reading and Study*

Gymnosperms (pp. 146–150)

This section gives examples of the group of seed plants known as gymnosperms and describes their features and how they reproduce.

Use Target Reading Skills

Before you read, preview the figure, The Life Cycle of a Gymnosperm, in the textbook. Then write two questions that you have about the diagram in the graphic organizer below. As you read, answer your questions.

The Life Cycle of a Gymnosperm
Q. How does gymnosperm pollination occur?
A.
Q.
A.

What Are Gymnosperms? (pp. 146–147)

1. What is a gymnosperm?

   _____

   _____

2. Is the following sentence true or false? Gymnosperms have seeds that are not enclosed by a fruit. _____

Seed Plants ▪ *Guided Reading and Study*

3. Is the following sentence true or false? Gymnosperms are the oldest type of seed plant. _____

Match the gymnosperms with their features. Some gymnosperms may be used more than once.

Features

_____ 4. Only one species exists today.

_____ 5. They are the largest group of gymnosperms.

_____ 6. These plants live in hot deserts and in tropical rain forests.

_____ 7. They grow in tropical and subtropical areas.

_____ 8. Most keep their needles year round.

_____ 9. These plants look like palm trees with giant cones.

_____ 10. Often planted along city streets because they tolerate air pollution.

Gymnosperms

a. cycads

b. ginkgoes

c. gnetophytes

d. conifers

Reproduction in Gymnosperms (pp. 148–149)

11. Most gymnosperms have reproductive structures called

_____.

12. Is the following sentence true or false? Male cones contain ovules at the base of each scale. _____

13. _____ groups of gymnosperms exist today.

14. A structure that contains an egg cell is a(n) _____.

15. What happens during pollination?

_____

_____

Seed Plants ▪ *Guided Reading and Study*

Gymnosperms *(continued)*

16. Is the following sentence true or false? In gymnosperms, wind often carries the pollen from the male cones to the female cones.

_____

17. Complete the cycle diagram showing the steps in the reproduction of gymnosperms.

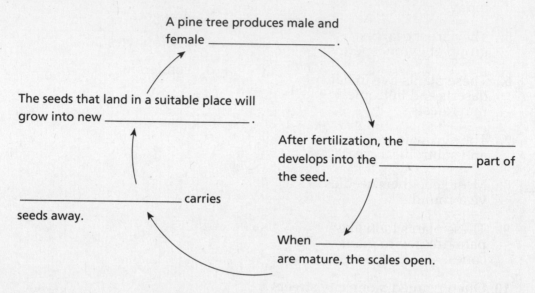

A pine tree produces male and female _____.

The seeds that land in a suitable place will grow into new _____.

After fertilization, the _____ develops into the _____ part of the seed.

_____ carries seeds away.

When _____ are mature, the scales open.

Gymnosperms in Everyday Life (p. 150)

18. Circle the letter of each product that conifers provide.
   a. fruit
   b. paper
   c. turpentine
   d. cotton fibers

19. Is the following sentence true or false? When adult trees in managed forests are cut down, no trees are planted to replace them.

_____

Name _____ Date _____ Class _____

Seed Plants · *Review and Reinforce*

Gymnosperms

Understanding Main Ideas

Study the diagram and read the following statements. Fill in the blank to complete each statement.

1. All gymnosperms produce naked seeds. Many have _____ or scalelike leaves, and deep root systems.

2. Cycads, ginkgoes, gnetophytes, and conifers are all gymnosperms. The plant shown is a _____.

3. The _____ shown on the plant are the reproductive structures.

4. The tree shown produces _____ in male cones.

5. The tree shown produces _____ in female cones.

Building Vocabulary

Answer the following question in the space provided.

pollen   ovule   pollination

6. Briefly describe reproduction in gymnosperms. Be sure to include the above terms in your description.

_____

_____

_____

_____

_____

Seed Plants • *Enrich*

From a Plant to Paper

The first known paper was made from the stems of a grasslike plant called *papyrus*. This plant was used because the stems contained long, strong fibers. The papyrus fibers were layered, pressed, and dried, forming sheets of paper.

Today, paper is made from many different sources. One of the most widely used sources is the wood of conifers. Conifers have long, strong fibers and produce strong paper.

Follow the diagram below as you read about the papermaking process. First, logs are loaded into a large, spinning drum, where the tumbling action removes the bark. Then, large knives cut the logs into small pieces or chips. The wood chips are beaten with water in a large vat to thoroughly separate the fibers and form a watery mixture called pulp. The pulp is then sent through a series of rollers. The rollers press about half of the water out of the newly-made paper. The paper passes through dryers, where the remaining water is removed. Now the paper is wound up into a giant roll. Then, some of the rolled paper is cut into sheets, and some is shipped on the rolls.

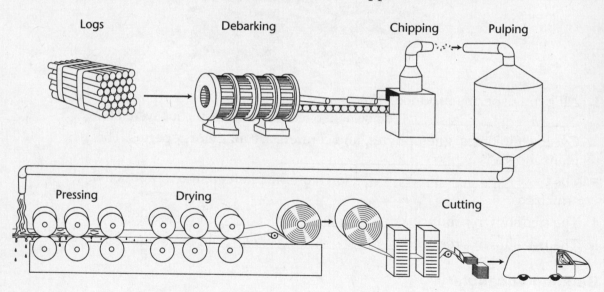

Answer the following questions on a separate sheet of paper.

1. What is a characteristic of a plant that is useful when making paper?
2. Why would you want to thoroughly separate the wood fibers in the pulp?
3. Why is it important to press and dry the newly made paper?
4. Name another fibrous plant you could use to make paper.

Angiosperms

🕐 *2–3 periods, 1 1/2–2 blocks*

Objectives

A.5.3.1 Describe the characteristics shared by angiosperms.
A.5.3.2 State the function of an angiosperm's flowers.
A.5.3.3 Explain how angiosperms reproduce.
A.5.3.4 Tell how monocots differ from dicots.

Local Standards

Key Terms

• angiosperm • flower • sepal • petal
• stamen • pistil • ovary • fruit • monocot
• dicot

PRETEACH

Build Background Knowledge
Invite students to describe flowers with which they are familiar.

 **Discover Activity** *What Is a Fruit?* **L1**

Targeted Resources

❏ **All in One** **Teaching Resources**
   L2 Reading Strategy: Building Vocabulary
❏ 💿 **PresentationExpress™ CD-ROM**

INSTRUCT

The Structure of Flowers Use a diagram to examine the reproductive parts of a flower.
Reproduction in Angiosperms Ask questions to help students understand the steps in reproduction of angiosperms.
Types of Angiosperms Compare and contrast the structures of monocots and dicots.
Angiosperms in Everyday Life Identify commercial uses of angiosperms.

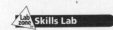 **Skills Lab** *A Close Look at Flowers* **L2**

Targeted Resources

❏ **All in One** **Teaching Resources**
   L2 Guided Reading, pp. 297–299
   L2 Transparencies A45, A46, A47
   L2 Lab: *A Close Look at Flowers*, pp. 302–304
❏ 📼 **Lab Activity Video/DVD**
   Skills Lab: *A Close Look at Flowers*
❏ **PHSchool.com** Web Code: cep-1053
❏ 💿 **Student Edition on Audio CD**

ASSESS

Section Assessment Questions
🕐 Have students use their definitions to answer the questions.
Reteach
Review the life cycle of angiosperms.

Targeted Resources

❏ **All in One** **Teaching Resources**
   Section Summary, p. 296
   L1 Review and Reinforce, p. 300
   L3 Enrich, p. 301

Seed Plants • *Section Summary*

Angiosperms

Key Concepts

- What characteristics do angiosperms share?
- What is the function of an angiosperm's flowers?
- How do angiosperms reproduce?
- How do monocots differ from dicots?

An **angiosperm** is a group of seed plants. **All angiosperms, or flowering plants, share two important characteristics. First, they produce flowers. Second, in contrast to gymnosperms, which produce uncovered seeds, angiosperms produce seeds that are enclosed in fruits.**

Flowers come in all sorts of shapes, sizes, and colors. But, despite their differences, all flowers have the same function—reproduction. A **flower** is the reproductive structure of an angiosperm. A flower bud is enclosed by leaflike structures called **sepals** that protect the developing flower. Most flowers have **petals**—colorful, leaflike structures. Within the petals are the flower's male and female reproductive parts. Thin stalks topped by small knobs inside the flower are **stamens,** the male reproductive parts. The thin stalk is called the filament. Pollen is produced in the knob, or anther, at the top of the stalk. The female parts, or **pistils,** are found in the center of most flowers. The sticky tip of the pistil is called the stigma. A slender tube, called a style, connects the stigma to the ovary, a hollow structure at the base of the flower. The ovary contains one or more ovules. An **ovary** is a flower structure that protects seeds as they develop.

For angiosperms to reproduce, **first, pollen falls on a flower's stigma. In time, the sperm cell and egg cell join together in the flower's ovule. The zygote develops into the embryo part of the seed.** As the seed develops, the ovary changes and eventually becomes a **fruit**—a ripened ovary and other structures that enclose one or more seeds.

Angiosperms are divided into two major groups: monocots and dicots. Monocots are angiosperms that have only one seed leaf. Grasses, including corn, wheat, and rice, and plants such as lilies and tulips, are monocots. **Dicots** produce seeds with two seed leaves. Dicots include plants such as roses, violets, and dandelions.

Angiosperms have many uses. People and many animals depend on various kinds of angiosperms for food. Fibers such as cotton and flax are used to make clothing. Angiosperms are used to make many medicines. These include digitalis, which is a heart medication.

Seed Plants ▪ *Guided Reading and Study*

Angiosperms (pp. 151–157)

This section describes the type of seed plants that produce fruit and their life cycle. It also explains the difference between two groups of plants that produce different kinds of seeds.

Use Target Reading Skills

Using a word in a sentence helps you think about how best to explain the word. After you read the section, reread the paragraphs that contain definitions of Key Terms. Use all the information you have learned to write a meaningful sentence using each Key Term.

Introduction (p. 151)

1. A plant that produces seeds that are enclosed in a fruit is called a(n) _____.

2. Circle the letter of the reproductive structure of an angiosperm.

   a. seed   **b.** flower
   c. petals   **d.** sepals

3. List two characteristics of angiosperms.

   a. _____

   b. _____

The Structure of Flowers (pp. 152–153)

Match the parts of the flower with their function.

Function		Flower Parts
_____ **4.** Male reproductive parts		**a.** petals
_____ **5.** Protect the developing flower		**b.** sepals
_____ **6.** Female reproductive parts		**c.** stamens
_____ **7.** Colorful structures that attract pollinators		**d.** pistils

Name _____ Date _____ Class _____

Seed Plants • *Guided Reading and Study*

Angiosperms *(continued)*

8. Label the parts of the flower in this diagram.

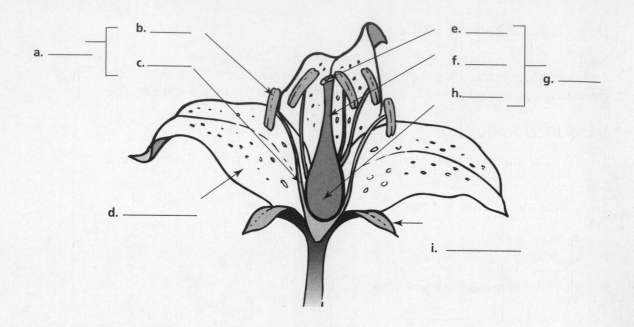

a. _____
b. _____
c. _____
d. _____
e. _____
f. _____
g. _____
h. _____
i. _____

Reproduction in Angiosperms (pp. 154–155)

9. When a flower is pollinated, a grain of pollen falls on a(n) _____.

10. In what part of the flower do the sperm cell and the egg cell join together?

_____

11. Is the following sentence true or false? All angiosperms rely on wind for pollination. _____

12. Describe how animals help to pollinate flowers.

_____

_____

_____

Name _____ Date _____ Class _____

Seed Plants · *Guided Reading and Study*

Types of Angiosperms (p. 156)

13. What are the two major groups of angiosperms?

a._____ b._____

14. The embryo in a seed gets food from the _____, or seed leaf.

Match each characteristic with the type of angiosperm. Each type of angiosperm may be used more than once.

Characteristics Types of Angiosperms

____ **15.** Have only one seed leaf

____ **16.** Have two seed leaves

____ **17.** Flower petals are in fours or fives.

____ **18.** Flower petals are in threes.

____ **19.** Leaves are wide with branching veins.

____ **20.** Leaves are narrow with parallel veins.

____ **21.** Roses, violets, and oak trees are examples.

____ **22.** Corn, wheat, and tulips are examples.

a. monocots

b. dicots

Angiosperms in Everyday Life (p. 157)

23. Circle the letter of each product made from angiosperms.

a. furniture
b. clothing
c. turpentine
d. steel

24. Is the following sentence true or false? Medicines, such as digitalis, come from angiosperms. _____

Name _____ Date _____ Class _____

Angiosperms

Understanding Main Ideas

Answer the following in the space provided.

1. Name two characteristics of angiosperms.

   _____

   _____

2. What do the male parts of the flower produce?

   _____

3. What do the female parts of the flower produce?

   _____

4. Briefly describe the process of embryo formation in an angiosperm.

   _____

   _____

   _____

5. What is the difference between a monocot and a dicot?

   _____

   _____

   _____

Building Vocabulary

Fill in the blank with the term that matches each numbered part of the flower in the figure.

6. _____

7. _____

8. _____

9. _____

10. _____

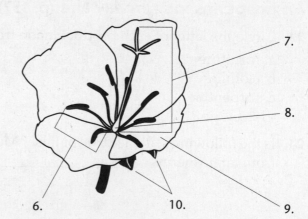

Seed Plants • *Enrich*

Counting Pollen

Millions of people suffer from allergies when they breathe in air containing certain kinds of pollen. They can develop allergic reactions similar to cold symptoms or even more severe. Pollen counts and pollen forecasts are issued to help people know what to expect from their pollen allergies.

Ragweed Pollen Forecast

One method used to count pollen is placing a greased microscope slide on the roof of a tall building and leaving it there for a certain amount of time, usually 24 hours. After this time, the slide is examined under a microscope and the various kinds of pollen that have fallen on the slide are counted. Pollen levels under 10 are usually not considered a problem for people with allergies. Levels above 60 can cause mild reactions, and a severe reaction can happen when levels go into the hundreds. A pollen forecast is different from a pollen count because it predicts what the pollen levels will be in the future, while a pollen count tells you the actual conditions on a specific day in the past.

Legend:
MA = Much above normal
A = Above normal
N = Near normal
B = Below normal
MB = Much below normal
NS = No ragweed season

Ragweed is an angiosperm found in nearly every region of the United States. It is a very hardy plant that likes hot weather. Ragweed plants release their pollen between 6 a.m. and 10 a.m. The figure above is a map showing a ragweed pollen forecast for the fall in the United States. The pollen count is for a specific fall day in a U.S. city.

Study the figures, then answer the following questions on a separate sheet of paper.

1. What type of reaction could most people allergic to ragweed pollen expect on the day the pollen count was taken?

2. If you suffered from ragweed allergies, in which area of the country would your allergies bother you the least?

3. According to the map, which area of the country (north, south, east, or west) is forecasted to have the highest levels of ragweed pollen? Why do you think this occurs?

4. If you lived in an area of high ragweed pollen, would it be helpful to keep your windows closed during the mornings? Explain your answer.

Seed Plants

Seed Plants · *Skills Lab*

A Close Look at Flowers

Problem

What is the function of a flower, and what roles do its different parts play?

Skills Focus

observing, inferring, measuring

Materials

paper towels	slide	tape
plastic dropper	large flower	water
hand lens	coverslip	metric ruler
microscope	scalpel	lens paper

Procedure

PART 1 The Outer Parts of the Flower

1. Tape four paper towel sheets on your work area. Obtain a flower from your teacher. While handling the flower gently, observe its shape and color. Use the ruler to measure it. Notice whether the petals have any spots or other markings. Does the flower have a scent? Record your observations with sketches and descriptions.

2. Observe the sepals. How many are there? How do they relate to the rest of the flower? (*Hint:* Sepals are often green, but not always.) Record your observations.

3. Use a scalpel to carefully cut off the sepals without damaging the structures beneath them. **CAUTION:** *Scalpels are sharp. Cut in a direction away from yourself and others.*

4. Observe the petals. How many are there? Are all the petals the same, or are they different? Record your observations.

Seed Plants ▪ *Skills Lab*

PART 2 The Male Part of the Flower

5. Carefully pull off the petals to examine the male part of the flower. Try not to damage the structures beneath the petals.

6. Observe the stamens. How many are there? How are they shaped? How tall are they? Record your observations.

7. Use a scalpel to carefully cut the stamens away from the rest of the flower without damaging the structures beneath them. Lay the stamens on the paper towel.

8. Obtain a clean slide and coverslip. Hold a stamen over the slide, and gently tap some pollen grains from the anther onto the slide. Add a drop of water to the pollen. Then place the coverslip over the water and pollen.

9. Observe the pollen under both the low-power objective and the high-power objective of a microscope. Draw and label a pollen grain.

PART 3 The Female Part of the Flower

10. Use a scalpel to cut the pistil away from the rest of the flower. Measure the height of the pistil. Examine its shape. Observe the top of the pistil. Determine if that surface will stick to and lift a tiny piece of lens paper. Record your observations.

11. Lay the pistil on the paper towel. Holding it firmly at its base, use a scalpel to cut the pistil in half at its widest point, as shown in the diagram below. **CAUTION:** *Cut away from your fingers.* How many compartments do you see? How many ovules do you see? Record your observations.

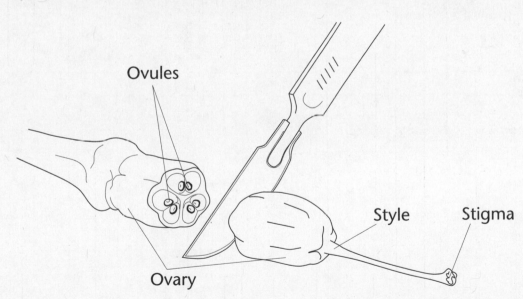

Ovules

Style   Stigma

Ovary

Seed Plants · *Skills Lab*

A Close Look at Flowers *(continued)*

Analyze and Conclude

Write your answers on a separate sheet of paper.

1. **Observing** Based on your observations, describe how the sepals, petals, stamens, and pistils of a flower are arranged.

2. **Inferring** How are the sepals, petals, stamens, and pistil involved in the function of this flower?

3. **Measuring** Based on your measurements of the heights of the pistil and stamens, how do you think the flower you examined is pollinated? Use additional observations to support your answer.

4. **Classifying** Did you find any patterns in the number of sepals, petals, stamens, or other structures? If so, describe that pattern. Is your flower a monocot or a dicot?

5. **Communicating** Write a paragraph explaining all you can learn about a plant by examining one of its flowers. Use your observations in this lab to support your conclusions.

More to Explore

Some kinds of flowers do not have all the parts found in the flower used in this lab. Obtain a different flower. Find out which parts this flower has, and which parts are missing. *Obtain your teacher's approval before carrying out this investigation.*

Plant Responses and Growth

ABILITY LEVELS KEY
L1 Basic to Average
L2 For All Students
L3 Average to Advanced

🕐 *2 periods, 1 block*

Objectives

A.5.4.1 Identify three stimuli that produce plant responses.

A.5.4.2 Describe how plants respond to seasonal changes.

A.5.4.3 State how long different angiosperms live.

Local Standards

Key Terms
* tropism • hormone • auxin
* photoperiodism • short-day plant
* long-day plant • critical night length
* day-neutral plant • dormancy • annual
* biennial • perennial

PRETEACH

Build Background Knowledge
Have students describe the usual direction of plant stem and root growth.

 **Discover Activity** *Can a Plant Respond to Touch?* **L1**

Targeted Resources

❑ **All in One Teaching Resources**
L2 Reading Strategy Transparency A48: Relating Cause and Effect
❑ 💿 **PresentationExpress™ CD-ROM**

INSTRUCT

Tropisms Identify plant responses to the stimuli of touch, light, and gravity.
Seasonal Changes Analyze the different ways plants respond to changing seasons.
Life Spans of Angiosperms Contrast the life spans of annuals, biennials, and perennials.

Targeted Resources

❑ **All in One Teaching Resources**
L2 Guided Reading, pp. 307–309
L2 Transparency A49
❑ **www.SciLinks.org** Web Code: scn-0154
❑ 💿 **Student Edition on Audio CD**

ASSESS

Section Assessment Questions
🖎 Have students use their Relating Cause and Effect graphic organizers to answer the questions.
Reteach
Sketch examples of tropisms, photoperiodism, and dormancy, and have students describe them.

Targeted Resources

❑ **All in One Teaching Resources**
Section Summary, p. 306
L1 Review and Reinforce, p. 310
L3 Enrich, p. 311

Seed Plants · *Section Summary*

Plant Responses and Growth

Key Concepts

- What are three stimuli that produce plant responses?
- How do plants respond to seasonal changes?
- How long do different angiosperms live?

A plant's growth response toward or away from a stimulus is called a **tropism. Touch, light, and gravity are three important stimuli to which plants show growth responses, or tropisms.**

A **hormone** produced by a plant is a chemical that affects how the plant grows and develops. In addition to tropisms, plant hormones also control germination, the formation of flowers, stems, and leaves, the shedding of leaves, and the development and ripening of fruit. One important plant hormone is named **auxin.** Auxin speeds up the rate at which a plant's cells grow.

The amount of darkness a plant receives determines the time of flowering in many plants. A plant's response to seasonal changes in length of night and day is called **photoperiodism. Short-day plants** flower when nights are *longer* than a critical night length. **Long-day plants** flower when nights are *shorter* than a critical night length. The **critical night length** is the number of hours of darkness that determines whether or not a plant will flower.

Short-day plants bloom in the fall or winter, when nights are growing longer. Long-day plants flower in the spring or summer, when nights are getting shorter. The flowering cycle of **day-neutral plants** is not sensitive to periods of light and dark.

As winter draws near, many plants prepare to go into a state of dormancy. **Dormancy** is a period when an organism's growth or activity stops. **Dormancy helps plants survive freezing temperatures and the lack of liquid water.**

Angiosperms are classified as annuals, biennials, or perennials based on the length of their life cycles. Flowering plants that flower and die in the same year are called **annuals.** Annuals include marigolds and petunias. Wheat and cucumbers are also annuals. **Biennials** complete their life cycle in two years. Parsley and celery are biennials. Flowering plants that live for more than two years are called **perennials.** Maple trees and peonies are examples of perennials.

Seed Plants · *Guided Reading and Study*

Plant Responses and Growth (pp. 160–164)

This section explains how plants respond to stimuli in their environment. It also describes the role of plant hormones and the life spans of flowering seed plants.

Use Target Reading Skills

As you read through the paragraphs under the heading Hormones and Tropisms, *identify four effects of plant hormones. Write the information in the graphic organizer below.*

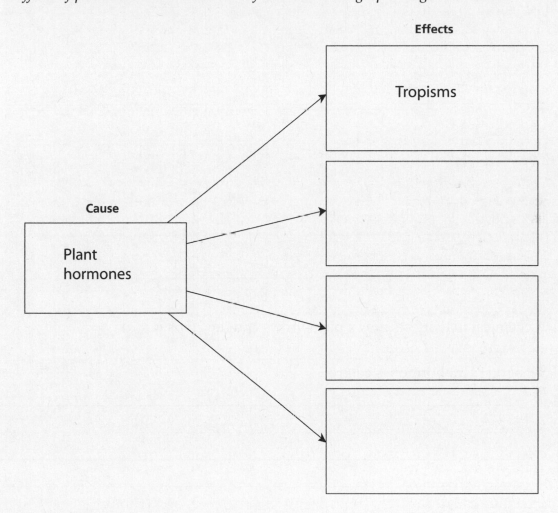

Effects

Tropisms

Cause

Plant hormones

Tropisms (pp. 160–161)

1. What is a tropism?

   _____

   _____

2. Is the following sentence true or false? If a plant grows toward the stimulus, it shows a negative tropism. _____

Seed Plants ▪ *Guided Reading and Study*

Plant Responses and Growth *(continued)*

3. Complete the concept map to show three stimuli to which plants respond.

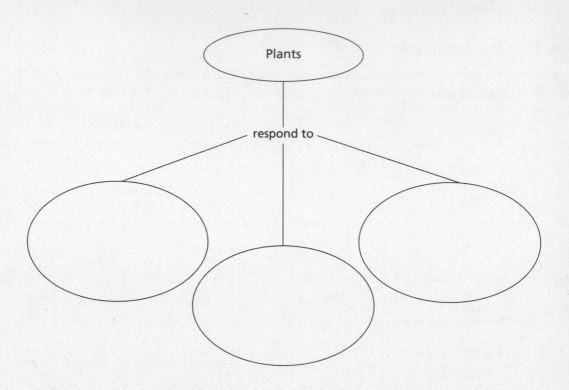

4. A chemical that affects how a plant grows and develops is a(n) _____ .

5. What do plant hormones control?

    a. _____

    b. _____

    c. _____

    d. _____

    e. _____

6. Auxin is a plant hormone that _____ the rate at which a plant's cells grow.

7. Describe how auxin controls a plant's response to light.

    _____

    _____

    _____

    _____

Seed Plants · *Guided Reading and Study*

_____

Seasonal Changes (pp. 162–163)

8. What determines the time of flowering in many plants?

_____

_____

9. What happens to a plant during dormancy?

_____

_____

Life Spans of Angiosperms (p. 164)

10. Circle the letter of the flowering plants that complete a life cycle within one growing season.

    a. perennials   **b.** biennials

    c. annuals   **d.** centennials

11. Is the following sentence true or false? Most annuals have woody stems.

    _____

12. Circle the letter of each sentence that is true about biennials.

    a. Biennials complete their life cycle in two years.
    b. In the first year, biennials produce seeds and flowers.
    c. In the second year, biennials germinate and grow roots.
    d. Once the flower produces seeds, the biennial dies.

13. How long is the life cycle of a perennial?

_____

_____

14. Circle the letter of the plant that is a perennial.

    a. parsley   **b.** peony

    c. cucumber   **d.** petunia

Seed Plants • *Review and Reinforce*

Plant Responses and Growth

Understanding Main Ideas

Study the diagram, then answer the following questions in the space provided.

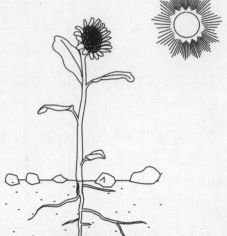

1. The plant in the figure is responding to what two types of stimulus?

   _____

   _____

   _____

2. What is the growth response shown in the figure called?

   _____

   _____

3. Are the plant's roots showing a positive or negative response?

   _____

   _____

   _____

4. Is the plant's flower showing a positive or negative response?

   _____

   _____

   _____

Building Vocabulary

Match each term with its definition by writing the letter of the correct definition in the right column on the line beside the term in the left column.

_____ 5. tropism   **a.** controls a plant's response to light

_____ 6. hormone   **b.** a plant's growth response toward or away from a stimulus

                     c. a chemical that affects how the plant grows and develops

_____ 7. auxin

Carnivorous Plants

A bladderwort is a *carnivorous plant*. This means that it traps and then digests insects and other small animals, obtaining their nitrogen. The Venus' flytrap is another example of the almost 400 species of carnivorous plants. Most carnivorous plants grow in marshy areas such as swamps and bogs where the soil is low in nitrogen. Because carnivorous plants do not have to rely on nitrogen absorbed from the soil by their roots, they are well suited to their environments.

Carnivorous plants respond to the stimulus of touch to trap insects and other small animals. For example, when an insect touches a hair on the leaf of a Venus' flytrap, this triggers a specific response. Water moves from cells on the inside of the flytrap to cells on the outside of the trap. This causes the leaf of the flytrap to snap shut quickly, catching the insect.

Carnivorous plants called sundews use another method to trap and digest insects. Sundews have small leaves that produce a sweet, sticky liquid at their tips. Insects fly into the stalks and stick to them. This triggers a different response. Other leaves begin to curl inward toward a trapped insect by using cell growth. The cells on one side of the stalks grow faster than the cells on the other side. This causes the leaves to bend. The leaves then produce a chemical that digests the insect, so it can be used to nourish the plant.

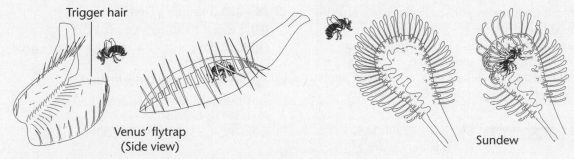

Trigger hair

Venus' flytrap
(Side view)

Sundew

Answer the following questions on a separate sheet of paper.

1. How do carnivorous plants get the nitrogen they need?
2. Why is it helpful to a sundew to produce the sweet, sticky liquid?
3. Do you think carnivorous plants also produce food by photosynthesis? Explain your answer.
4. What is one advantage that quick movement gives to a Venus' flytrap?
5. Why doesn't the sundew have to move as quickly as the Venus' flytrap to imprison an insect?

Feeding the World

⏱ *1–2 periods, 1/2–1 block*

Objectives
A.5.5.1 Identify technologies that may help farmers produce more crops.

Local Standards

Key Terms
- precision farming • hydroponics
- genetic engineering

PRETEACH

Build Background Knowledge
Elicit ideas of a typical farm 100 years ago, today, and 100 years from today.

 **Discover Activity** *Will There Be Enough to Eat?* **L1**

Targeted Resources

- ❑ **All in One Teaching Resources**
  L2 Reading Strategy Transparency A50: Identifying Main Ideas
- ❑ 💿 **PresentationExpress™ CD-ROM**

INSTRUCT

Precision Farming Discuss precision farming and its benefits.
Hydroponics Describe hydroponics and identify an example of its use.
Engineering Better Plants State what genetic engineering is and apply to an example.

 **Technology Lab** *Design and Build a Hydroponic Garden* **L2**

Targeted Resources

- ❑ **All in One Teaching Resources**
  L2 Guided Reading, pp. 314–316
  L3 Lab: *Design and Build a Hydroponic Garden,* pp. 319–320
- ❑ 📼 **Lab Activity Video/DVD**
  Technology Lab: *Design and Build a Hydroponic Garden*
- ❑ **www.SciLinks.org** Web Code: scn-0155

ASSESS

Section Assessment Questions
🔄 Have students use their graphic organizers of main ideas and details to answer the questions.
Reteach
Summarize the benefits of the technologies that increase crop yields.

Targeted Resources

- ❑ **All in One Teaching Resources**
  Section Summary, p. 313
  L1 Review and Reinforce, p. 317
  L3 Enrich, p. 318

Seed Plants · *Section Summary*

Feeding the World

Key Concept

■ What technologies may help farmers produce more crops?

On farms, new, efficient, farming practices are being used. In laboratories, scientists are developing plants that are more resistant to insects, disease, and drought.

Farmers are using satellite images and computer analysis to determine the water and fertilizer needs of different fields. This is called **precision farming. Precision farming can benefit farmers by saving time and money. It also increases crop yields by helping farmers maintain ideal conditions in all fields.**

In some areas of the world, food crops are being grown using hydroponics. **Hydroponics** is a method by which plants are grown in solutions of nutrients instead of in soil. **Hydroponics allows people to grow crops in areas with poor soil to help feed a growing population.** Hydroponics is costly but allows people to grow crops in areas with poor farmland.

In **genetic engineering,** scientists alter an organism's genetic material to produce an organism with qualities that people find useful. **Scientists are using genetic engineering to produce plants that can grow in a wider range of climates. They are also engineering plants to be more resistant to damage from insects.**

Seed Plants • *Guided Reading and Study*

Feeding the World (pp. 165–167)

This section describes different ways farmers can produce more crops.

Use Target Reading Skills

As you read the section, write the main idea in the graphic organizer below. Then write three supporting details that give examples of the main idea.

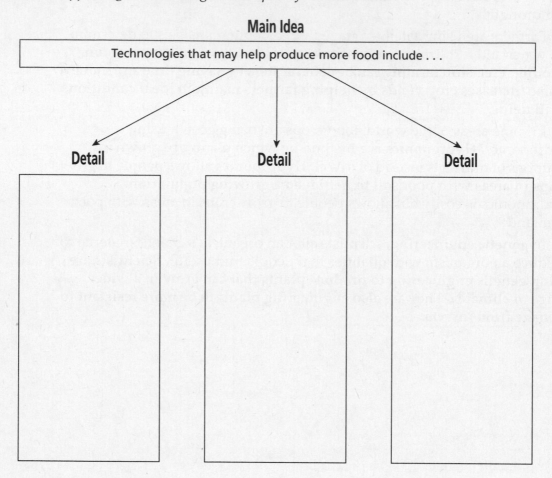

Main Idea

Technologies that may help produce more food include . . .

Detail

Detail

Detail

Introduction (p. 165)

1. List three ways scientists and farmers are working to grow enough food to feed the growing population of people.

   a. _____

   _____

   b. _____

   _____

   c. _____

   _____

Seed Plants ▪ *Guided Reading and Study*

Precision Farming (p. 166)

2. Is the following sentence true or false? In precision farming, farmers know how much water and fertilizer different fields need.
    _____

3. Complete the flowchart to show the process of precision farming.

Precision Farming

A(n) _____ takes images of a farmer's field.

A computer analyzes the images to determine the makeup of the
_____ in different fields on the farm.

The computer prepares a(n)_____and
_____ plan for each field.

4. List three ways in which precision farming benefits farmers.

    a. _____   b. _____

    c. _____

5. Is the following sentence true or false? Precision farming benefits the environment by using more fertilizer than the soil needs.
    _____

Seed Plants · *Guided Reading and Study*

Feeding the World *(continued)*

Hydroponics (p. 166)

6. What is hydroponics?

   _____

   _____

   _____

7. Is the following sentence true or false? Hydroponics can be used to grow crops in places with poor soil. _____

Engineering Better Plants (p. 167)

8. What are four major sources of food for people?

   _____

   _____

9. Is the following sentence true or false? Farmers can easily feed more people without increasing the production of crops.

   _____

10. What two challenges do farmers face in producing more crops?

    a. _____

    b. _____

11. Scientists change an organism's genetic material to produce an organism with useful qualities in the process of _____.

Name _____ Date _____ Class _____

Feeding the World

Understanding Main Ideas

Study the diagram of the experimental cornfield and read the following statements. If the statement could be true, write true. *If it is false, change the underlined word or words so that the statement could be true.*

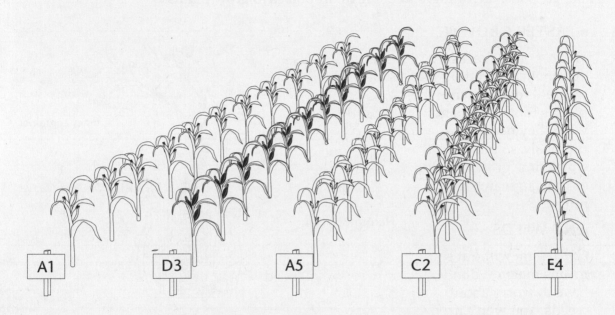

A1   D3   A5   C2   E4

_____ 1. The field shown is being used to test <u>genetically</u> engineered corn.

_____ 2. Scientists are developing plants that are more resistant to insects, disease, and <u>water</u>.

_____ 3. Scientists are developing plants that can grow in a <u>wider</u> range of climates.

_____ 4. Precision farming means knowing just how much water and <u>sunlight</u> different fields require.

_____ 5. Hydroponics is a <u>cheap</u> way for people to grow crops in areas with poor farmland.

Building Vocabulary

Write the definition of the terms below in the space provided.

6. hydroponics

_____

_____

7. genetic engineering

_____

_____

Seed Plants · *Enrich*

Hydroponics

Hydroponics is the science of growing plants without soil. A solution of nutrients is used in place of the soil. Plants can be grown by hydroponics either outdoors or indoors. The following figure shows how a plant can be grown without soil.

There are some advantages to using hydroponics to grow plants.

■ FASTER GROWTH

Hydroponics works by automatically getting the nutrients and water to the plant's roots. Plants get what they need con-tinuously, so they don't waste time growing a lot of roots to search for nutrients.

■ NO WEEDS

Gardening without soil means that you don't have to worry about weeds. You won't need any weed sprays.

■ NO PESTS

Because most pests live in the soil, you won't have to use any pesticides or other toxic chemicals.

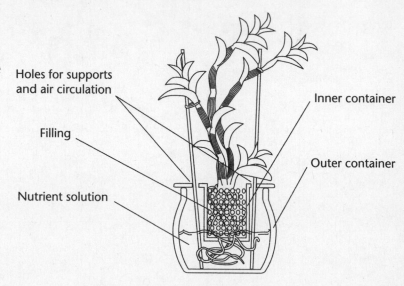

The major disadvantage of hydroponics is that it is costly.

Answer the following questions on a separate sheet of paper.

1. What do you think is the purpose of the filling?

2. Will the nutrient solution have to be replaced from time to time? Explain your answer.

3. If plants are grown indoors using hydroponics, what else must be provided for the plants' needs besides the nutrient solution?

4. Do you think hydroponics would be a good method to grow food during long space flights? Explain your answer.

5. Since you don't need weed sprays or pesticides, what do you think makes hydroponics costly?

Seed Plants · *Technology Lab*

Design and Build a Hydroponic Garden

Problem

Can you design and build a system for growing plants without soil?

Skills Focus

designing a solution, redesigning

Materials

potted plant

2 different types of seedlings

nutrient solution

empty 2-liter soda bottles

paper towels

optional materials provided by your teacher

Procedure

PART 1 Research and Investigate

1. Copy the data table onto a sheet of paper.
2. Carefully examine the potted plant your teacher gives you. Think about all the factors that are required in order for the plant to grow. List these factors in the first column of the data table.
3. Use your knowledge of plants and additional research to fill in the second column of the data table.
4. For each factor listed in the table, decide whether or not it is "essential" for plant growth. Write this information in the third column of the data table.

PART 2 Design and Build

5. To test whether soil is essential for plant growth, design a "garden" system for growing plants without soil. Your garden must
   - include at least two different types of seedlings
   - use only the amount of nutrient solution provided by your teacher
   - be built using materials that are small and lightweight, yet durable
6. Sketch your garden design on a sheet of paper and make a list of the materials you will use. Then obtain your teacher's approval and build your garden.

Seed Plants · *Technology Lab*

Design and Build a Hydroponic Garden *(continued)*

Data Table

Factor Required for Plant Growth	What This Factor Provides for the Plant	Essential or Nonessential?

Evaluate and Redesign

7. Test your garden design by growing your plants for 2 weeks. Each day, measure and record the height of your plants and the number of leaves. Also note the overall appearance of your plants.

8. Evaluate your design by comparing your garden and plants with those of your classmates. Based on your comparison, decide how you might improve your garden's design. Then make any needed changes and monitor plant growth for one more week.

Analyze and Conclude

1. **Identifying a Need** In Part 1, did you list soil as a factor required for plant growth? If so, did you think it was an essential or nonessential factor? Explain your thinking.

2. **Designing a Solution** How did the information you gathered in Part 1 help you in designing your garden in Part 2? How did your garden design provide for each of the essential growth factors you listed?

3. **Redesigning** What changes did you make to your garden design and why? Did the changes lead to improved plant growth?

4. **Working With Design Constraints** How did the design constraints in Step 5 limit your design? How did you overcome those limitations?

5. **Evaluating the Impact on Society** Hydroponic gardens are planned for future space flights and as a way to grow plants in cold climates. Explain why hydroponic gardens are a good choice for each of these situations. Then, identify two more situations in which hydroponic gardens would be a good choice and explain why.

Communicate

Create a brochure highlighting the benefits of hydroponic gardening. Be sure to provide details about how a plant's needs are met and about the problems that hydroponic gardens could solve.

Seed Plants · *Key Terms*

Key Terms

How fast can you solve this crossword puzzle? You'll need to use what you've learned about seed plants. Go!

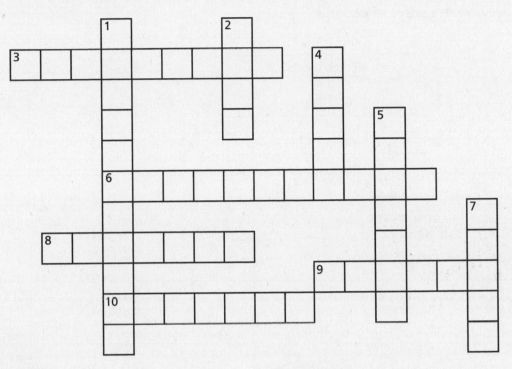

Clues down

1. A method by which plants are grown in solutions of nutrients instead of soil
2. The reproductive structure in gymnosperms
4. A ripened ovary that encloses one or more seeds
5. A plant's growth response
7. Vascular tissue through which water and minerals travel

Clues across

3. Seed leaf in which food is stored
6. The transfer of pollen from a male structure to a female structure
8. Angiosperms with only one seed leaf
9. The female part of a flower
10. Layer of cells that divide to produce new phloem and xylem

Name _____ Date _____ Class _____

Seed Plants · *Connecting Concepts*

Connecting Concepts

Develop a concept map that uses the Key Concepts and Key Terms from this chapter. Keep in mind the big idea of this chapter. The concept map shown is one way to organize how the information in this chapter is related. You may use an extra sheet of paper.

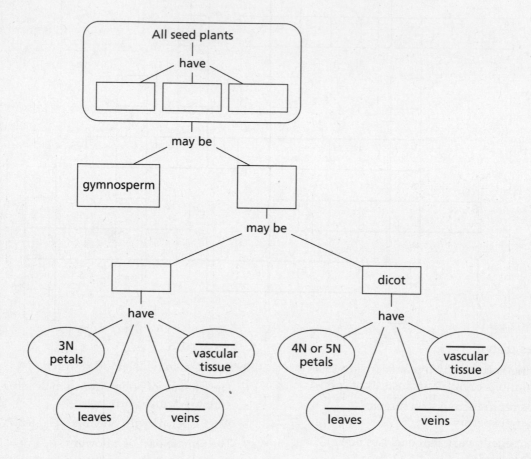

Investigating Hormones That Control Germination

Key Concept

Plant hormones control different plant functions.

Skills Focus

observing, inferring, designing experiments, controlling variables

Time

60 minutes and an observation period of 10 minutes a day for 8 days

Materials *(per group)*

wide, shallow bowl

metal or wooden spoon

tomatoes (2 or more varieties)

strainer

plastic cup

tap water

brush

funnel

beaker

glass-marking pencil

filter paper

4 plastic petri dishes

paper towel

Advance Preparation

Obtain several of each of two tomato varieties such as plum, cherry, and beefsteak. If time is limited, crush the tomatoes, wash the seeds, and strain the extract before class.

Teaching Tips

(More to Explore) Students could boil the extract from variety A tomato and then use it to see if it still inhibits seed germination.

Name _____ Date _____ Class _____

Seed Plants · *Laboratory Investigation*

Investigating Hormones That Control Germination

Pre-Lab Discussion

Tomato seeds usually germinate when exposed to moisture, oxygen, and a fairly warm temperature. Yet inside the tomato, where these conditions are met, seeds do not germinate. How do tomato seeds know when to develop and when not to develop?

Plants produce chemicals called hormones that control how the plants grow and develop. Only a small amount of hormone is needed to control plant processes such as the growth of the plant toward light.

In this investigation, you will explore the plant hormone that controls seed germination.

1. How can you tell if a seed is germinating?

   _____

   _____

2. Besides germination, what other processes do plant hormones control?

   _____

   _____

   _____

Problem

Do tomatoes have a hormone that affects seed germination?

Materials *(per group)*

wide, shallow bowl	funnel
metal or wooden spoon	beaker
tomatoes (2 or more varieties)	glass-marking pencil
strainer	filter paper
plastic cup	4 plastic petri dishes
tap water	paper towel
brush	

Name _____ Date _____ Class _____

Seed Plants · *Laboratory Investigation*

Safety

Review the safety guidelines in Appendix A of your textbook.

Handle glass objects carefully. If they break, tell the teacher. Do not pick up broken glass.

Procedure

1. Use a spoon to crush a whole tomato (variety A) in a bowl. Strain the crushed tomato and collect the liquid extract in a beaker. With a glass-marking pencil, label the beaker "Extract A" and set it aside.

2. Empty the pulp from the strainer onto a paper towel and blot the pulp to remove some of the moisture. Separate 20 seeds from the pulp and rub them gently with a paper towel to remove the jelly-like capsule from the outside of the seeds.

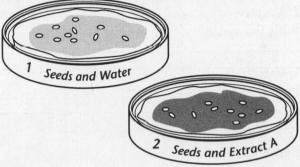

3. Clean the strainer. (Use a brush, if necessary, to remove the pulp.) Place the 20 seeds in the strainer and rinse with water. Empty the seeds out on a fresh paper towel and blot them dry.

Figure 1

4. Label two petri dishes as shown in Figure 1. Line the petri dishes with filter paper. Place 10 seeds in each dish.
   Wet the filter paper in dish 1 with water;
   wet the paper in dish 2 with tomato extract. Cover the dishes.

5. Crush a different kind of tomato (variety B). Remove 20 seeds and wash them.

6. Line two more petri dishes with filter paper. Place 10 seeds in each petri dish.

7. Wet the filter paper in one dish with water. Label this dish 3. Wet the filter paper in the other dish with Extract A. Label it dish 4. Cover these two dishes.

8. Observe the seeds in the four dishes for several days, adding more water or tomato extract to keep the filter paper moist.

9. Each day record the total number of seeds that have germinated in each dish in the appropriate place in the Data Table.

Seed Plants · *Laboratory Investigation*

Investigating Hormones That Control Germination (continued)

Observations

Data Table

Dish	Day 1	Day 2	Day 3	Day 4	Day 5	Day 6	Day 7	Day 8
1: Variety A with Water								
2: Variety A with Extract A								
1: Variety B with Water								
1: Variety B with Extract A								

Analyze and Conclude

1. What is the purpose of dish 1?

   _____

   _____

2. What conclusion can you draw after observing the results in dishes 1 and 2? Do tomatoes contain a hormone that inhibits germination? Give evidence to support your answer.

   _____

   _____

   _____

3. What conclusions can you draw after studying the results in dishes 3 and 4? Does the juice from variety A inhibit germination of seeds from variety B? Give evidence to support your answer.

   _____

   _____

   _____

   _____

Name _____ Date _____ Class _____

Critical Thinking and Applications

1. Explain why some of the seeds in dishes 1 and 3 may not have germinated, even though they had all the necessary conditions for growth.

   _____

   _____

2. Explain why many seeds that do not contain hormones that inhibit germination might begin to germinate outside during late spring.

   _____

   _____

   _____

3. What are three fruits and / or vegetables (besides tomatoes) that you think contain hormones that inhibit germination?

   _____

   _____

More to Explore

New Problem Is the hormone that inhibits the germination of tomato seeds a protein? (*Hint:* Proteins lose their effectiveness when boiled.)

Possible Materials Consider which materials you can use from the previous part of this lab. What else will you need?

Safety Be careful when boiling a liquid. Use a hot plate and heat-resistant beakers for heating. Use oven mitts to handle hot containers. Wear safety goggles and a lab apron.

Procedure Make a hypothesis that answers and explains the problem. Consider your data from the lab when developing your hypothesis. Make sure to keep a control to compare with the experimental dishes. Write your procedure on a separate sheet of paper. Have the teacher approve your procedure before carrying out the investigation.

Observations On a separate sheet of paper, make a data table to record your data.

Analyze and Conclude Is the hormone responsible for inhibiting seed germination a protein? Give a reason for your answer.

_____

_____

_____

Modeling an Angiosperm

Students are presented with the problem of creating a model of either a monocot or a dicot. To solve this problem, students will apply the concepts they have learned about angiosperms, flowers, and leaves.

Expected Outcome

Students' models will vary, but should include a flower, stem, and several leaves. Each leaf should include a cuticle and stomata. For example, a student could model the upper surface of a leaf with waxed paper to indicate the cuticle. The bottom surface of a leaf could be made from construction paper with tiny holes punched into it to represent stomata. The shape of the leaves should represent students' choice of monocot or dicot; the leaves of monocots should be narrow with parallel veins, and the leaves of dicots should be wide with branching veins.

Students' flowers should include a stigma, style, ovary, anthers, filaments, pollen, sepals, and petals. For example, a student could model a style and an ovary with modeling clay. A stigma could be modeled with a small piece of masking tape with the sticky side facing up. A student could model filaments with wires and attach small pieces of clay to the ends to represent anthers. Pollen could be modeled by coating the anthers with a thin layer of glue and then dusting them with corn meal. Sepals could be modeled with pieces of construction paper. A student could model petals with construction paper or pieces of fabric. The number of petals should be based on whether a monocot or dicot is being modeled. Students should attach their flower and leaves to a stem modeled from a thin wooden dowel.

Students should mount their model on cardboard and label each of its structures and their functions. They should also indicate where pollination and fertilization occur.

Content Assessed

The Performance Assessment tests students' understanding of concepts relating to angiosperms, leaves, flowers, monocots, and dicots.

Skills Assessed

making models, applying concepts

Materials

- Provide students with materials and tools for making their models such as toothpicks, construction paper, waxed paper, scissors, glue, small pieces of fabric, wire, modeling clay, markers or colored pencils, wire cutters, corn meal, masking tape, and cardboard.

- Each student will need a small wooden dowel about 1 cm in diameter to use as a "stem." Dowels can be purchased at a hardware or do-it-yourself store.

Time

40 minutes

Monitoring the Task

- Consider placing the materials in two or three central locations where all students will have access to them rather than distributing each material to each student.

- When students are labeling their models, remind them to include the function of each structure as well as its name.

- At the end of the Performance Assessment, allow students to walk around the classroom and examine each other's models.

Seed Plants · *Performance Assessment*   **Scoring Rubric**

Modeling an Angiosperm

In assessing students' performance, use the following rubric.

	4	3	2	1
Constructing the Model	Student models the cuticle and stomata of leaves. Student models the stigma, style, ovary, anthers, filaments, pollen, sepals, and petals of a flower. Student models at least one other part of an angiosperm, such as roots or the veins in leaves. Each part and its function is clearly labeled. Student correctly indicates where pollination and fertilization take place. The shape of the leaves and the number of petals correspond to student's choice of either a monocot or dicot.	Student models the cuticle and stomata of leaves. Student models the stigma, style, ovary, anthers, filaments, pollen, sepals, and petals of a flower. Most parts and their functions are labeled. Student correctly indicates where pollination and fertilization take place. The shape of the leaves and the number of petals correspond to student's choice of either a monocot or dicot.	Student models the cuticle and stomata of leaves. Student models only five or six of the following: the stigma, style, ovary, anthers, filaments, pollen, sepals, and petals of a flower. Many parts are labeled, but a few functions are unlabeled or incorrect. Student correctly indicates where either pollination or fertilization takes place. Student's model represents a monocot or dicot by either the shape of the leaves or the number of petals.	Student models either the cuticle or stomata of leaves. Student models less than five of the following: the stigma, style, ovary, anthers, filaments, pollen, sepals, and petals of a flower. A few parts and most functions are unlabeled or incorrect. Student fails to indicate where pollination and fertilization take place. Student's model represents a monocot or dicot by either the shape of the leaves or the number of petals.
Concept Understanding	Student demonstrates a mastery of concepts relating to angiosperms, leaves, and flowers.	Student demonstrates a good understanding of concepts relating to angiosperms, leaves, and flowers.	Student demonstrates a partial understanding of concepts relating to angiosperms, leaves, and flowers.	Student demonstrates a minimal understanding of concepts relating to angiosperms, leaves, and flowers.

Seed Plants • *Performance Assessment*

Modeling an Angiosperm

Problem

How can you make a model of a monocot or a dicot that includes a flower, stem, and leaves?

Suggested Materials

small wooden dowel

toothpicks

construction paper

waxed paper

scissors

glue

small pieces of fabric

wire

modeling clay

markers or colored pencils

wire cutters

cardboard

corn meal

masking tape

Devise a Plan

1. Choose either a monocot or a dicot to model. Study the materials and decide how you could use them to make a model of a flower. Be sure to include the following: stigma, style, ovary, anthers, filaments, pollen, sepals, and an appropriate number of petals.

2. Next, determine how you could use the materials to make leaves and a stem for your angiosperm. Be sure to include the cuticle and stomata of the leaves. Consider what shape the leaves and their veins should have based on whether you chose a monocot or a dicot to model.

3. Assemble your model. Mount it on cardboard, and then label its parts and their functions. Indicate where pollination and fertilization occur.

Analyze and Conclude

After following the plan you devised, answer the following questions on a separate sheet of paper.

1. Describe how you modeled a flower, stem, and leaves of an angiosperm.
2. What characteristics of leaves weren't you able to show in your model?
3. If you were to model a gymnosperm, what reproductive structures would you include? How would these structures be similar to the one you modeled for an angiosperm? How would they be different?
4. In what part of your angiosperm's flower are seeds produced? Name three ways that these seeds could be dispersed.
5. How could you change your model to illustrate phototropism?

Seed Plants

Multiple Choice
Write the letter of the correct answer on the line at the left.

1. The vascular tissue through which food travels from the leaves to the stems and roots is called
   a. xylem.
   b. phloem.
   c. cotyledon.
   d. stomata.

2. Leaves perform all of the following EXCEPT
   a. capture energy from the sun.
   b. make food.
   c. release carbon dioxide.
   d. produce seeds.

3. The process by which plants lose water through their leaves is
   a. transpiration.
   b. absorption.
   c. germination.
   d. pollination.

4. A plant with needlelike leaves is a(n)
   a. gymnosperm.
   b. angiosperm.
   c. monocot.
   d. dicot.

5. Pollination is the transfer of pollen from
   a. female to male reproductive structures.
   b. male to female reproductive structures.
   c. ovaries to sepals.
   d. filaments to stamens.

6. Once a female cone is pollinated, the cone
   a. shrinks.
   b. moves to a lower branch.
   c. falls off the tree.
   d. closes its scales.

7. Sepals
   a. protect developing flowers.
   b. attract insects.
   c. produce pollen.
   d. produce ovaries.

8. An example of positive phototropism is
   a. a stem growing upward.
   b. roots growing downward.
   c. a plant wilting in the sun.
   d. flowers growing to face the sun.

9. A plant that has a two year life cycle is called a(n)
   a. annual.
   b. biennials
   c. perennial.
   d. cambium

10. In precision farming, performing computer analysis on satellite images of fields can tell farmers
    a. the makeup of the soil in different fields.
    b. which fields have more insects.
    c. which fields have more food per plant.
    d. the expected yield of each field.

Completion

Fill in the blank to complete each statement.

11. All seed plants have roots, _____, and leaves.

12. Gymnosperms have neither flowers nor _____.

13. Pollen is produced by _____ cones.

14. Plants that produce seeds enclosed in a fruit are called _____.

15. Growing plants in solutions of nutrients instead of soil is called

_____.

True or False

If the statement is true, write true. If it is false, change the underlined word or words to make the statement true.

_____ 16. All seed plants have <u>vascular tissue</u> and produce seeds.

_____ 17. Stomata open and close to control the flow of <u>food</u>.

_____ 18. A conifer is a kind of <u>angiosperm</u>.

_____ 19. Stamens are the <u>male</u> reproductive parts of flowers.

_____ 20. Auxin controls a plant's response to light by <u>speeding up</u> the rate at which some cells grow.

Seed Plants ▪ *Chapter Test*

Using Science Skills

Use the diagram below to answer the following questions.

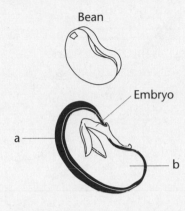

21. **Interpret Illustrations** What label should replace (a)? What is the function of this part of the seed?

   _____

   _____

22. **Applying Concepts** What label should replace (b)? How will the embryo use this part of the seed?

   _____

   _____

Essay

Write an answer for each of the following.

23. Name three functions of roots.

   _____

   _____

   _____

24. Describe three ways seeds can be dispersed.

   _____

   _____

   _____

25. Briefly explain how angiosperms reproduce.

   _____

   _____

   _____

Name _____ Date _____ Class _____

Using Science Skills

Use the diagram below to answer the following questions.

26. Classifying Is the flower in the figure above a monocot or a dicot? How can you tell?

_____

_____

27. Applying Concepts What role do petals play for a flower?

_____

_____

28. Classifying Is this an angiosperm or gymnosperm? What role do flowers play in plants?

_____

_____

Essay

Write an answer for each of the following.

29. Describe why it is advantageous for seeds to be dispersed by pods that burst open rather than just dropping to the ground.

_____

_____

30. Describe two ways scientists are trying to improve plants using genetic engineering.

_____

_____

Chapter Project Worksheet 1

1. Answers will vary. Sample: I'm going to grow a pea plant. I've seen them sprout before, so I expect in a few days I'll see the two little leaves growing out of the soil. Then it will grow bigger leaves. In a few weeks it will bloom.

2. Check that students' drawings show the seed coat, embryo, and stored food. Drawings should be large enough to see details of the inside of the seed.

3. Students data table entries should be daily and detailed. Quantifiable observations are good, such as number of leaves and height of the plant, but qualitative observations, such as "The leaves get limp when I don't water the plant enough" are also important.

Chapter Project Worksheet 2

1. Answers will vary. Sample: The pea plant grew quickly and seemed healthy. It grew especially fast after the first two weeks, and always grew toward the window. A few flowers were produced but no seeds. I think the plant would have produced seeds if the project had gone on longer.

2. Answers will vary. Sample: The seed leaves emerged from the ground on day 6, and I could see the first true leaves forming about day 9. Each day I could tell the plant was growing toward the light, so every couple of days I turned the tray so the plant would grow straighter. The true leaves always appeared in pairs. The first tendril appeared on day 13, after the second pair of true leaves. The first flower appeared on day 25. I pollinated the flowers on day 29.

3. Answers will vary. Sample: I will make 3 sketches of the entire plant, one of the germinating plant, another when the plant has 4 leaves and the first tendrils, and one of the full grown plant with flowers. I will make separate drawings of the seed, a close-up of a leaf, one showing how the tendril curls around an object, and one of the flower. Each drawing will have labels for the important parts and text to explain what is happening.

The Characteristics of Seed Plants
Guided Reading and Study

Use Target Reading Skills
The Characteristics of Seed Plants
I. What Is a Seed Plant?
   A. Vascular tissue
   B. Seeds
II. How Seeds Become New Plants
   A. Seed Structure
   B. Seed Dispersal
   C. Germination
III. Roots
   A. Types of Roots
   B. The Structure of a Root
IV. Stems
   A. The Structure of a Stem
   B. Annual Rings
V. Leaves
   A. The Structure of a Leaf
   B. The Leaf and Photosynthesis
   C. Controlling Water Loss

1. c, d
2. sporophyte, gametophyte
3. **a.** It helps support the plants; **b.** It transports food, water, and minerals through the plants.
4. b
5. a
6. leaves
7. roots
8. A seed is a plant structure that contains a young plant inside a protective covering.
9. true
10. b
11. c
12. a
13. Seeds need light, water, and nutrients.
14. false
15. Animals, Water, Wind, Shooting out of plant
16. Germination is the sprouting of the embryo out of a seed.
17. b, d
18. **a.** Anchor plants in the ground; **b.** Absorb water and minerals from the soil; **c.** Store food
19. **a.** Fibrous roots, **b.** Taproot
20. b
21. d
22. a
23. c
24. d
25. **a.** Carry substances between the leaves and roots; **b.** Support the plant and hold up the leaves; **c.** Store food

26. false
27. Heartwood is an inner layer of old, inactive xylem that provides support to woody stems.
28. a
29. true
30. Leaves capture the sun's energy and carry out the food-making process of photosynthesis.
31. c
32. b
33. e
34. f
35. a
36. d
37. true
38. transpiration
39. true

The Characteristics of Seed Plants
Review and Reinforce

1. Accept any of the following: have vascular tissue, produce pollen, produce seeds, have leaves, stems, and roots
2. embryo, stored food, seed coat
3. Accept one of the following: captures the sun's energy, carries out photosynthesis
4. a layer of cells that divides to produce new phloem and xylem
5. root
6. contains a young plant inside a protective covering
7. xylem
8. phloem
9. protects the growing tip of the root from injury
10. stomata
11. Accept one of the following: carries substances between the roots and leaves, provides support for the plant, holds up leaves so they are exposed to the sun
12. a seed leaf where food can be stored

The Characteristics of Seed Plants
Enrich

1. Accept either air bubbles or gas bubbles.
2. One leaf has stomata on one side only, while the other leaf has stomata on both sides.
3. Much of the air inside the leaf might escape through the stalk.
4. Water would be more readily lost from the upper surface of the leaves, because that is the side more exposed to sun and wind. Having few or no stomata on the upper surface of the leaves reduces the places from which water can escape, and this helps control water loss.
5. on the top—the surface that is exposed to air

Gymnosperms
Guided Reading and Study

Use Target Reading Skills
Possible questions and answers include:
How does gymnosperm pollination occur?
(Pollen is transferred from a male reproductive structure to a female reproductive structure; wind often carries pollen from male to female cones.)
How does gymnosperm fertilization occur?
(Pollen collects in a sticky substance produced by ovules. Female scales close to seal in pollen and fertilization occurs.)
1. A gymnosperm is a seed plant that produces naked seeds.
2. true
3. true
4. b
5. d
6. c
7. a
8. d
9. a
10. b
11. cones
12. false
13. Four
14. ovule
15. Pollen moves from a male reproductive structure to a female reproductive structure.
16. true
17. cones; fertilized egg; embryo; seeds; Wind; plants
18. b, c
19. false

Gymnosperms
Review and Reinforce

1. needlelike
2. conifer
3. cones
4. pollen
5. ovules or egg cells
6. Answers may vary. Sample: First, pollen falls from a male cone onto a female cone. This is called pollination. In time, a sperm cell and an egg cell join together in an ovule on the female cone. After fertilization occurs, the zygote develops into the embryo part of the seed.

Gymnosperms
Enrich

1. long, strong fibers
2. Answers may vary. Sample: You want the fibers thoroughly separated in the pulp so the finished paper will be thin and smooth, with no lumps.
3. Answers may vary. Sample: The paper is pressed and dried so it can be flat and smooth.
4. Answers may vary. Samples: flax, cotton, hemp, straw, corn stalks, bamboo, grasses

Angiosperms
Guided Reading and Study

Use Target Reading Skills
Have students write what they know about each key term before reading the definitions in the section. As they read each passage that contains key terms, remind them to write the definitions in their own words.
1. angiosperm
2. b
3. **a.** Produce flowers; **b.** Produce fruits
4. c
5. b
6. d
7. a
8. **a.** Stamen, **b.** Anther, **c.** Filament, **d.** Petal, **e.** Stigma, **f.** Style, **g.** Pistil, **h.** Ovary, **i.** Sepal
9. stigma
10. They join together in the ovule.
11. false
12. Animals feeding on flower nectar also become coated with pollen. Animals pollinate flowers by brushing pollen onto the flower's stigma as they leave the flower or as they enter the next flower.
13. **a.** monocots **b.** dicots
14. cotyledon
15. a
16. b
17. b
18. a
19. b
20. a
21. b
22. a
23. a, b
24. true

Angiosperms
Review and Reinforce

1. They produce flowers and fruits.
2. pollen
3. eggs

4. Pollen falls on the stigma. The sperm cell and egg cell join in the ovule. The zygote develops into an embryo.
5. Monocots are angiosperms that have only one seed leaf. Dicots produce seeds with two seed leafs.
6. stamen
7. pistil
8. ovary
9. petal
10. sepals

Angiosperms
Enrich

1. a mild reaction
2. the Northwest
3. The South has the highest levels of ragweed pollen, because ragweed grows best in hot climates.
4. Yes, because ragweed plants release their pollen between 6 and 10 a.m.

A Close Look at Flowers
Skills Lab

For answers see, Teacher's Edition.

Plant Responses and Growth
Guided Reading and Study

Use Target Reading Skills
Effects: Tropisms; Germination; Forming flowers, stems, leaves; Shedding leaves; Development and ripening of fruit
1. A tropism is a plant's growth response toward or away from a stimulus.
2. false
3. Touch, Light, Gravity
4. hormone
5. **a.** tropisms, **b.** germination, **c.** the formation of flowers, stems, and leaves, **d.** the shedding of leaves, **e.** the development and ripening of fruit
6. speeds up
7. Auxin builds up in the shaded side of the stem. The cells on the shaded side begin to grow faster. Eventually, the cells on the stem's shady side are longer than those on its sunny side. So the stem bends toward the light.
8. the amount of darkness a plant receives
9. During dormancy, a plant's growth or activity stops.
10. c
11. false
12. a, d
13. A perennial usually lives for more than two years.
14. b

Plant Responses and Growth
Review and Reinforce

1. gravity and light
2. tropism
3. positive (to gravity)
4. positive (to light)
5. b
6. c
7. a

Plant Responses and Growth
Enrich

1. by digesting insects and other animals that they trap
2. The sweet, sticky liquid acts as bait and trap for insects.
3. Yes, the plants still need to make food even though they digest insects to obtain nitrogen.
4. Answers may vary. Sample: Speed allows the Venus' flytrap to trap an insect by surprising it. The trap closes before the insect can fly away.
5. The sticky liquid traps the insect. Therefore, the plant can move relatively slowly to imprison and digest it.

Feeding the World
Guided Reading and Study

Use Target Reading Skills
Possible details: Precision farming—uses satellite images and computers to determine the amount of water and fertilization needed; Hydroponics—plants are grown in solutions of nutrients instead of in soil; Genetic engineering—genetic material is altered to produce organisms with useful qualities
1. a. Scientists are developing plants that are more resistant to insects, disease, and drought. b. People are developing methods for growing plants in areas with poor soil. c. Efficient, new technologies are being used on farms.
2. true
3. satellite, soil, water, fertilizing
4. a. Saves time, b. Saves money, c. Increases crop yields
5. false
6. Hydroponics is a method by which plants are grown in a solution of nutrients instead of soil.
7. true
8. Wheat, corn, rice, and potatoes are the major food sources.
9. false

10. a. Food crops can grow only in certain climates. b. The size and structure of crop plants limit how much food they can produce.
11. genetic engineering

Feeding the World
Review and Reinforce

1. true
2. drought
3. true
4. fertilizer
5. costly
6. a method by which plants are grown in solutions of nutrients instead of soil
7. the process by which scientists alter an organism's genetic material to produce an organism with qualities that people find useful

Feeding the World
Enrich

1. The filling is used to support the roots of the plants.
2. Yes, because the plant will eventually use up all the nutrients in the solution.
3. Plants must also be provided with appropriate amounts of light.
4. Answers may vary. Sample: Yes, because plants will grow faster, saving scarce room on the ship, pesticides will not be needed, and carrying heavy soil can be avoided.
5. Answers may vary. Sample: Special containers and supports must be purchased for the plants. Also, plants grown with hydroponics might need more care to keep the water and nutrient level right.

Design and Build a Hydroponic Garden
Technology Lab

For answers, see the Teacher's Edition.

Key Terms

Down:
1. hydroponics
2. cone
4. fruit
5. tropism
7. xylem
Across:
3. cotyledon
6. pollination
8. monocot
9. pistil
10. cambium

Connecting Concepts

This concept map is only one way to represent the main ideas and relationships in this chapter. Accept other logical answers from students.

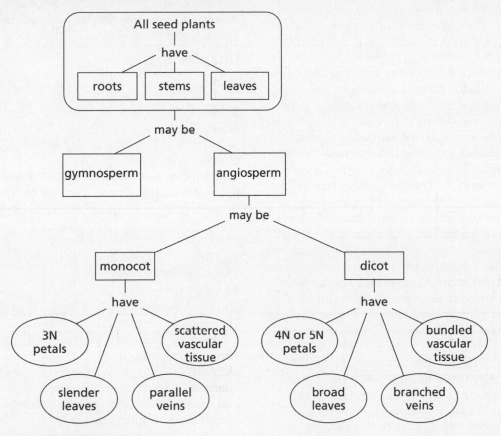

Laboratory Investigation

Investigating Hormones That Control Germination
Pre-Lab Discussion

1. Usually a root emerges from the seed.
2. Plant hormones control the formation of flowers, stems, and leaves; the shedding of leaves; and the development and ripening of fruit.

Observations

Students' data should show the following trends: Dish 1: Most seeds germinate. Dish 2: Few or no seeds germinate. Dish 3: Most seeds germinate. Dish 4: Most seeds germinate.

Analyze and Conclude

1. Dish 1 is a control for the experiment. It provides a comparison for dish 2.
2. Yes, tomatoes contain a hormone that inhibits seed germination. No seeds, or very few, germinated in the tomato extract. The extract must contain the hormone.

3. Answers may vary depending on the varieties used. Most hormones that inhibit seed germination are specific to the variety from which they are collected and may not inhibit germination in other varieties.

Critical Thinking and Applications

1. Some seeds that were used in the experiment may have been dead.
2. During late spring, in many areas, the necessary conditions for seed germination—warmth and moisture—become available.
3. Answers will vary. Examples could include apples, oranges, watermelons, squash, cucumbers, and so on.

More to Explore

Results should show that the hormone inhibits seed germination of variety A even after it's boiled, so it's not a protein. The hormone is abscisic acid.

Students could boil the extract from variety A tomato and then use it to see if it still inhibits seed germination.

Chapter Performance Assessment

Analyze and Conclude

1. Answers will vary. Sample: I modeled the upper surface of leaves with waxed paper to represent the cuticle. For the bottom surface of the leaves, I used construction paper with tiny holes punched into it to represent stomata. The leaves are long and narrow with parallel veins to show that the plant is a monocot.

I modeled the style and the ovary of the flower with modeling clay. For a stigma, I used a small piece of masking tape with the sticky side facing up. I modeled filaments with wires and attached small pieces of clay to the ends to represent anthers. To show pollen, I coated the anthers with a thin layer of glue and then dusted them with corn meal. I modeled sepals with pieces of construction paper. I modeled petals with pieces of pink fabric. My flower has six petals (a multiple of three) to show that it is a monocot. I attached the flower and leaves to a stem modeled from a thin wooden dowel.

2. Answers may vary. Sample: I wasn't able to show that leaves have chloroplasts where photosynthesis occurs. I also wasn't able to show that leaves have xylem and phloem. Phloem is the vascular tissue through which food moves. Xylem is the vascular tissue through which water and nutrients move.

3. The reproductive structures of most gymnosperms are cones. Gymnosperms have male cones that produce pollen and female cones that produce ovules. The flowers of most angiosperms have female parts that produce ovules and male parts that produce pollen. In both types of plants, the egg cell of an ovule is fertilized by a sperm cell that forms from a pollen grain. Once the egg is fertilized, the ovule of both cones and flowers develops into a seed. The seeds of a gymnosperm are naked, while the seeds of an angiosperm are enclosed in an ovary that develops into a fruit. Cones are pollinated by the wind, but most flowers rely on animals such as insects or birds for pollination.

4. A seed is produced in an ovary. As the seed develops, the ovary develops into a fruit. Methods of dispersal may vary. Samples: An animal may eat the fruit. The seeds inside the fruit pass through the animal's digestive system and are deposited in a new area. A fruit may fall into water such as a stream or river and may be carried to a new area by the current. Some fruits, such as those of dandelions, may be blown to new areas by the wind.

5. Answers may vary. Sample: Instead of using a wooden dowel, I would have to model a stem out of something flexible such as a pipe cleaner or a thick wire. Then I could bend the stem, flower, and leaves so that they leaned towards a light source.

Chapter Test

1. b
2. d
3. a
4. a
5. b
6. d
7. a
8. d
9. b
10. a
11. stems
12. fruits
13. male
14. angiosperms
15. hydroponics
16. true
17. gases
18. gymnosperm
19. true
20. true
21. seed coat; the seed coat protects the embryo and its food from drying out
22. stored food; the embryo will use the stored food to begin to grow during germination
23. anchor the plant; absorb water and minerals from the soil; store food
24. Any three of the following: seeds pass through animals' digestive systems; fruits, containing seeds hook to an animal's fur; float in bodies of water; blown by the wind; seeds are dispersed by the sudden force of seedpods opening
25. First, pollen falls on a stigma. In time, the sperm cell and egg cell join together in the flower's ovule. The zygote develops into the embryo part of the seed.
26. a monocot; the flower parts are in threes and the leaves have parallel veins
27. The colors and shapes of petals attract pollinators.
28. Angiosperm; flowers are the reproductive structures of angiosperms.
29. Seeds that are dispersed away from the parent plant do not have to compete with the parent for light, water, and nutrients.
30. Any two of the following: making plants more resistant to insects; more resistant to disease; more resistant to drought

Color Transparency Planner

Transparencies

A2 Redi's Experiment

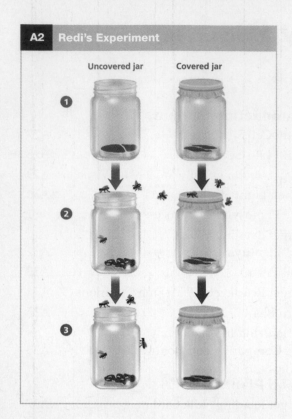

Uncovered jar   Covered jar

① ② ③

A4 Target Reading Skill: Asking Questions

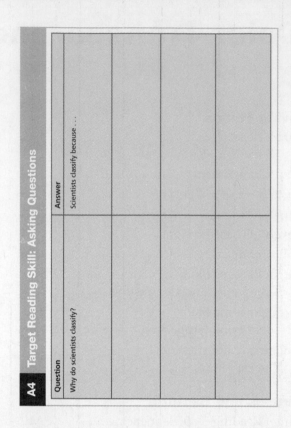

Question	Answer
Why do scientists classify?	Scientists classify because . . .

A1 Target Reading Skill: Using Prior Knowledge

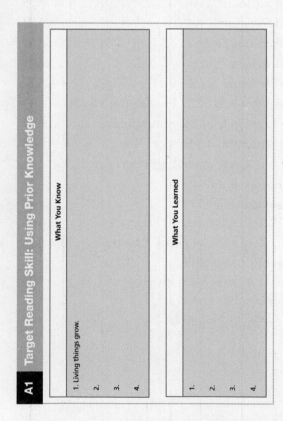

What You Know

1. Living things grow.
2.
3.
4.

What You Learned

1.
2.
3.
4.

A3 Pasteur's Experiment

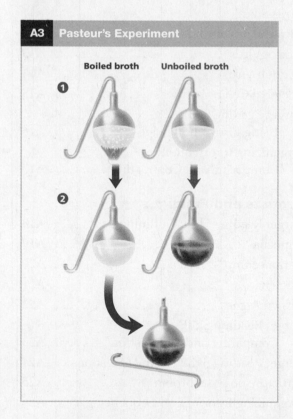

Boiled broth   Unboiled broth

① ②

A6 A Taxonomic Key

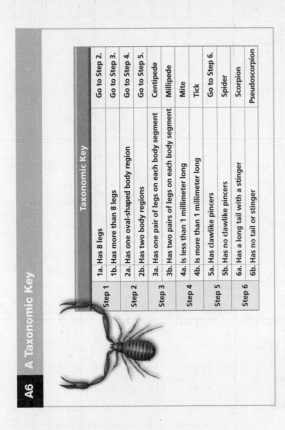

Taxonomic Key

Step 1	1a. Has 8 legs	Go to Step 2.
	1b. Has more than 8 legs	Go to Step 3.
Step 2	2a. Has one oval-shaped body region	Go to Step 4.
	2b. Has two body regions	Go to Step 5.
Step 3	3a. Has one pair of legs on each body segment	Centipede
	3b. Has two pairs of legs on each body segment	Millipede
Step 4	4a. Is less than 1 millimeter long	Mite
	4b. Is more than 1 millimeter long	Tick
Step 5	5a. Has clawlike pincers	Go to Step 6.
	5b. Has no clawlike pincers	Spider
Step 6	6a. Has a long tail with a stinger	Scorpion
	6b. Has no tail or stinger	Pseudoscorpion

A8 Target Reading Skill: Identifying Supporting Evidence

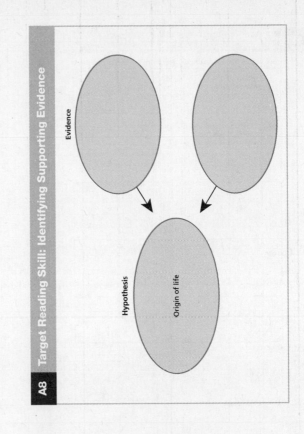

Evidence

Hypothesis

Origin of life

A5 Levels of Classification

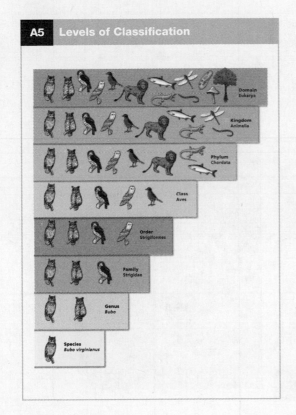

Domain Eukarya

Kingdom Animalia

Phylum Chordata

Class Aves

Order Strigiformes

Family Strigidae

Genus Bubo

Species Bubo virginianus

A7 Target Reading Skill: Comparing and Contrasting

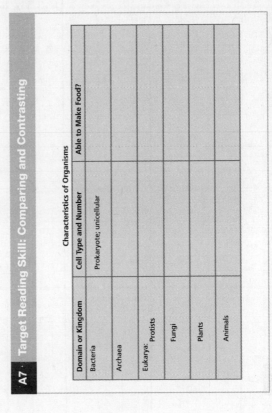

Characteristics of Organisms

Domain or Kingdom		Cell Type and Number	Able to Make Food?
Bacteria		Prokaryote; unicellular	
Archaea			
Eukarya:	Protists		
	Fungi		
	Plants		
	Animals		

A10 Target Reading Skill: Sequencing

How Active Viruses Multiply

Virus attaches to the surface of a living cell

↓

Virus injects genetic material into cell

↓

[ ]

↓

[ ]

↓

[ ]

How Hidden Viruses Multiply

[ ]

↓

[ ]

↓

[ ]

↓

[ ]

↓

[ ]

↓

[ ]

A9 Organizing Information: Concept Mapping

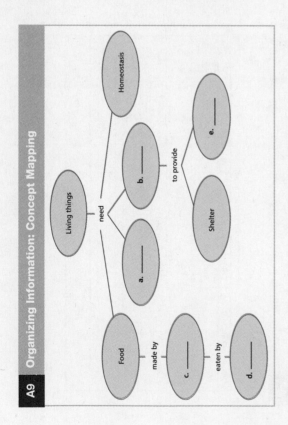

Living things — need — a. ___ and b. ___

Homeostasis

b. ___ — to provide — e. ___ and Shelter

Food — made by — c. ___ — eaten by — d. ___

A12 Virus Structure and Infection

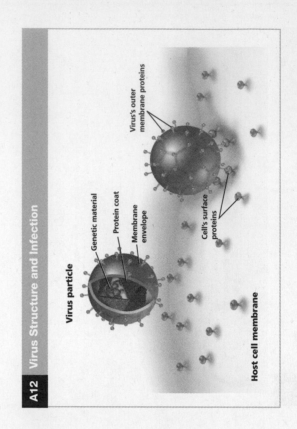

Virus particle

Genetic material

Protein coat

Membrane envelope

Virus's outer membrane proteins

Cell's surface proteins

Host cell membrane

A11 Virus Sizes

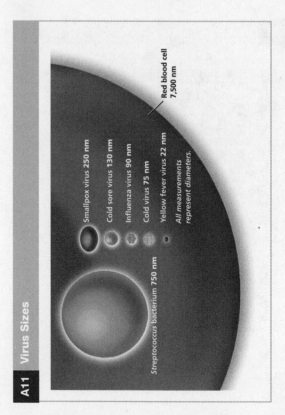

Smallpox virus 250 nm

Cold sore virus 130 nm

Influenza virus 90 nm

Cold virus 75 nm

Yellow fever virus 22 nm

All measurements represent diameters.

Red blood cell 7,500 nm

Streptococcus bacterium 750 nm

A14 Hidden Virus

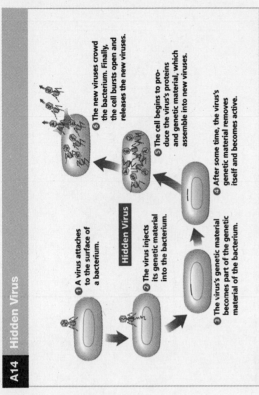

Hidden Virus

① A virus attaches to the surface of a bacterium.

② The virus injects its genetic material into the bacterium.

③ The virus's genetic material becomes part of the genetic material of the bacterium.

④ After some time, the virus's genetic material removes itself and becomes active.

⑤ The cell begins to produce the virus's proteins and genetic material, which assemble into new viruses.

⑥ The new viruses crowd the bacterium. Finally, the cell bursts open and releases the new viruses.

A16 Target Reading Skill: Using Prior Knowledge

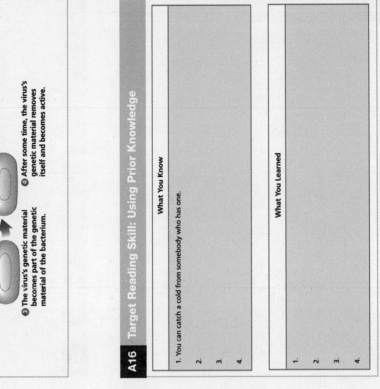

What You Know

1. You can catch a cold from somebody who has one.

2.

3.

4.

What You Learned

1.

2.

3.

4.

A13 Active Virus

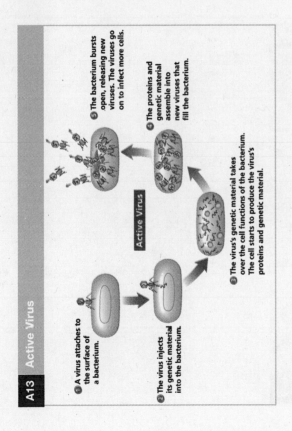

Active Virus

① A virus attaches to the surface of a bacterium.

② The virus injects its genetic material into the bacterium.

③ The virus's genetic material takes over the cell functions of the bacterium. The cell starts to produce the virus's proteins and genetic material.

④ The proteins and genetic material assemble into new viruses that fill the bacterium.

⑤ The bacterium bursts open, releasing new viruses. The viruses go on to infect more cells.

A15 Bacterial Cell Structures

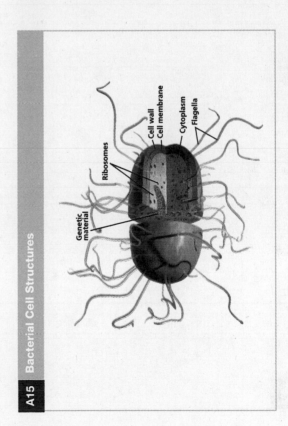

Genetic material

Ribosomes

Cell wall
Cell membrane

Cytoplasm

Flagella

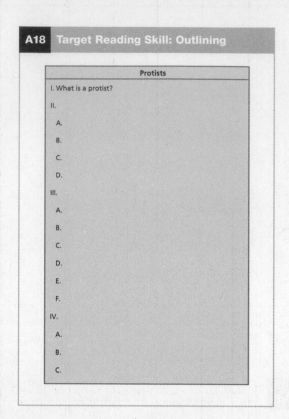

A18 Target Reading Skill: Outlining

Protists
I. What is a protist?
II.
A.
B.
C.
D.
III.
A.
B.
C.
D.
E.
F.
IV.
A.
B.
C.

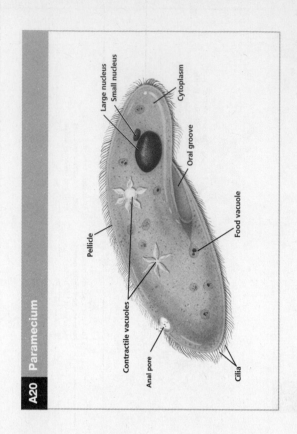

A20 Paramecium

Large nucleus
Small nucleus
Cytoplasm
Oral groove
Food vacuole
Pellicle
Contractile vacuoles
Anal pore
Cilia

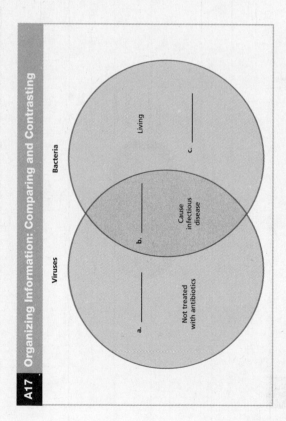

A17 Organizing Information: Comparing and Contrasting

Bacteria
Viruses
Living
c.
b.
Cause infectious disease
a.
Not treated with antibiotics

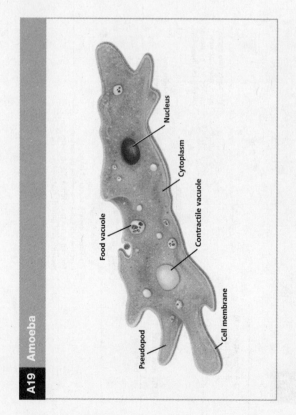

A19 Amoeba

Nucleus
Cytoplasm
Food vacuole
Contractile vacuole
Pseudopod
Cell membrane

A22 Brown Algae

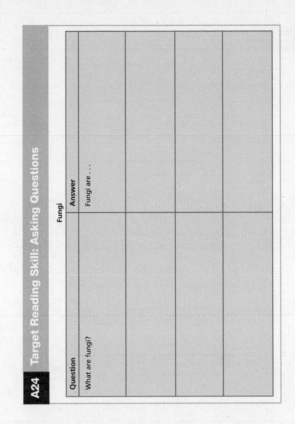

Blade

Bladder   Stalk

Holdfast

A21 Euglena

Chloroplast (used in food production)

Nucleus

Contractile vacuole

Eyespot

Pellicle

Flagellum

A24 Target Reading Skill: Asking Questions

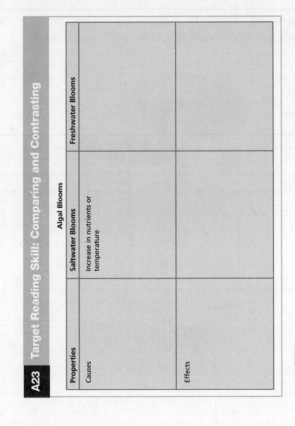

Fungi

Question	Answer
What are fungi?	Fungi are . . .

A23 Target Reading Skill: Comparing and Contrasting

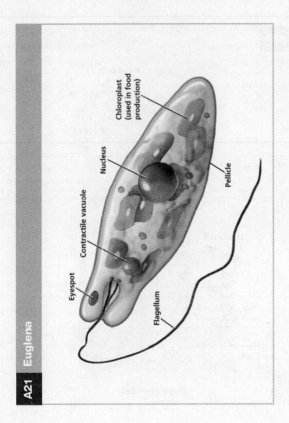

Algal Blooms

Properties	Saltwater Blooms	Freshwater Blooms
Causes	Increase in nutrients or temperature	
Effects		

Transparencies

A26 Organizing Information: Sequencing

Excess nutrients flow into a lake.

↓

a. _____

↓

b. _____

↓

c. _____

↓

Fishes and other organisms in the water die.

A28 Plant Life Cycle

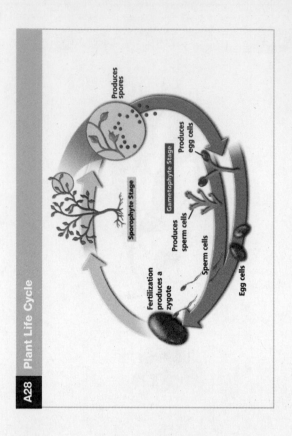

Produces spores

Sporophyte Stage

Gametophyte Stage

Produces egg cells

Produces sperm cells

Sperm cells

Egg cells

Fertilization produces a zygote

A25 Structure of a Mushroom

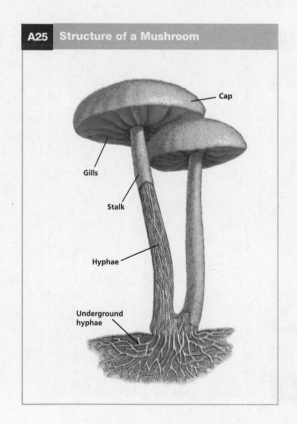

Cap

Gills

Stalk

Hyphae

Underground hyphae

A27 Plant Cell Structures

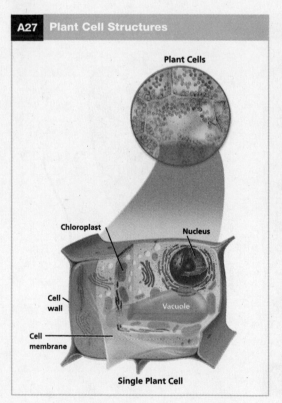

Plant Cells

Chloroplast

Nucleus

Cell wall

Cell membrane

Vacuole

Single Plant Cell

A30 When Light Strikes Objects

A32 Target Reading Skill: Identifying Main Ideas

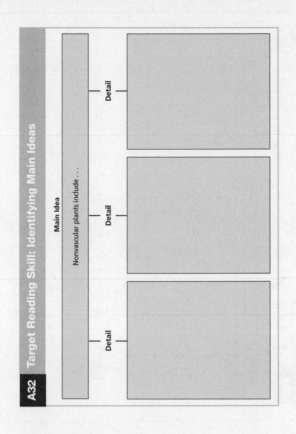

Main Idea

Nonvascular plants include . . .

Detail | Detail | Detail

A29 Target Reading Skill: Previewing Visuals

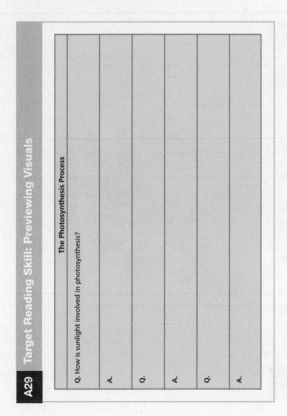

The Photosynthesis Process

Q: How is sunlight involved in photosynthesis?

A:

Q:

A:

Q:

A:

A31 The Photosynthesis Process

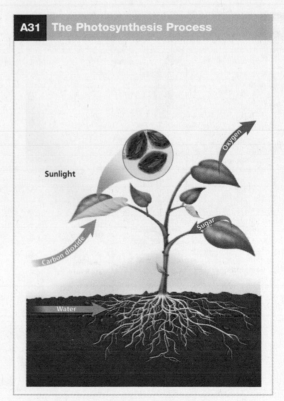

Sunlight

Oxygen

Carbon dioxide

Sugar

Water

Target Reading Skill: Asking Questions

Question	Answer
What are the characteristics of seedless vascular plants?	Seedless vascular plants have . . .

Organizing Information: Comparing and Contrasting

Characteristic	Moss	Fern
Size	a. _____	Can be tall
Environment	Moist	b. _____
Body parts	Rootlike, stemlike, and leaflike structures	c. _____
Familiar generation	d. _____	Sporophyte
Is true vascular tissue present?	No	e. _____

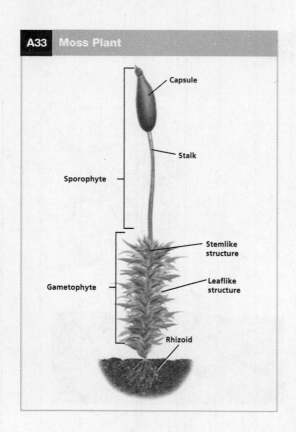

Capsule
Stalk
Sporophyte
Stemlike structure
Gametophyte
Leaflike structure
Rhizoid

Root
Stem
Frond

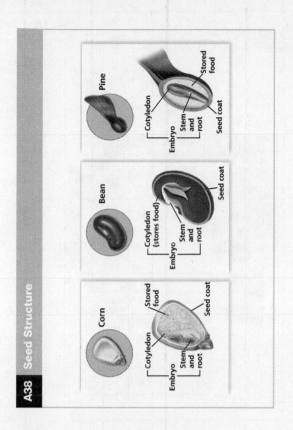

Pine

Stored food

Cotyledon

Embryo

Stem and root

Seed coat

Bean

Seed coat

Cotyledon (stores food)

Embryo

Stem and root

Corn

Cotyledon

Stored food

Seed coat

Embryo

Stem and root

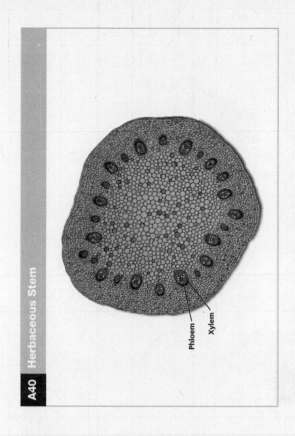

Phloem

Xylem

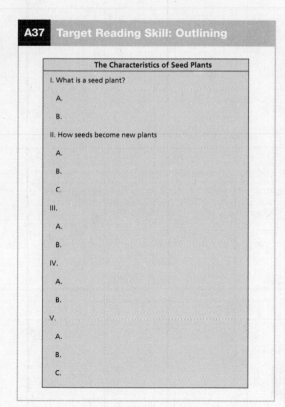

The Characteristics of Seed Plants

I. What is a seed plant?

  A.

  B.

II. How seeds become new plants

  A.

  B.

  C.

III.

  A.

  B.

IV.

  A.

  B.

V.

  A.

  B.

  C.

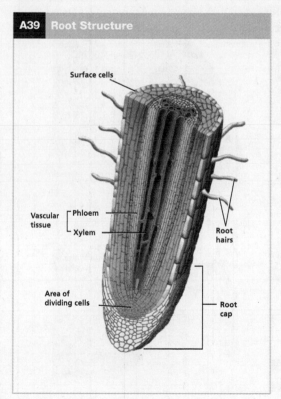

Surface cells

Vascular tissue

Phloem

Xylem

Root hairs

Area of dividing cells

Root cap

A42 The Structure of a Leaf

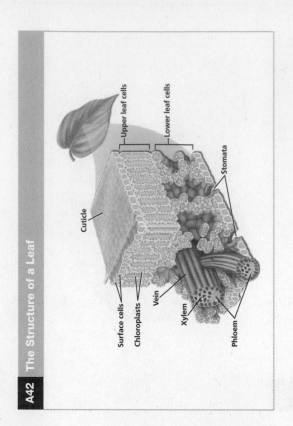

- Upper leaf cells
- Lower leaf cells
- Cuticle
- Surface cells
- Chloroplasts
- Vein
- Xylem
- Phloem
- Stomata

A44 The Life Cycle of a Gymnosperm

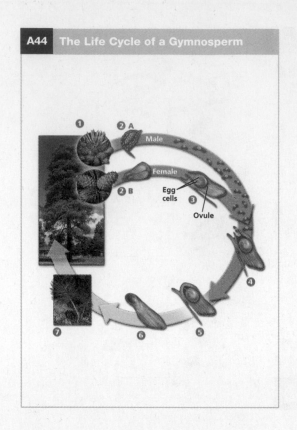

- ① ② A
- Male
- ② B
- Female
- ③ Egg cells
- Ovule
- ④
- ⑤
- ⑥
- ⑦

A41 Woody Stem

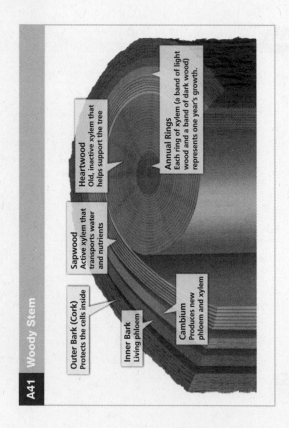

Heartwood
Old, inactive xylem that helps support the tree

Annual Rings
Each ring of xylem (a band of light wood and a band of dark wood) represents one year's growth.

Sapwood
Active xylem that transports water and nutrients

Outer Bark (Cork)
Protects the cells inside

Inner Bark
Living phloem

Cambium
Produces new phloem and xylem

A43 Target Reading Skill: Previewing Visuals

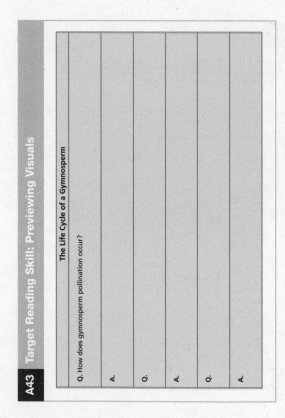

The Life Cycle of a Gymnosperm

Q. How does gymnosperm pollination occur?

A.

Q.

A.

Q.

A.

© Pearson Education, Inc., publishing as Pearson Prentice Hall. All rights reserved.

352

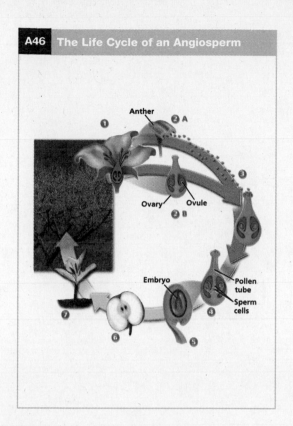

A46 The Life Cycle of an Angiosperm

- Anther
- Ovary
- Ovule
- Embryo
- Pollen tube
- Sperm cells

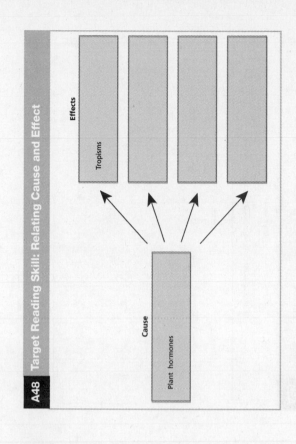

A48 Target Reading Skill: Relating Cause and Effect

Cause

Plant hormones

Effects

Tropisms

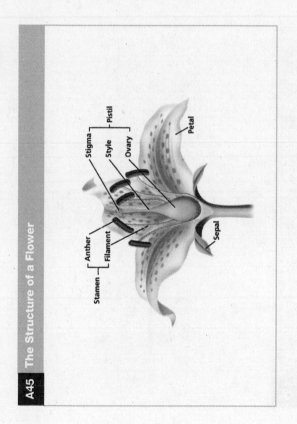

A45 The Structure of a Flower

- Stigma
- Style — Pistil
- Ovary
- Petal
- Anther
- Filament — Stamen
- Sepal

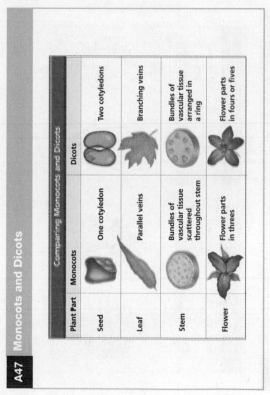

A47 Monocots and Dicots

Comparing Monocots and Dicots

Plant Part	Monocots	Dicots
Seed	One cotyledon	Two cotyledons
Leaf	Parallel veins	Branching veins
Stem	Bundles of vascular tissue scattered throughout stem	Bundles of vascular tissue arranged in a ring
Flower	Flower parts in threes	Flower parts in fours or fives

Transparencies

Target Reading Skill: Identifying Main Ideas

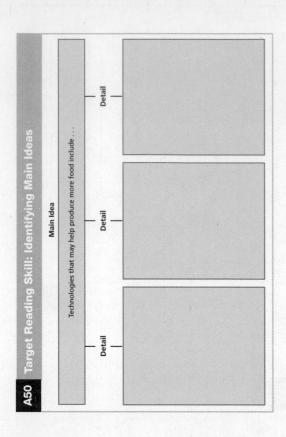

Main Idea

Technologies that may help produce more food include . . . .

Detail

Detail

Detail

Short-Day and Long-Day Plants

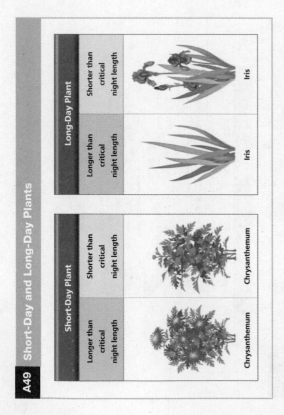

Short-Day Plant

Longer than critical night length	Shorter than critical night length
Chrysanthemum	Chrysanthemum

Long-Day Plant

Longer than critical night length	Shorter than critical night length
Iris	Iris

Organizing Information: Concept Mapping

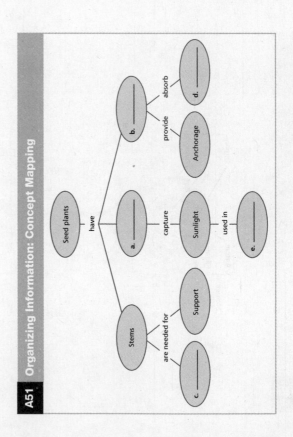

Seed plants

have

a.

capture

Sunlight

used in

e.

b.

absorb

d.

provide

Anchorage

Stems

are needed for

Support

c.
